ISOZYMES

Current Topics in
Biological and Medical Research

Volume 8

CELLULAR LOCALIZATION, METABOLISM, AND PHYSIOLOGY

ISOZYMES

Current Topics in Biological and Medical Research

Five Volumes Constituting the Proceedings of the 4th International Congress on Isozymes

ISOZYMES

Current Topics in Biological and Medical Research

Volume 8

CELLULAR LOCALIZATION, METABOLISM, AND PHYSIOLOGY

The second of five volumes constituting the proceedings of the 4th International Congress on Isozymes held in Austin, Texas, June 14–19, 1982

Editors

Mario C. Rattazzi
Department of Pediatrics at Children's Hospital
State University of New York, Buffalo

John G. Scandalios
Department of Genetics
North Carolina State University, Raleigh

Gregory S. Whitt
Department of Genetics and Development
University of Illinois, Urbana

Alan R. Liss, Inc., New York

Address all Inquiries to the Publisher
Alan R. Liss, Inc., 150 Fifth Avenue, New York, NY 10011

Library of Congress Cataloging in Publication Data

International Congress on Isozymes (4th : 1982 : Austin, Tex.)
  Cellular localization, metabolism, and physiology.

  (Isozymes ; v. 8)
  "The second of five volumes constituting the proceedings of the
4th International Congress on Isozymes, held in Austin, Texas,
June 14–19, 1982."
  Includes bibliographies.
  1. Isoenzymes—Congresses. I. Rattazzi, Mario C.
II. Scandalios, John G. III. Whitt, Gregory S.
IV. Title. V. Series. [DNLM: 1. Isozymes—Congresses.
W1 IS62 v.8 / QU 135 I5876 1982c]
QP601.I77   vol. 8   574.19'25s [574.19'25]   83-7915
ISBN 0-8451-0257-5

Contents

Contributors

Dharam P. Agarwal [175] Institute of Human Genetics, University of Hamburg, 2000 Hamburg 54, Butenfeld 32, Federal Republic of Germany

Thomas J. Bazzone [219] Center for Biochemical and Biophysical Sciences and Medicine, Harvard Medical School, Boston, Massachusetts 02115

James N. Burnell [155] School of Science, Griffith University, Nathan 4111; *present address* CSIRO Division of Plant Industry, Canberra, ACT, Australia

Graham S. Byng [115] Center for Somatic-cell Genetics and Biochemistry, State University of New York at Binghamton, Binghamton, New York 13901

P. Boon Chock [141] Laboratory of Biochemistry, National Heart, Lung, and Blood Institute, National Institutes of Health, Bethesda, Maryland 20205

G.P. Dobson [91] Department of Zoology, University of British Columbia, Vancouver, BC V6T 2A9, Canada

John A. Duley [155] School of Science, Griffith University, Nathan 4111, Queensland, Australia

H. Werner Goedde [175] Institute of Human Genetics, University of Hamburg, 2000 Hamburg 54, Butenfeld 32, Federal Republic of Germany

Shoji Harada [175] Institute of Human Genetics, University of Hamburg, 2000 Hamburg 54, Butenfeld 32, Federal Republic of Germany

Marija Herbert [23] Institute of Plant Physiology and Cell Biology, Free University of Berlin, Königin-Luise-Str. 12-16a, D-1000 Berlin 33, Federal Republic of Germany

P.W. Hochachka [91] Department of Zoology, University of British Columbia, Vancouver, BC V6T 2A9, Canada

Roger S. Holmes [155] School of Science, Griffith University, Nathan 4111, Queensland, Australia

Roy A. Jensen [115] Center for Somatic-cell Genetics and Biochemistry, State University of New York at Binghamton, Binghamton, New York 13901

Ingo Krüger [23] Institute of Plant Physiology and Cell Biology, Free University of Berlin, Königen-Luise-Str. 12-16a, D-1000 Berlin 33, Federal Republic of Germany

Colin Masters [1] School of Science, Griffith University, Brisbane 4111, Queensland, Australia

David E. McMillin [67] Department of Biological Sciences, North Texas State University, Box 5318, Denton, Texas 76203

T.P. Mommsen [91] Department of Zoology, University of British Columbia, Vancouver, BC V6T 2A9, Canada; *present address* Department of Biology, Dalhousie University, Halifax, Nova Scotia, Canada

Regina Pietruszko [195] Center of Alcohol Studies, Rutgers University, New Brunswick, New Jersey 08903

The number in brackets is the opening page number of the contributor's article.

Sue Goo Rhee [141] Laboratory of Biochemistry, National Heart, Lung, and Blood Institute, National Institutes of Health, Bethesda, Maryland 20205

John G. Scandalios [67] Department of Genetics, North Carolina State University, Box 5487, Raleigh, North Carolina 27650

Claus Schnarrenberger [23] Institute of Plant Physiology and Cell Biology, Free University of Berlin, Königin-Luise-Str. 12-16a, D-1000 Berlin 33, Federal Republic of Germany

Norman F. Weeden [53] Department of Seed and Vegetable Sciences, Cornell University, Geneva, New York 14456

Bert L. Vallee [219] Center for Biochemical and Biophysical Sciences and Medicine, Harvard Medical School, Boston, Massachusetts 02115

Akira Yoshida [245] Department of Biochemical Genetics, City of Hope Research Institute, Duarte, California 91010

Contents of Other Volumes Containing the Proceedings of The 4th International Congress of Isozymes

Volume 7
Molecular Structure and Regulation

Volume 9
Gene Expression and Development

Volume 11
Medical and Other Applications

Preface

Since the origin of the isozyme concept and the recognition of the biological significance of isozymes in 1959, by Clement L. Markert, these gene products have served as powerful probes of molecular, genetic, developmental, physiological, and evolutionary mechanisms. The present series **Isozymes: Current Topics in Biological and Medical Research**, founded in 1977, has been used to review the progress of research in all the various biological disciplines utilizing isozymes. This series has been successful in making the point that the isozyme concept and technology transcend traditional biological disciplines.

The general theme of the series continues to be the roles of isozymes in the biology of prokaryotes, plants, man, and other animals. One goal is to provide the reader with the most contemporary concepts and state-of-the-art technology in the area of isozyme research. The other goal is to illustrate the diversity of experimental approaches used to study isozymes and the versatility of isozymes as research tools. The editors believe that it is important to communicate these diverse perspectives which have proven successful in testing hypotheses at different levels of biological organization.

Isozymes are present in the cells of all organisms. Ultimately, all enzymes exist as allelic isozymes, but many also exist as multilocus isozymes, and as isozymes formed by epigenetic events. Because isozymes can have different genetic and molecular bases as well as different functional roles, they are not only intrinsically interesting, from a structural or functional point of view, to protein chemists, molecular and cellular biologists, and physiologists, but are also powerful probes of fundamental mechanisms such as gene regulation, transmission, and evolution, and can provide an insight into the molecular mechanisms of pathological processes. This series, therefore, is aimed at readers with very diverse backgrounds and interests. By stressing the interdisciplinary nature of isozyme research, the editors hope to encourage the reader to bridge the apparent conceptual gap between the role of isozymes in the molecular ecology of the cell and the impact they have at the organismic and species levels.

After the publication of the proceedings of the 4th International Congress on Isozymes in topical volumes 7, 8, 9, 10, and 11 each successive volume will continue to provide different general and specific topics, ensuring a wide coverage of established fields as well as burgeoning new ones to which the study of isozymes is significantly contributing.

M.C.R.
J.G.S.
G.S.W.

Foreword

Since the recognition of multiple molecular forms of enzymes in 1959, isozymes have been studied or used as markers in a wide range of biochemical, biological, and biomedical investigations. On four occasions since the birth of isozymes as a concept, researchers from around the world have gathered to discuss their work and to be brought up to date on the technologies employed and the novel applications of these probes. These International Congresses on Isozymes have proven to be extremely stimulating interdisciplinary events. Each has resulted in significant publications that have proved helpful to scientists from many disciplines.

The Fourth International Congress on Isozymes was held on the campus of the University of Texas at Austin, Texas, in June of 1982. There were 265 participants, 85 symposium presentations, 5 workshop exhibitions, and 65 poster displays. The symposium presentations illustrated well the many genetic and molecular bases of isozymes, their tissue-specific and subcellular localization, their control in development and disease, and their practical application to biomedical problems. Many presentations also illustrated the power of isozymes for analyzing genetic linkage, evolution, systematics, breeding, biochemical pathways, gene regulation, nucleic acid metabolism, and mutagenesis. The edited proceedings of these symposia, which will be presented in volumes 7, 8, 9, 10, and 11 of **Isozymes: Current Topics in Biological and Medical Research**, provide a state-of-the-art perspective on isozyme research.

Finally, we would like to acknowledge the financial help for the Congress provided by the National Science Foundation, Yale University, The University of Texas, and a number of private contributors: Alan R. Liss, Inc. (New York, New York); Bayer AG/Cutter/Miles (Elkhart, Indiana); Beckman Instruments (Palo Alto, California); Boehringer-Mannheim (Indianapolis, Indiana); Cetus Corporation (Berkeley, California); Chemetron (Milano, Italia); Continental Water Company (Austin, Texas); Fisher Scientific Co. (Houston, Texas); Isolab, Inc. (Akron, Ohio); The Monsanto Company (St. Louis, Missouri); New England Nuclear (Boston, Massachusetts); Newport Corporation (Fountain Valley, California); Revlon Corporation (Tuckahoe, New York); Sartorius Filters (Haywood, California); Schering-Plough (Bloomfield, New Jersey); and Warner-Lambert Diagnostics (Morris Plains, New Jersey).

Michael J. Siciliano,
Organizer of the 4th
International Congress on Isozymes
Mario C. Rattazzi
John G. Scandalios
Gregory S. Whitt

Subcellular Localization of Isozymes—an Overview

Colin Masters

School of Science, Griffith University, Brisbane 4111, Australia

I. INTRODUCTION

A notable characteristic of isozymes is their specific localization—a phenomenon which is observable not only at the tissue and cellular level, but also at the subcellular level. Just as the tissue-specific patterns of activity tend to be associated with the metabolic advantages of such separate positioning, so the subcellular distributions of activity tend to reflect intracellular organization and compartmentation of cellular functions which is of fundamental importance in higher organisms. Hence, an understanding of the subcellular distribution of isozymes would seem essential to any satisfying comprehension of the cellular processes [Holmes and Masters, 1979].

There are technical difficulties which attend any definitive specifications of the subcellular disposition of multiple enzyme forms, however, and the nature of these difficulties and the experimental alternatives need to be defined at an early stage of any overview of this topic. The most widely used technique employed in the study of the subcellular localization of enzymes, for example, is undoubtedly *differential centrifugation,* where tissues are homogenized and their organelles separated on the basis of their different size-shape-density characteristics [Hogeboom, 1955]. Cell fractionation studies such as these have proved of immense general value to cell biologists, but, in the present context it needs to be recognized that it is difficult to completely obviate the possibility of artifactual modification during the separatory process. Apart from the trauma associated with homogenization, one of the greatest difficulties arises from the necessary choice of a suspension medium for the cell components. Ideally this medium should so approximate the soluble phase of the cytoplasm that the cellular constituents remain unaltered, but the perfect medium has not yet been devised. Most of the available fractionation procedures are subject to the criticism that their use may lead to the loss of water-soluble components from the particulate fractions, the transfer of substances between the soluble phases, and the retention of such substances by adsorption to the membranes and organelles, or a degree of cross-contamination within the particulate fractions. These possibilities emphasize the need for cautious interpretation of results, especially in regard to the exactitude of the intracellular distribution of isozymes.

Particularly difficult problems occur in relation to the exact definition of subcellular localization in the case of the so called "soluble" enzymes, ie, the enzymes which are normally characterized as components of the cytosol. This is particularly unfortunate in the present context as many of the archetypal and best-characterized isozyme systems are classified as "soluble" and are often resolved on the basis of their charge characteristics. Nevertheless, as we shall see in a later section of this review, evidence from a number of sources has been mounting in recent years, and a meaningful statement on the microlocalization and interactions of many of these cytosol enzymes now seems possible.

In this overview of the subcellular distribution of isozymes, examples are given of the characteristic distribution of isozymes among the subcellular compartments in mammalian systems, mention is made of the physiological advantage conferred by this distribution in some instances, and attention is directed toward the genetic, epigenetic, and evolutionary involvements of these phenomena. In addition, two particular aspects of the subcellular distribution of isozymes, which are the center of considerable topical interest, have been developed in more detail—namely, the interactions between ambiquitous (newly coined term) isozymes, subcellular structure, and metabolic regulation, and the contributions which knowledge of the subcellular distribution of isozymes can make to complex biological phenomena such as organelle biogenesis.

II. ISOZYMES PREDOMINANTLY LOCALIZED WITHIN INDIVIDUAL SUBCELLULAR COMPARTMENTS

A. Cytoplasmic Isozymes

Where the total activity of a particular enzyme has been identified as existing within one particular subcellular compartment, it follows that the multiple forms of that activity will also be similarly located, and there are a large number of isozyme systems whose gross activities have been identified as being associated with individual subcellular fractions.

On the basis of studies involving the classical methods of subcellular fractionation, the enzymes of glycolysis and the pentose phosphate pathway, for example, are commonly recognized as "soluble" enzymes, and many of the individual components have been intensively studied with respect to the existence and molecular basis of isozymic contributions. It is beyond the scope of this review to examine each glycolytic enzyme in detail, but the major features have been listed in Table I. Pyruvate kinase may be taken as one example of the possibilities of metabolic divergence and differential function offered by these systems. Liver pyruvate kinase (B_4) is an allosteric enzyme which is positively modulated by fructose diphosphate and negatively modulated by adenosine triphosphate (ATP) and alanine [Cardenas et al, 1975]. Consequently, the isozyme may be viewed as possessing a significant control function. In contrast, the muscle isozyme (A_4) is nonallosteric and is geared kinetically to the rapid metabolic activity required for glycolysis in muscle.

However, the differential distribution of glycolytic isozymes cannot always be explained in terms of kinetic parameters of tissue distribution; other

TABLE I. Multiple Forms of Glycolytic Enzymes

Enzyme	Multiple forms
Hexokinase	A, B, C, D, E
Phosphoglucomutase	A, B, C
Phosphofructokinase	A_4, B_4, AB hybrids, C_4, AC hybrids
Aldolase	A_4, B_4, AB hybrids, C_4, AC hybrids
Fructose bisphosphatase	A_4, B_4
Phosphoglycerate kinase	A, B
Enolase	A2, AB hybrids, B_2, C_2, BC hybrids
Pyruvate kinase	A_4, B_4, BC hybrids, C_4, AB hybrids
Lactate dehydrogenase	A_4, AB hybrids, B_4, C_4, BC hybrids

factors such as enzyme turnover, microlocalization, macromolecular associations, and independent gene regulation also need to be considered [Masters, 1977].

B. Nuclear Isozymes

The DNA and RNA polymerases may be taken as examples of isozyme systems which are predominantly localized within the nucleus. In the latter case, for example, the DNA-dependent RNA polymerase (E.C.2.7.7.6) from eukaryotes exists as structurally distinct species designated I, II, and III [Roeder, 1976]. These enzymes mediate the synthesis, respectively, of the large ribosomal RNAs (rRNA), the heterogeneous nuclear RNAs, and the 5S and transfer RNA (tRNA) and are compartmentalized within the nucleus in the nucleolus (class I) and the nucleoplasm (classes II and III).

C. Microsomal Isozymes

Carboxylesterases may be cited as an example of microsomal isozyme systems. Subcellular fractionation studies have demonstrated that carboxylesterases are predominantly localized in the "microsomal" fraction of liver extracts [Dixon and Webb, 1964] and, at the fine structural level, electron microscopic analyses of mammalian tissue sections have reported the histochemical reaction products to be deposited primarily on the membranous elements of the smooth and rough endoplasmic reticulum.

A characteristic feature of carboxylesterases is the extensive degree of multiplicity which is often displayed [review by Masters and Holmes, 1975]. Mouse esterases, in particular, have been extensively studied and at least 13 esterase structural genes have been demonstrated for this organism [reviewed by Chapman et al, 1978].

D. Peroxisomal Isozymes

L-α-hydroxyacid oxidase (E.C.1.1.3.1; HAOX) is a flavoenzyme that catalyzes the oxidation of L-α-hydroxyacids according to the following reaction:

$$
\begin{array}{ccc}
R & & R \\
| & & | \\
CHOH & + \; O_2 \rightleftharpoons & CO \; + \; H_2O_2 \\
| & & | \\
COO^- & & COO^-
\end{array}
$$

The enzyme exists as two isozymes in mammalian tissues, the properties of which have been recently reviewed [Masters and Holmes, 1977]. HAOX-A_4 (commonly referred to as glycolate oxidase or the liver isozyme of HAOX) preferentially oxidizes short-chain aliphatic hydroxyacids, whereas HAOX-B_4 (the kidney isozyme) exhibits no activity with glycolate but oxidizes a variety of other L-α-hydroxyacids, particularly long-chain aliphatic and aromatic hydroxyacids [Ushijima and Nakano, 1969].

The isozymes are predominantly localized within liver and kidney peroxisomes [de Duve and Baudhuin, 1966; McGroarty et al, 1974]; however, significant activities are also found in the cytoplasm of liver and kidney extracts [Duley, 1976].

E. Lysosomal Isozymes

β-glucuronidase is differentially localized in mammalian liver extracts between the microsomal, Golgi, and lysosomal fractions and exhibits extensive heterogeneity and a distinct pattern in the subcellular distribution of the multiple forms. The forms are apparently epigenetically derived from a single polypeptide chain by means of sialation and proteolysis, and may represent different stages in the biosynthesis and intracellular transport of the enzyme to the lysosomes. Their biochemical properties, intracellular localization, and genetic control have been extensively studied, and readers are referred to an excellent review on this area for further details [Lusis and Paigen, 1978].

III. ISOZYMES DIFFERENTIALLY DISTRIBUTED BETWEEN CELLULAR COMPARTMENTS

Simply on the basis of the structural divergences of multiple enzyme forms it would not be surprising to find that differential subcellular distributions of isozymes are a relatively common occurrence, and, indeed, there are a large number of such examples in the literature. Some examples of the major types of subcellular distribution are listed in this section.

A. Mitochondrial and Cytoplasmic Isozymes

Several enzymes exist as genetically distinct forms which are differentially distributed between the mitochondria and the cytoplasm (Table II). These include a number of the tricarboxylic acid cycle enzymes in the soluble matrix, enzymes involved in amino acid transamination, or functioning in gluconeogenesis, NADPH generation, detoxification of aldehyde and superoxide radicals, and in energy transfer.

Malate dehydrogenase (MDH; E.C.1.1.1.37), for example, functions in malate oxidation by catalyzing the following reversible reaction in the citric acid cycle: L-malate + NAD^+ $\rightleftharpoons$ oxaloacetate + $NADH$ + H^+. Early studies on this enzyme demonstrated a differential localization of two isozymes in the cytoplasm and in mitochondria [Kitto and Kaplan, 1966]. The isozymes are encoded by distinct nuclear genes in the mouse [Shows et al, 1970] and have dimeric subunit structures [Kitto and Kaplan, 1966].

Cytoplasmic and mitochondrial MDH are broadly distributed in mammalian tissues and apparently perform distinct physiologic roles in the cell. Their behavior is consistent with the mitochondrial enzyme catalyzing malate oxidation (a reaction necessary for proper functioning of the citrate cycle) and with the soluble enzyme being involved with the reduction of oxaloacetate (thus ensuring an adequate supply of cytoplasmic malate required in lipogenic and reducing-equivalent "shuttle" reactions) [Hanson et al, 1971].

TABLE II. Isozymes Differentially Distributed Between the Mitochondria and Cytoplasm

Mitochondrial function	Enzyme
Citrate cycle	Malate dehydrogenase
	Isocitrate dehydrogenase
	Aconitase
Amino acid metabolism	Aspartate aminotransferase
	Alanine aminotransferase
	Tryosine aminotransferase
Gluconeogenesis	PEP carboxykinase
Detoxification	Aldehyde dehydrogenase
	Superoxide dismutase
Energy transfer/ Phosphorylation	Deoxycytidine kinase
	Thymidine kinase
	Creatine kinase
	Adenylate kinase
NADPH generation	Malic enzyme

B. Lysosomal and Cytoplasmic Isozymes

The acid phosphatases provide one example of an isozyme system which displays differential distributions of activity between the lysosomal and cytoplasmic compartments. These enzymes (E.C.3.1.32) can be broadly subdivided into two major classes on the basis of molecular weight, subunit structure, and subcellular localization. The low-molecular-weight isozyme is localized in the cytoplasm of red cells and all tissues examined [Swallow et al, 1973], while the high-molecular-weight (100,000–120,000) isozymes are localized in the lysosomes [de Aranjo et al, 1976] of placenta, liver, and other tissues. Sialic acid residues apparently contribute to the molecular heterogeneity of tissue acid phosphatases [Harris and Hopkinson, 1976].

C. Peroxisomal and Cytoplasmic Catalase

A number of studies have demonstrated a differential subcellular distribution of catalase. In the mouse, catalase exhibits a distinctive multiplicity of the five major forms of activity [Masters and Holmes, 1977], the most acidic form (catalase-1) being localized in liver peroxisomes, whereas the cytoplasm exhibited four major forms of activity (catalases-2, -3, -4, -5). Genetic and biochemical analyses have demonstrated an epigenetic basis of multiplicity, apparently associated with a process of progressive desialation of the fully sialated form in peroxisomes and microsomes [Jones and Masters, 1975; Holmes and Duley, 1975], and the significance of this phenomenon with respect to catalase microlocalization and turnover is discussed in a later section of this review.

D. Microsomal and Soluble Isozymes

Glucose-6-phosphate dehydrogenase (G6PH) exists as two isozymes in mammalian cells which catalyze the reaction: glucose-6-phosphate $+$ NADP$^+$ $\rightleftharpoons$ 6-phosphogluconate $+$ NADPH $+$ H$^+$. The isozymes show considerable differences in biochemical properties and genetic control and have been designated as separate enzymes by the Enzyme Commission because of their distinct substrate specificities. One (G6PD) is specific for glucose-6-phosphate and NADP (E.C.1.1.1.49), whereas the other (hexose-6-phosphate dehydrogenase, H6PD; glucose dehydrogenase) can utilize various hexose-6-phosphates and glucose as substrates with either NAD or NADP as the coenzyme (E.C.1.1.1.47) [Beutler and Morrison, 1967].

G6PD is predominantly localized in the cytoplasm of vertebrate cells, whereas H6PD is most active in the endoplasmic reticulum of liver and kidney extracts [Beutler and Morrison, 1967]. G6PD is sex linked in eutherian and marsupial mammals [Richardson et al, 1971], while H6PD is autosomally inherited in mammals [Shaw, 1976; Ohno et al, 1966].

The physiologic function of cytoplasmic G6PD is well known to consist of catalyzing the essential first step of the pentose phosphate pathway and providing adequate levels of NADPH for reductive synthesis of steroids and fatty acid. In contrast, the metabolic role of H6PD is not clearly understood, although it has been proposed that the isozyme facilitates the oxidation of hexoses other than glucose and also glucose utilization in livers of species with undetectable levels of glucokinase [Shatton et al, 1971].

IV. AN OVERVIEW OF SUBCELLULAR LOCALIZATION

The above examples provide an outline of the basic characteristics of the subcellular distribution of isozymes—the broad picture which emerges from an examination and analysis of the literature on this topic. The reader is referred to specialized reviews for more detailed comments [Holmes and Masters. 1979].

Despite the brevity of the foregoing comments, however, it should be clear that there is substantial evidence of a differential localization of isozymes within the cell and a distinct indication of metabolic and evolutionary advantage in such dispositions.

It should also be kept in mind, however, that these reported localizations are not universal or absolute in nature and are subject to many individual variables. The details of isozyme distribution may differ significantly between tissues in the same species, between the same organs in different species, or between different developmental stages of a particular organism [Holmes and Masters, 1979]. Clearly, care is necessary in relating particular findings to a more general context.

As to the basis of ontogenetic and phylogenetic variation of isozyme distribution, much of this information may be rationalized in terms of the occurrence of distinctive binding sites on these enzymes, ie, sites for the binding of substrates and sites governing interactions between enzyme and structure (Fig. 1).

Whether the isozymes are the products of the multiple loci or are formed by posttranslational changes of the product of a single locus [Markert and Whitt, 1968; Masters and Holmes, 1975]—for example, their qualitatively similar substrate specificity may be taken as indicating a conservation of the active site and modification of the respective "carrier" protein. If such modifications alter the charge characteristics within an isozyme set, the changes may be seen as likely to affect not only their separation in vitro, but also the relative positioning of the isozymes in regard to other charged elements of cellular architecture in vivo.

If, on the other hand, the modifications between isozymes are of a character that affect the disposition of uncharged residues in the carrier protein, they

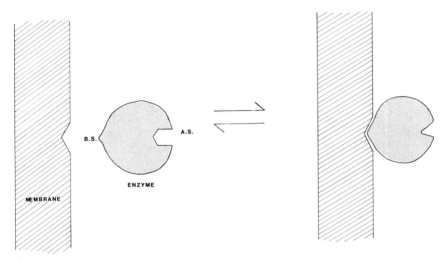

Fig. 1. Diagrammatic representation of the interaction between a soluble isozyme and cellular structure. The principle features are the presence of sites for both substrate (A.S.) and binding activities (B.S.) on the enzyme, the occurrence of reversible binding between soluble and particulate components, and the possibility of attendant conformational changes.

would still be expected to influence the conformation of the protein and its binding affinity for other cellular components. Such alterations may result in a change of the disposition of hydrophobic groups in a contact site affecting protein:protein interaction, for example, or have an influence on the shape or polarity of a recognition site concerned with protein:lipid or protein:carbohydrate interactions. In any of the cases a marked alteration in the dispositional tendencies of the isozyme within the cell may result.

Despite a tendency toward the opposite conclusion in the earlier literature, both functional and structural considerations indicate that the differential subcellular localization of isozymes may logically be viewed as a general expectation rather than an exception.

V. INTERACTIONS BETWEEN ISOZYMES AND CELLULAR STRUCTURE

A. Examples of Interactions

In recent years there has been increasing acceptance of the possibility that the enzymes of the cytosol may interact with the cellular matrices or be organized into multienzymic complexes. The available data are now strongly in favor of these possibilities, the occurrence of sites on these enzymes which govern the interactions, and the isozyme-specific characteristics of binding to cellular structure [Masters, 1981].

One further aspect of major importance in considerations of the role of cytosolic enzymes in interactions is the influence of adsorption on the catalytic properties of the enzyme. It is becoming increasingly clear that binding to particulate material may significantly modify the kinetic parameters of an enzyme. This being so, the role of the enzyme in metabolism may also be influenced, and, to cite one case in point, the data of Karadsheh and Uyeda [1977] might be mentioned (Fig. 2). These workers have shown that there is a specific interaction between phosphofructokinase and the inner surface of the erythrocyte membrane. Associated with this binding is a change in the allosteric properties of the enzyme. Unlike free phosphofructokinase, the membrane bound enzyme is not inhibited by ATP or 2,3-diphosphoglycerate, and its fructose-6-phosphate saturation curve reverts to a nonsigmoidal shape. Apparently the interaction has reduced or "frozen" the conformational flexibility of the enzyme. Results such as these obviously imply that the classical regulatory role of this key allosteric enzyme may be markedly influenced by adsorption to cellular structure and that the biological function of other enzymes may also be quite different than that assumed on the basis of monophasic kinetics.

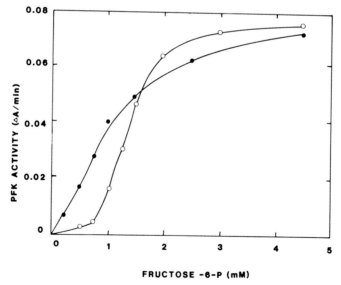

Fig. 2.   Fructose-6-phosphate saturation curves for membrane-bound phosphofructokinase (●) and the free soluble enzyme [after Karasheh and Uyeda, 1977].

This specific interaction behavior has been observed with a number of other isozyme systems too—eg, lactate dehydrogenase, hexokinase, aldolase, creatine phosphokinase, and glyceraldehyde-3-phosphate dehydrogenase have all been shown to exhibit kinetics which are modified by the interactions with cellular structure—and hence a major new element is introduced to considerations of the role of isozymes in cellular metabolism and its regulation [Masters, 1981].

B. Enzyme Ambiquity

Adding further point to the significance of such interactions is the fact that a number of investigators have reported that the subcellular distribution of some enzymes may not be invariant even in a single tissue of defined maturity—rather, the degree of interaction may be a dynamic characteristic which alters in response to the changing metabolic needs of the cell [Masters, 1981]. To describe such a situation where the distribution of an enzyme between soluble and particulate forms may vary with the metabolic status of the cell, the term "ambiquitous enzyme" has been coined [Wilson, 1978].

An example of ambiquity in an in vivo situation is that provided by the multiple forms of certain glycolytic enzymes in mammalian tissues. Several of these enzymes have been shown to bind significantly to the thin filaments of muscle, for example, and when these muscles are stimulated a quite considerable redistribution of enzyme activity occurs between the soluble: particulate fractions. As indicated in Table III, when one hindlimb of a sheep

TABLE III. Effect of Tetanic Stimulation on Enzyme Binding and Glycolysis in Sheep M. Semitendinosus[a]

	Bound (%)	
	Control	Stimulated
Hexokinase	6.2 ± 2.4	4.9 ± 0.7
Glucose phosphate isomerase	6.6 ± 0.1	7.6 ± 0.8
Phosphofructokinase	12.8 ± 6.3	26.1 ± 5.5
Aldolase	35.0 ± 4.4	45.6 ± 5.1
Triose phosphate isomerase	11.0 ± 3.4	9.1 ± 2.1
Glyceraldehyde-3-phosphate dehydrogenase	25.3 ± 1.5	39.1 ± 7.8
Phosphoglyceric kinase	15.4 ± 1.8	16.8 ± 0.2
Phosphoglyceric mutase	10.5 ± 7.4	15.0 ± 0.3
Enolase	13.0 ± 4.4	16.4 ± 5.0
Pyruvate kinase	14.1 ± 2.2	15.2 ± 0.6
Lactate dehydrogenase	12.0 ± 1.6	15.4 ± 0.2

[a]For experimental details, see Walsh et al, 1981.

was electrically stimulated, the proportion of certain enzymes in these two fractions was significantly altered by comparison with that in the control limb. The extent of these alterations was dependent on a number of factors, such as the extent of stimulation and the individual muscle type involved, but the overall effect was an increased binding of phosphofructokinase, aldolase, and glyceraldehyde-3-phosphate dehydrogenase, in particular. Similarly, when the effect of anoxia and ischemia on the distribution of glycolytic enzymes in perfused rat heart was studied, marked increases in binding were observed which were especially dramatic in the case of aldolase activity.

Further examples of redistribution of enzyme localization with physiological stimuli are also evident in the literature. Knull et al [1974] have demonstrated a redistribution of brain hexokinase between the mitochondrial and cytosolic fractions during ischemia. From all of these experiments, it should be quite apparent that changes in the extent of binding of enzymes to structure occur along with alteration of the functional status of tissues.

C. Implications of Interactions

Surveys of the literature reveal that a substantial body of evidence is now available to support the biological reality of interactions between the enzymic components of the cytosol and the structural elements of cells. The characteristics of such binding have been studied in some detail in both in vivo and in vitro systems, and it is clear that the kinetic parameters of the enzymes may be significantly modified by these interactions with structure and that alterations in the extent of binding occur in response to changes in the metabolic state of a tissue. It is also clear that the binding is isozyme-specific in many cases. When considered in toto, these findings appear to indicate that such interactions display the scope for a major contribution to metabolic regulation.

Further information is required in relation to many aspects of these interactions of isozymes, however. It has not yet been established, for example, whether or not a multiplicity of pathways catalyzing similar functions may exist in a cell or tissue, in the same manner that isozymes are distributed with high specificity, or whether such multiple metabolic alternatives play a significant role in cellular regulation. It must be conceded as possible, for example, that the high degree of multiplicity which is observable in the individual glycolytic enzymes, and their demonstrably different adsorption characteristics, may lead to the presence of a number of discrete systems of glycolytic components in individual tissues and the effective partitioning of these functional systems between different subcellular or tissue compartments. Ureta [1978] has suggested that there may be up to ten separate polyisozymic complexes associated with glucose metabolism in some tissues. Such considerations stress the need for continuing studies at this level of organization in order to achieve a satisfying comprehension of the manner in which the cell may utilize these characteristics of multiplicity and interaction in determining its remarkably versatile metabolic capabilities.

VI. ORGANELLE BIOGENESIS

One further example of the increasing role of isozymes and their subcellular distribution in cellular biology is provided by a consideration of organelle biogenesis.

A. Catalase Multiplicity and Subcellular Distribution

In the case of peroxisomes, for example, we have already noted that the enzyme catalase is differentially distributed between the cytoplasmic and peroxisomal compartments. This subcellular distribution affords unique insight into the processes involved in peroxisomal biogenesis.

In the peroxisomes of mouse liver, for example, catalase is typically present as the anodic form (cat-1), whereas the cytosol is represented by the more cathodic forms (cats-2, -3, -4, -5) (Fig. 3). When taken in conjunction with other differential inhibitory and cytochemical studies on the distinctive nature of peroxisomal and cytosolic catalase [Jones and Masters, 1972; Roel,

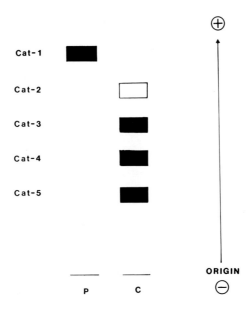

Fig. 3. Zymograms of mouse liver catalase from the peroxisomal (left-hand slot) and cytosolic fractions (right-hand slot).

1976], these data may be taken as providing strong evidence for the *native occurrence* of catalase activity in the *cytosol*—a delineation which is difficult to establish on the basis of differential centrifugation alone.

These data also provide a useful means of studying the temporal relationships of these pools. The incorporation of radioactive iron has been followed into the individual catalase heteromorphs of mouse liver, for example, with catalase-1 being indicated as the first synthesized form, and with subsequent progressive desialation leading to the forms characteristic of the cytosol [Jones and Masters, 1974; Fig. 4]. Clearly then, a *precursor-product* relationship exists between the peroxisomal and cytosolic pools of catalase.

It has also been possible to distinguish between two pools of catalase activity within the peroxisome by means of fractional extraction procedures. One pool of activity may be extracted with buffer alone (the peroxisomal aqueous extract, PAE), whereas the second pool of activity requires treatment of the peroxisome with detergent such as Triton X-100 (the peroxisomal detergent extract, PDE). When this methodology was used in combination with the analysis of incorporation of isotope into the multiple forms of catalase (Figs. 4,5), evidence was provided that the major portion of the newly synthesized catalase was rapidly incorporated into the peroxisome membrane.

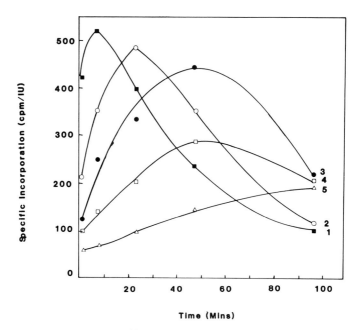

Fig. 4. The temporal sequence of ^{55}Fe incorporation into catalase isozymes. Catalase-1 (■), -2 (○), -3 (●), -4 (□), -5 (△).

Later, the catalase became freed from this tight association and existed within the peroxisome in a form which was readily extractable in aqueous solution. This catalase was then released into the cytosol and eventually degraded. Hence the multiplicity of mouse liver catalase may be taken as a manifestation of the intracellular sequestration and degradation of the enzyme [Masters and Holmes, 1977, 1979].

In looking at the nature of the degradation sequence in cytosol in more detail, the multiple forms of mouse liver catalase were separated by means of an *isoelectric focussing* fractionation, and the heme content, specific activity, and specific incorporation of amino triazole in these fractions were studied (Table IV). While the heteromorphs did display differences in their heme content, these differences did not appear to be of a magnitude or proportion which was sufficient to explain the marked differences in specific

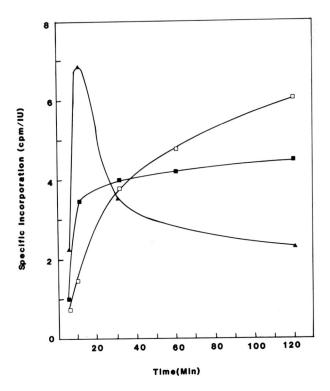

Fig. 5. The temporal sequence of ^{55}Fe incorporation into the detergent extract of the peroxisomal fraction (▲), the aqueous extract of the peroxisomal fraction (□), and the supernatant fraction (■).

TABLE IV. Properties of the Aged Forms of Catalase[a]

Activity pool	Specific activity (IU/mg)	Specific activity heme	Specific activity ^{14}C-AT incorporation
Pool 2	75,000	18,800	12.0
Pool 3	65,000	18,800	10.9
Pool 4	34,500	10,100	11.7
Pool 5	25,600	8,500	11.2

[a]Catalase was separated into its heteromorphs by narrow-range isoelectric focussing (pH 8.5). Peaks of activity were pooled, dialyzed, and concentrated. Hematin was determined by the pyridine hemochromagen method, and irreversible inactivation with ^{14}C-amino-triazole.

activity. On the other hand, an excellent correlation was found to exist between the specific activities and specific incorporations of amino triazol into the different heteromorphs [Jones and Masters, 1975]. Since amino triazol is known to bind to histidine-74 of catalase and to require a fully active heme group before covalent binding occurs, these facts would seem to indicate that degradation of this enzyme in the cytosol is accompanied not only by desialation, but also by chemical and or *conformational changes* which affect the active site of the molecule. These changes probably include the conversion of heme to biliverdin and other related pigments.

One further example of the way in which catalase multiplicity may afford interesting insight into the *temporal relationships* of the separate pools of catalase within the liver cells might be cited. Figure 6 shows the kinetics of induction in the peroxisomal and cytosolic pools of liver catalase activity with mice which had been injected with ethyl chlorophenoxyisobutyrate (CPIB). As a result of treatment with this hypolipidemic agent and peroxisome pro-liferator, catalase activity is seen to increase rapidly in the supernatant pool and to reach a peak value of nearly ten times that of control after five days. In the granular pool of catalase activity, by contrast, there was an initial decrease in catalase activity following this treatment. A level of less than half of the controls occurred at three days after the beginning of treatment, and, thereafter, the level of activity progressively increased in the pool to reach a peak value at five days. Examination of the electrophoretic nature of the catalase confirmed that the increase in cytosol activity involved ca-talases-3–5 (ie, the "oldest" catalase species).

The *simplest interpretation* of these results, and one with interesting control connotations, is that the level of supernatant catalase determines the level of peroxisomal catalase. Thus, the initial increase in catalase activity in the cytosol with this treatment results from an increased efflux of this enzyme

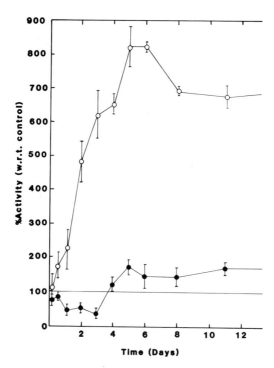

Fig. 6. Diagrammatic representation of the response of liver catalase in the mouse to treatment with clofibrate (CPIB) ● cytoplasmic catalase; ○ peroxisomal catalase.

from the peroxisome, and this increase in activity of the active "end products" of catalase metabolism may act to feed back and trigger an increased synthesis of peroxisomal catalase.

B. A Model for Peroxisomal Biogenesis and Turnover

Taken in conjunction, the data from these separate aspects of peroxisomal turnover have allowed formulation of a model of peroxisomal biogenesis and catalase transport—the essential characteristics of which are represented in Figure 7.

In accord with the concepts of the signal hypothesis [Blobel and Dobberstein, 1975], the newly synthesized catalase apomonomer is envisaged as containing a putative signal sequence, which interacts with a receptor of the membrane of the nascent peroxisome and apomonomer is viewed as passing through the resulting pore in the peroxisomal membrane, but not completely—it remains attached by the carboxy terminal peptide. No proteolytic

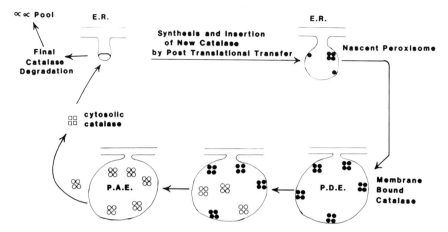

Fig. 7. A representation of the role of catalase in peroxisomal biogenesis. Aged catalase (□) binds to specialized areas of the endoplasmic reticulum, triggers the synthesis of catalase monomers which are inserted into the nascent peroxisome, where catalase is present initially in association with the membrane (●) and then is converted to a more loosely associated form (○).

excision of the signal peptide is envisaged at this stage. Subsequently, heme group insertion and formation of the tetrameric enzyme takes place in peroxisome.

The peroxisomal enzyme may subsequently be traced through a stage of decreased association with the peroxisomal membrane and, after release of catalase into the cytosol, this stage is followed by a series of chemical changes to the enzyme, including desialation and conformational modifications to the active site. In this working model, it is suggested that this aged form of catalase still retains the signal sequence, and hence the capacity to bind receptor sites on specialized regions of the endoplasmic reticulum. The conversion of newly synthesized catalase to an aged form of the enzyme thus completes a feedback loop in peroxisomal turnover.

In further support of the relevance of feedback considerations to this model, it may be noted that the recent experiments in our laboratory have shown that incubation of a mouse liver cytosol extract with endoplasmic reticulum results in an appreciable uptake of the slowest moving cytosol catalase multiple forms, ie, aged catalase.

Mention should also be made of the fact that the case for a logical connection between catalase levels in the cell and microbody proliferation has circulated in the literature previously [Svoboda and Azarnoff, 1966]. These suggestions seem to have been discounted because of the lack of correlation between the specific activity of peroxisomal catalase and proliferation but, as indicated in the present data, the establishment of the cytoplasmic pool of aged catalase as the relevant index sheds new light on this possibility.

Finally, it may be pointed out that the present model is in accordance with the kinetics of labeling of catalase, reported earlier, which showed that the various subcellular parts of activity are related to each other in a distinct precursor product relationship. The existence of feedback relationships may require the retention of the signal region in the catalase molecule throughout the full cycle of synthesis, membrane attachment, release from peroxisomes, aging, and stimulation of peroxisomal proliferation; and hence this model favors the concept of a retained or internal form of signal in this case.

At this stage, there are still a number of aspects of this model which warrent further investigation, but hopefully these data have provided a useful example of how an extremely complex biological process (ie, peroxisomal biogenesis) may obtain clarification from a knowledge of the subcellular distribution of isozymes.

VII. CONCLUSIONS

In summary, then, the intracellular localization of isozymes is viewed as an aspect of enzyme multiplicity which seems bound to attract increasing consideration in future years, and one which should contribute significantly to many areas of topical interest in cellular biology.

In relation to the evolutionary aspects, phylogenetic variations in the subcellular distributions of isozymes may now be rationalized in terms of the existence of two classes of sites on these isozymes—active sites governing the expression of enzyme activity, and interactive sites governing the interactions between enzyme and subcellular structures.

Similarly, the realization that the subcellular distribution of isozymes is not invariant for a particular species of a particular stage of ontogeny, but may vary significantly and rapidly with the metabolic status of a tissue, opens new vistas in relation to the regulation of metabolism, and may also be analyzed in terms of separate active and interactive sites.

In regard to organelle biogenesis, studies of lysosomal and mitochondrial biogenesis have already shown the benefits of the isozyme approach, and this technique is likely to be much more widely utilized in future studies of this type.

VIII. ACKNOWLEDGMENTS

The author wishes to acknowledge the contributions of Roger Holmes, Denis Crane, Michael Kuter, and Stephen Reid in these investigations, and the financial assistance of the Australian Research Grants Committee.

IX. REFERENCES

Beutler E, Morrison M (1967): Localization and characteristics of hexose 6-phosphate dehydrogenase (glucose dehydrogenase). J Biol Chem 242:5289–5293.

Blobel G, Dobberstein B (1975): Transfer of proteins across membranes. I. J Cell Biol 67:835–844.

Cardenas JM, Dyson RD, Strandholm JJ (1975): Bovine and chicken pyruvate kinase isozymes intraspecies and interspecies hybrids. In Markert CL (ed): "Isozymes. I, Molecular Structure." New York: Academic, pp 523–541.

Chapman A, Hoogenraad NG, Holmes RS (1978): Purification of aldolase from rabbit liver. Biochem J 175:377–382.

de Aranjo PS, Mies V, Miranda O (1976): Subcellular distribution of low- and high-molecular-weight acid phosphatases. Biochim Biophys Acta 452:121–130.

de Duve C, Baudhuin P (1966): Peroxisomes (microbodies and related particles). Physiol Rev 46:323–357.

Dixon M, Webb EC (1964): "Enzymes." London: Longmans.

Duley JA (1976): "L-α-Hydroxyacid Oxidase Isozymes." Doctoral dissertation, La Trobe University, Australia.

Hanson RW, Patel MS, Rashet L, Ballard FJ (1971): The role of pyruvate carboxylase and Penolpyruvate carboxylase in rat adipose tissue. In Söling HD, Willms B (eds): "Regulation of Gluconeogenesis." New York: Academic, pp 255–276.

Harris H, Hopkinson DA (1976): "Handbook of Enzyme Electrophoresis in Human Genetics." Amsterdam: North Holland.

Hogeboom GH (1955): Fractionation of cell components of animal tissues. Methods Enzymol 1:16–19.

Holmes RS, Duley JA (1975): Biochemical and genetic studies of peroxisomal multiple enzyme systems: α-hydroxyacid oxidase and catalase. In Markert CL (ed): "Isozymes. I. Molecular Structure." New York: Academic pp 191–211.

Holmes RS, Masters CJ (1979): Subcellular localization of isozymes. Isozymes: Curr Top Biol Med Res 3:53–114.

Jones GL, Masters CJ (1972): On the differential inhibition of the multiple forms of catalase in mouse tissues. FEBS Lett 21:207–210.

Jones GL, Masters CJ (1974): On the synthesis and degradation of the multiple forms of catalase in mouse liver. Arch Biochem Biophys 161:601–609.

Jones GL, Masters CJ (1975): On the nature and characteristics of the multiple forms of catalase in mouse liver. Arch Biochem Biophys 169:7–21.

Karadsheh NS, Uyeda K (1977): Changes in allosteric properties of phosphofructokinase bound to erythrocyte membranes. J Biol Chem 252:7418–7420.

Kitto GB, Kaplan NO (1966): Purification and properties of chicken heart mitochondrial and supernatant malic dehydrogenases. Biochemistry 5:3966–3980.

Knull HR, Taylor WF, Wells WH (1974): Insulin effects on brain energy metabolism and the related hexokinase distribution. J Biol Chem 249:6930–6935.

Lusis AJ, Paigen K (1978): Mechanisms involved in the intracellular localization of mouse glucuronidase. In Ratazzi MC, Scandalios JG, Whitt GS (eds): "Isozymes: Current Topics in Biological and Medical Research." New York: Alan R. Liss, Vol 2.

Markert CL, Whitt GS (1968): Molecular varieties of isozymes. Experientia 24:977–991.

Masters CJ (1977): Metabolic regulation and the microenvironment. Curr Top Cell Regul 12:75–105.

Masters CJ (1981): Interactions between soluble enzymes and subcellular structure. CRC Crit Rev Biochem 11:105–144.

Masters CJ, Holmes RS (1975): "Haemoglobin, Isoenzymes and Tissue Differentiation." Amsterdam: North Holland.

Masters CJ, Holmes RS (1977): Peroxisomes: New aspects of cell biology and biochemistry. Physiol Rev 57:816–882.

Masters CJ, Holmes RS (1979): Peroxisomes: Their metabolic roles in mammalian tissues. TIBS 4:233–236.

McGroarty E, Hsieh B, Wied DM, Gee R, Tolbert NE (1974): Alpha hydroxyacid oxidation by peroxisomes. Arch Biochem Biophys 161:194–210.

Ohno S, Payne HW, Morrison M, Beutler E (1966): Hexose 6-phosphate dehydrogenase found in human liver. Science 153:1015–1016.

Richardson BJ, Czuppon AP, Sharman GB (1971): Inheritance of glucose 6-phosphate dehydrogenase variation in kangaroos. Nature 230:154–155.

Roeder RG (1976): Eukaryotic nuclear RNA polymerase. In Losick R, Chamberlain M (eds): "RNA Polymerases." Cold Spring Harbor Press, New York, pp 285–329.

Roel SF (1976): Cytochemical demonstration of extraperoxisomal catalase. J Histochem Cytochem 24:713–724.

Shatton JB, Halver JB, Weinhouse S (1971): Glucose (hexose 6-phosphate) dehydrogenase in liver of rainbow trout. J Biol Chem 246:4878–4885.

Shaw CR (1976): Glucose 6-phosphate dehydrogenase: Homogolcous molecules in deer mouse and man. Science 153:1013–1015.

Shows TB, Chapman VM, Ruddle FH (1970): Mitochondrial malate dehydrogenase and malic enzyme: Mendelian inherited variants in the mouse. Biochem Genet 4:707–718.

Svoboda DJ, Azarnoff DL (1966): Response of hepatic microbodies to a hypolipidemic agent, ethyl chlorophenoxyisobutyrate (CPIB). J Cell Biol 32:442–450.

Swallow DM, Povey S, Harris H (1973): Activity of the "red cell" acid phosphatase locus in other tissues. Ann Hum Genet 37:31–38.

Ureta T (1978): The role of isozymes in metabolism: A model of metabolic pathways as the basis for the biological role of isozymes. In Horecker BL, Stadtman ER (eds): "Current Topics in Cellular Regulation." New York: Academic Press, Vol *13* pp 233–258.

Ushijima Y, Nakano M (1969): Aliphatic L-α-hydroxyacid oxidases from rat liver. Biochim Biophys Acta 178:429–433.

Walsh TP, Masters CJ, Morton DJ, Clarke FM (1981): The reversible binding of glycolytic enzymes in ovine skeletal muscle in response to tetanic stimulation. Biochim Biophys Acta 675:27–39.

Wilson JE (1978): Ambiquitous enzymes: Variation in intracellular distribution as a regulatory mechanism. Trends Biochem Sci 3:124–125.

Isozymes: Current Topics in Biological and Medical Research
Volume 8: Cellular Localization, Metabolism, and Physiology 23–51

Intracellular Compartmentation of Isozymes of Sugar Phosphate Metabolism in Green Leaves

Claus Schnarrenberger, Marija Herbert, and Ingo Krüger

Institute of Plant Physiology and Cell Biology, Free University of Berlin, Königin-Luise-Str. 12-16a, D-1000 Berlin 33, Federal Republic of Germany

I. INTRODUCTION

The existence, development, and regulation of plant isozymes have been described in numerous reports. Plant isozymes have also been recognized in the case of a limited number of enzyme activities, and plant species as products of multiple genes or alleles. These include, eg, isozymes for catalase, alcohol dehydrogenase, peptidase, glutamate oxalacetate transaminase, starch-metabolizing enzymes, and others, mostly from wheat and corn [see literature cited in Scandalios, 1974; Hart, 1979a; Jaaska, 1976; Ott and Scandalios, 1978; Boyer and Preiss, 1978, 1981]. Such genetically defined isozymes, in turn, have been the basis for successful classification of plant populations or for the detection of evolutionary relationships among plant populations, eg, date palms [Torres and Tisserat, 1980], avocado plants [Torres and Bergh, 1978], beans [Gates and Boulter, 1979], Clarkia [Gottlieb and Weeden, 1979; Gottlieb, 1977, 1973], wheat [Jaaska, 1976; Hart, 1979a], potatoes [Stegemann and Loeschcke, 1977], or rice [Park and Stegemann, 1979].

Another approach to isozymes was developed when it was discovered that isozymes existed in plant tissues in which an enzyme activity was present in more than one subcellular location. In such cases the enzyme activity in the different cellular compartments was due to different isozymes. One of the earliest and most prominent examples were three to five isozymes of malate dehydrogenase which were specifically located either in the mitochondria, in the peroxisomes, or in the cytosol, eg, from spinach leaves [Yamazaki and Tolbert, 1969; Rocha and Ting, 1970], from corn [Longo and Scandalios, 1969], or from watermelon cotyledons [Hock, 1973]. These isozymes are thought to function as a shuttle system for transferring reducing equivalents between several cell compartments. At the same time Anderson and Advani [1970] reported two isozymes each of aldolase, triosephosphate isomerase, and 3-P-glycerate kinase in pea leaves, one in the chloroplasts and the other in the cytosol of a cell. During the last decade similar isozymes have been detected for other activities of sugar phosphate metabolism. Today, evidence exists for duplicate sets of isozymes for glycolysis, gluconeogenesis, and for the oxidative pentose phosphate pathway which are compartmentalized in the chloroplast and in the cytosol. In this paper we will summarize the evidence for cell-compartment-specific isozymes of sugar phosphate metabolism in various plants and point out their function in providing duplicate pathways in cellular spaces which are seperated by the semipermeable inner chloroplast envelope membrane. In addition we will show immunological evidence for major structural differences between such isozymes.

II. MATERIALS AND METHODS

A. Materials

The following plant species have been used: The C_3 plants Spinacia oleracea L (spinach), Triticum aestivum L (wheat), Nicotiana tabacum L (tobacco), the C_4 plants Zea mays L (corn), Saccharum officinale L (sugarcane), Coix lacryma-jobi L, Atriplex spongiosa L, Portulaca oleracea L, the CAM plants Crassula lycopodioides Lam, Bryophyllum calycinum Salisb, Sedum rubrotinctum R T Clausen, and the green algae Chlorella vulgaris Beyerinck, strain *211-11f*, and Chlamydomonas reinhardii Dangeard, strain *137C*, mating type + , a derivative of strain *CW-2* [Davies and Plaskit, 1971].

B. Enzyme Assays

All enzymes have been assayed spectrophotometrically in a 1-ml mixture at 20° C by measuring absorbance changes at 340 nm. The following assay procedures are listed in Herbert et al [1979]: phosphoglucomutase (EC 2.7.5.1), glucose-6-phosphate dehydrogenase (EC 1.1.1.49), 6-phosphogluconate dehydrogenase (EC 1.1.1.43), glucosephosphate isomerase (EC 5.3.1.4), hydroxypyruvate reductase (1.1.1.81), cytochrome *c* oxidase (EC 1.9.3.1), phosphoenolpyruvate carboxylase (EC 4.1.1.31), and ribulosebisphosphate carboxylase (EC 4.1.1.39). Phosphofructokinase (EC 2.7.1.11) was assayed according to Kelly and Latzko [1977], hexosediphosphatase (EC 3.1.3.11) at pH 8.8 according to Latzko et al [1974], fructose-bisphosphate aldolase (EC 4.1.2.13) according to Wu and Racker [1959], glyceraldehyde-phosphate dehydrogenase ($NADP^+$) (phosphorylating) (EC 1.2.1.13) and glyceraldehyde-phosphate dehydrogenase (EC 1.2.1.12) according to Heber et al [1963], glyceraldehyde-phosphate dehydrogenase ($NADP^+$) (EC 1.2.1.9) according to Kelly and Gibbs [1973], phosphoglycerate kinase (EC 2.7.2.3) according to Pacold and Anderson [1975], phosphoglycerate phosphomutase (EC 5.4.2.1) and enolase (EC 4.2.1.11) according to Kahl et al [1969], chlorophyll according to Arnon [1949], and protein according to Bradford [1976]. Triosephosphate isomerase (EC 5.3.1.1) was coupled to glyceraldehyde-phosphate dehydrogenase and phosphoglycerate kinase; the reaction was initiated with 10 mM dihydroxy-acetonephosphate instead of 3-phosphoglycerate in the assay system described by Velick [1955]. $(NH_4)_2SO_4$ and sucrose concentrations were determined by refractometry.

C. Cell Fractionation

Cell organelles were prepared from spinach leaves by isopycnic centrifugation in sucrose gradients as described by Schnarrenberger and Burkhard

[1977]. Glycylglycine (20 mM pH 7.5) was used as buffer in both grinding medium and gradient.

D. Isolation of Mesophyll Protoplasts and Bundle Sheath Strands

Mesophyll protoplasts and bundle sheath strands were prepared from the C_4 plants corn and Atriplex spongiosa according to the enzymatic method published by Kanai and Edwards [1973] and Huber and Edwards [1975]. Details were described in the paper by Herbert et al [1979].

E. Separation and Purification of Isozymes

Two methods have been used to separate isozymes from plant tissues, ie, anion-exchange chromatography on diethylaminoethyl (DEAE)-cellulose and $(NH_4)_2SO_4$ gradient solubilization. Both methods were described in detail in Schnarrenberger and Oeser [1974]. Particularly during chromatography on DEAE-cellulose it was essential to control strictly pH and salt concentrations in order to bind all activity and to avoid artifacts.

Glucosephosphate isomerase-2 from spinach leaves was purified to homogeneity by a newly developed method and glucosephosphate isomerase-1 was enriched 80-fold [Herbert and Schnarrenberger, 1982]. Glucosephosphate isomerase-1 from Escherichia coli and rabbit antibodies against it [Schreyer and Böck, 1980] were a gift from Drs. R. Schreyer and A. Böck (University of Munich, FRG). Yeast and rabbit muscle glucosephosphate isomerase were obtained from Boehringer (Mannheim, FRG) or Sigma (Munich, FRG), respectively. Aldolase-1 and -2 from spinach and the aldolase from corn were purified to homogeneity by the combined procedures of Fluri et al [1967], Anderson et al [1975], and Heil and Lebherz [1978; Krüger and Schnarrenberger, unpublished].

F. Preparation of Antibodies and Immunochemical Assays

Antibodies against purified glucosephosphate isomerases were prepared in guinea pigs by injecting 30 to 100 μg of protein emulsified with complete Freund's adjuvant into the footpads of guinea pigs three times in weekly intervals [Herbert and Schnarrenberger, 1982]. After an additional three days the animals were exsanguinated. Antibodies against purified aldolases were prepared by immunizing a rabbit or a guinea pig [Krüger and Schnarrenberger, unpublished].

Cross-reaction between glucosephosphate isomerases was tested by the Ouchterlony double diffusion test [Ouchterlony, 1949]. In another assay, the immune complexes were absorbed to protein A on the cell wall of Staphylococcus aureus Cowan I cells [Kessler, 1975] by mixing and incubating 20 μl of enzyme and 20 μl antiserum (or dilutions of it) for ten minutes in Eppendorf tubes and adding 5 μm of 12% Immuno-Precipitin (Bethesda

Research Laboratories, Neuisenburg, FRG). After an additional incubation for five minutes the suspension was centrifuged and nonbound glucosephosphate isomerase activity was determined in the supernatant fraction [Herbert and Schnarrenberger, 1982].

III. RESULTS

A. Isozymes in Spinach Leaves

1. Intracellular localization of enzyme activities. It was a major task during the late 1950s and early 1960s to determine the intracellular location of enzymes of sugar phosphate metabolism, particularly of the Calvin cycle enzymes. Based on aqueous and nonaqueous cell fractionation studies it was found that all Calvin cycle enzymes were present in the chloroplasts and some of them were in the cytosol as well [see eg Smillie, 1963].

In this paper we have employed isopycnic centrifugation in a sucrose gradient to separate cell organelles. Peroxisomes, mitochondria, and whole and broken chloroplasts were identified by the respective marker enzymes hydroxypyruvate dehydrogenase, cytochrome c oxidase, NADP: glyceraldehyde-phosphate dehydrogenase, and the two chlorophyll peaks [Schnarrenberger and Fock, 1976]. All enzymes of sugar phosphate metabolism (except three) show activity in the whole chloroplast and in the supernatant fraction, the latter representing activity of cytosolic enzymes and of solubilized enzymes (Fig. 1). Some of the enzymes show also a smaller peak of activity in the broken chloroplast fraction. These have been found to be enzymes bound to thylakoids [for literature see Ben-Bassat and Anderson, 1981].

The enzymes found in the chloroplasts are due to enzymes in this compartment. However, the presence of an additional enzyme in the supernatant is difficult to assess since preparative conditions during organelle isolation may have a different impact on stability, and thus recovery, of different enzymes and isozymes unless specified for each enzyme. Besides enzymes in the chloroplasts there are three enzymes which are fully restricted to the supernatant fraction, ie, the nonreversible glyceraldehyde-phosphate dehydrogenase (NADP$^+$), the phosphoglycerate mutase, and the enolase. The glyceraldehyde-phosphate dehydrogenase reaction can be accomplished by other glyceraldehyde-phosphate dehydrogenases in the chloroplasts and cytosol despite the exclusive localization of the nonreversible glycerladehyde-phosphate dehydrogenase in the cytosol. However, the exclusive compartmentation of the mutase and enolase implies that sugar phosphate metabolism beyond 3-phosphoglycerate cannot take place in the chloroplasts.

2. Separation and intracellular compartmentation of isozymes. The primary strategy in separating isozymes is to apply preparative methods. This

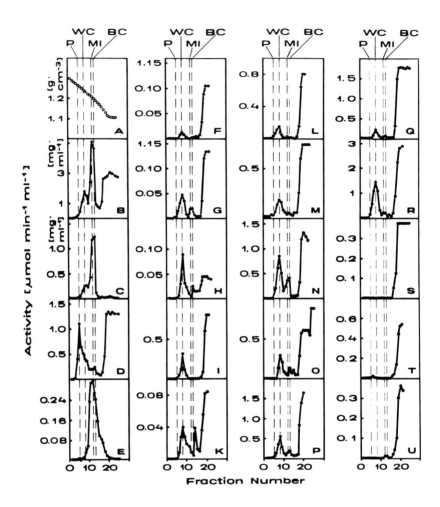

Fig. 1. Distribution of enzyme activities in fractions of a sucrose gradient after separation of cell organelles from spinach leaves by isopycnic centrifugation. (WC) A. Sucrose density. B. Protein. C. Chlorophyll for whole (BC) (small peak) and broken (P) chloroplasts (large peak). D. Hydroxypyruvate dehydrogenase for peroxisomes (MI). E. Cytochrome *c* oxidase for mitochondria (MI). F. Glucose-6-phosphate dehydrogenase. G. 6-phosphogluconate dehydrogenase. H. Phosphorylase. I. Hexosediphosphatase. K. Phosphofructokinase. L. Phosphoglucomutase. M. Glucosephosphate isomerase. N. Fructose-bisphosphate aldolase. O. Triosephosphate isomerase. P. Glyceraldehyde-phosphate dehydrogenase. Q. Glyceraldehyde-phosphate ($NADP^+$) (phosphorylating). R. Phosphoglycerate kinase. S. Glyceraldehyde-phosphate dehydrogenase ($NADP^+$). T. Phosphoglycerate mutase. U. Enolase.

way many causes of artifacts can be avoided and preparations can be used subsequently for biochemical characterization and purification of isozymes. The most successful methods in the past proved to be ion-exchange chromatography, $(NH_4)_2SO_4$ gradient solubilization, and isoelectric focusing. With few exceptions, molecular weights of plant isoenzymes differ too little to yield satisfactory separation by methods depending solely on molecular size.

If proteins of spinach leaves are separated by anion-exchange chromatography of DEAE-cellulose or by $(NH_4)_2SO_4$ gradient solubilization (Fig. 2) two isozymes can be recognized from the type of elution pattern for the following activities: phosphoglucomutase, glucose-6-phosphate dehydrogenase, 6-phosphogluconate dehydrogenase, glucosephosphate isomerase, hexosediphosphatase, phosphofructokinase, fructose-bisphosphate aldolase, triosephosphate isomerase, and phosphoglycerate kinase. For the latter two the separation is not very clear-cut by the method applied. If instead proteins from isolated chloroplasts are used only one homogeneous peak of activity is recovered. These results imply that two isozymes exist in spinach leaf cells for the activities tested and that only one of these is located in the chloroplasts. Based upon the data in Figure 1 the cytosol would be the only other cellular compartment in question for the other isozymes.

For glycerladehyde-phosphate dehydrogenase there are an nicotinamide-adenine dincleotide (NAD)-dependent enzyme and a nonreversible, NADP-dependent enzyme in the cytosol and two isozymes in the chloroplasts which both can utilize either $NADP^+$ or NAD^+ as a cofactor. The latter two isozymes had also been found by Cerff and Chambers [1979] in mustard and barley, while the nonreversible enzyme was described first by Kelly and Gibbs [1973].

Phosphoglycerate mutase and enolase appear to exist as single enzymes in the cytosol of spinach leaf cells [Achenbach, 1980].

3. Implications of multiple pathways by isozymes. The existence and intracellular compartmentation of two isozymes for activities of sugar phosphate metabolism has mainly been developed for spinach and pea leaves. Subsequently this was extended for developing and germinating castor bean (Ricinus communis L) seeds by also showing that one of each two isozymes was restricted to isolated plastids. Recently, Weeden and Gottlieb [1979, 1980a] have demonstrated the localization of similar isozymes in pollen of several plants. When soaked for four hours in an appropriate buffer pollen only releases cytosolic isozymes but not isozymes from plastids. Table I shows a synopsis of evidence for plastid/cytosol compartmentalized isozymes from the literature.

The conclusion from the data in Table I and Figure 2 is that complete pathways exist in plant cells in the form of duplicate sets of isozymes, located seperately in the plastids and in the cytosol. This applies in green leaves to

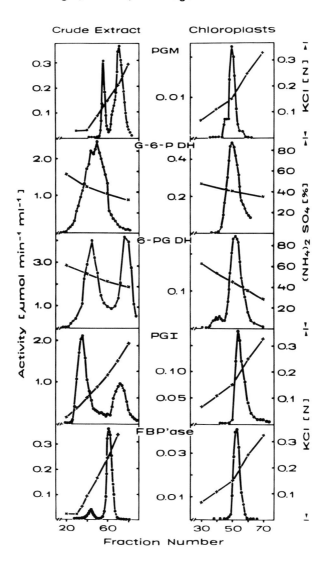

Fig. 2.   Separation of isoenzymes from a crude extract (left) or chloroplast preparations (right) of spinach leaves by anion-exchange chromatography on diethylaminoethyl (DEAE)-cellulose or by $(NH_4)_2SO_4$ gradient solubilization. Closed circles represent activities and crosses represent KCl concentrations or $(NH_4)_2SO_4$ saturations. PGM, phosphoglucomutase; G-6-P DH, glucose-6-phosphate dehydrogenase; 6-PG DH, 6-phosphogluconate dehydrogenase; PGI, glucose-phosphate isomerase; FBP'ase, hexosediphosphatase; PFK, phosphofructokinase; Aldolase, fructose-bisphosphate aldolase; TPI, triosephosphate isomerase; $NAD^+/NADP^+$ GAP DH, NAD^+ (○)- and $NADP^+$ (●)-dependent glyceraldehyde-phosphate dehydrogenase; 3-PGA Kinase, 3-phosphoglycerate kinase.

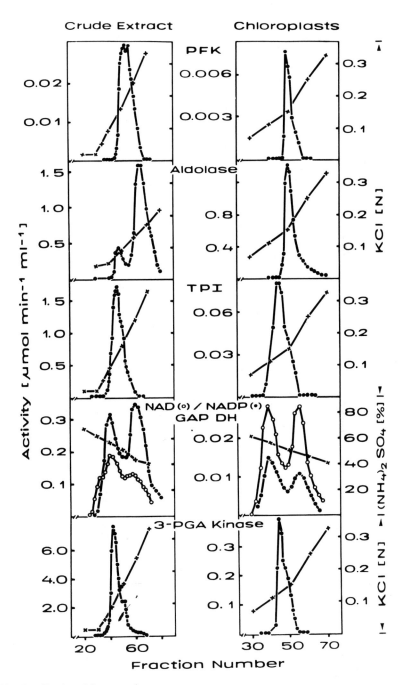

Fig. 2. Continued from previous page.

TABLE I. Evidence for Specific Isoenzymes in Plastids and Cytosol

Enzyme activity	Plant tissue	Isoenzymes in plastids/cytosol	References
1. Starch phosphorylase	Spinach and pea leaves	1/1	Steup and Latzko [1979]
		2/1	Steup et al [1980]
2. Phosphogluco-mutase	Spinach leaves	1/1	Mühlbach and Schnarrenberger [1978]
	Spinach and pea pollen	1/1	Weeden and Gottlieb [1980a]
	Ricinus, germinating endosperm	1/1	Nishimura and Beevers [1981]
3. Glucose-6-phosphate dehydrogenase	Spinach leaves	1/1	Schnarrenberger et al [1973]
	Pea leaves	1/1	Anderson et al [1974]
4. 6-Phosphogluconate dehydrogenase	Spinach leaves	1/1	Schnarrenberger et al [1973]
	Ricinus, developing endosperm, germinating endosperm	1/1	Simcox and Dennis [1978] Nishimura and Beevers [1981]
5. Glucose-phosphate isomerase	Spinach leaves	1/1	Schnarrenberger and Oeser [1974]
		1/1	Herbert et al [1979]
		1/1	Weeden and Gottlieb [1979, 1980a]
	Ricinus, germinating endosperm	1/1	Nishimura and Beevers [1981]
6. Ribosephosphate isomerase	Pea leaves		Anderson [1971b]

Enzyme	Source	Ratio	Reference
7. Phosphofructokinase	Spinach leaves	1/1	Kelly and Latzko [1977]
	Ricinus, developing and germinating endosperm	1/1	Garland and Dennis [1980]
		1/1	Nishimura and Beevers [1981]
8. Hexosediphosphatase	Spinach leaves	1/1	Latzko et al [1974]
9. Fructose-bisphosphate aldolase	Ricinus, germinating endosperm	1/1	Nishimura and Beevers [1981]
	Pea leaves	1/1	Anderson and Advani [1970]
		1/1	Anderson and Pacold [1972]
10. Triosephosphate isomerase	Pea leaves	1/1	Anderson and Advani [1970]
		1/1	[Anderson 1971a]
	Spinach and pea pollen	1/1	Weeden and Gottlieb [1980a,b]
	Ricinus, developing endosperm	1/1	Miernyk and Dennis [1982]
11. Glyceraldehyde-phosphate dehydrogenase	Spinach leaves	1/1	Heber et al [1963]
	Pea pollen	2/1	Cerff and Chambers [1978]
	Ricinus, developing endosperm	1/1	Miernyk and Dennis [1982]
12. Phosphoglycerate kinase	Pea leaves	1/1	Anderson and Advani [1970]
		1/1	Pacold and Anderson [1975]
	Ricinus, developing endosperm	1/1	Miernyk and Dennis [1982]

glycolysis and gluconeogenesis for all reactions between starch and 3-phosphoglycerate and to the oxidative pentose phosphate pathway for most reactions including the two key dehydrogenases. For reactions beyond 3-phosphoglycerate, there are only enzymes in the cytosol, restricting the pathways to this compartment. This holds true for 3-phosphoglycerate mutase from pea shoots [Stitt and ap Rees, 1979] and spinach leaves [Achenbach, 1980] and for enolase in spinach leaves [Achenbach, 1980]. However, Miernyk and Dennis [1982] have recently described an additional isozyme for 3-phosphoglycerate mutase and enolase in plastids from developing castor bean endosperm, so that such isozymes may have to be looked for in green leaf cells again.

The functional significance for duplicate sets of isozymes for glycolysis, gluconeogenesis, and the oxidative pentose phosphate pathway is to be seen in the limited permeability of the inner chloroplast envelope membrane for most substrates and cofactors of the enzymes involved [Walker, 1976]. If exchange of metabolites between chloroplasts and cytosol does not proceed via diffusion, there are only four translocators for a direct or indirect transport by diffusion-limited countercurrent exchange, ie, a phosphate translocator, a dicarboxylate translocator, an adenylate translocator [Heldt, 1976], and a glucose translocator [Schäfer and Heber, 1977]. In order to bypass the limited permeability of the inner chloroplast envelope membrane, plant cells have apparently developed and/or maintained duplicate sets of isoenzymes for three pathways of the sugar phosphate metabolism. This makes the general function of these three pathways possible in both the chloroplasts and the cytosol despite the limited permeability of the inner chlorplast envelope membrane. These four possibilities of interaction between chloroplasts and cytosol are summarized in Figure 3.

Isozymes can function in more than one pathway in a particular cell compartment. This is obvious for most activities of glycolysis and gluconeogenesis in the chloroplasts and in the cytosol. On the other hand, Calvin cycle metabolism is restricted to the chloroplasts even though many activities of the Calvin cycle exist as isozymes in the chloroplasts and in the cytosol. This is so since the lack of the two key reactions of the Calvin cycle in the cytosol, ie, of ribulose-5-phosphate kinase and ribulosebisphosphate carboxylase, and the impermeability of the inner chloroplast envelope membrane [Walker, 1976] do not allow this cycle to proceed in the cytosol.

Most pairs of isozymes have very similar catalytic properties and molecular weights. The most consistent differences between pairs of isozymes are the charge of the proteins—the chloroplast isozymes being mostly, but not always, more negatively charged than the cytosolic isozyme. In addition, chloroplast isozymes appear to be much more sensitive to surhydryl oxidation than the cytosolic counterparts. Differences in regulatory properties are lim-

Semipermeability of the chloroplast envelope

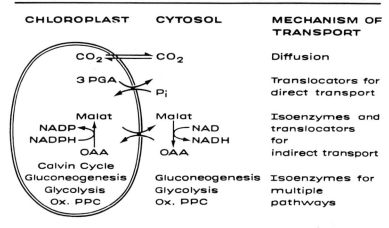

Fig. 3. Scheme illustrating four principles dealing with the semipermeability of the inner chloroplast envelope membrane, ie, diffusion, direct transport, indirect transport, and duplicate pathways by isoenzymes. 3PGA, 3-phosphoglycerate; OAA, oxalacetate; Ox. PPC, oxidative pentose phosphate cycle.

ited, but highly significant, particularly during dark-light-dark transitions in leaves. Some chloroplast isozymes are far more regulated by light-dependent changes of stromal pH and Mg^{2+} concentrations than the cytosolic counterparts, eg, hexosediphosphatase and 3-phosphoglycerate kinase, or by light modulation, eg, the NADP-dependent glyceraldehyde-phosphate dehydrogenase, hexosediphosphatase, glucose-6-phosphate dehydrogenase, and phosphofructokinase [see Anderson, 1979] or by inorganic phosphate [Kelly and Latzko, 1977].

B. Isozymes in Other Plants

1. Survey for isozymes in C_3, C_4, and CAM plants and algae. Whether the isozymes specific for chloroplasts and cytosol are present in all green plant cells or not is an intriguing question. In an extensive survey Bukowiecki and Anderson [1974] have shown by isoelectric focusing that two isozymes each of aldolase and triosephosphate isomerase are present in such diverse species as pea, Gingko biloba, Dioon spinulosum, Adiantum capillusveneris, Equisetum hymale, Psilotum nudum, Marchantia polymorpha, Pylaisiella selwnyii, and Euglena gracilis. In another survey Herbert et al [1979] have looked for isozymes in plants which differed in their mode of photosynthetic CO_2 fixation, ie, in the C_3 plants spinach, tobacco, and wheat, in the C_4 plants corn, sugarcane, Atriplex spongiosa, Portulaca oleracea, and Coix lacryma-jobi, in the CAM plants Crassula lycopodioides, Bryophyllum calycinum, and Sedum rubrotinctum, and in the two algae Chlamydomonas reinhardii and Chlorella vulgaris. For the four enzyme activities phosphoglucomutase, glucosephosphate isomerase, glucose-6-phosphate dehydrogenase, and 6-phosphogluconate dehydrogenase two isozymes each could be resolved by ion-exchange chromatography on DEAE-cellulose and $(NH_4)_2SO_4$ gradient solubilization in all species of C_3 plants, CAM plants, and algae (Table II). However, in all five species of C_4 plants three isozymes each were resolved for phosphoglucomutase and glucosephosphate isomerase. Only a single enzyme each for the two dehydrogenases was found in corn, sugarcane, and Coix lacryma-jobi and two isoenzymes in Atriplex spongiosa and Portulaca oleracea (Fig. 4).

C_4 plants were first recognized by Haberlandt [1881] as plants with a typical Kranz anatomy of their leaves—ie, there are just two layers of photosynthetic cells arranged as a wreath around each vascular bundle, a layer of bundle sheath cells inside and a layer of mesophyll cells outside (Fig. 5A). Today we know that C_4 plants have a higher potential photosynthetic capacity than C_3 plants. C_4 plants fix CO_2 twice, first by the C_4 dicarboxylate cycle in the mesophyll cells and, after liberation, a second time by the Calvin cycle in the bundle sheath cells [Hatch and Osmond, 1976].

2. Cellular distribution of isozymes in C_4 plants. The exclusive occurrence of more than two isozymes only in the C_4 plants implies that such isozymes might be specifically distributed between mesophyll and bundle sheath cells. When the two cell types were separated from corn (Fig. 5B,C)

TABLE II. Number of Isozymes Present in Several Plant Species as Revealed by Anion-Exchange Chromatography and $(NH_4)_2SO_4$ Gradient Solubilization

Plant type	Plant species	Phospho-gluco-mutase	Glucose-phosphate isomerase	Glucose-6-phosphate dehydrogenase	6-phospho-gluconate dehydrogenase
C_3 plants	Spinach	2	2	2	2
	Tobacco	2	2	2	2
	Wheat	2	2	2	2
C_4 plants	Corn	3	3	1	1
	Sugarcane	3	3	1	1
	Coix	3	3	1	1
	Atriplex	3	3	2	2
	Portulaca	3	3	2	2
CAM plants	Crassula	2	2	2	2
	Bryophyllum	2	2	2	2
	Sedum	2	2	2	2
Algae	Chlorella	2	2	2	2
	Chlamydomonas	2	2	2	2

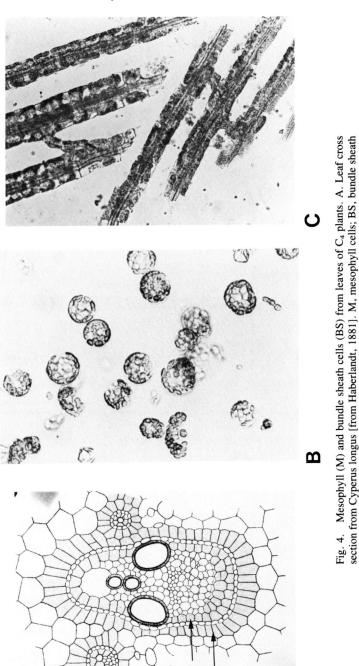

Fig. 4. Mesophyll (M) and bundle sheath cells (BS) from leaves of C_4 plants. A. Leaf cross section from Cyperus longus [from Haberlandt, 1881]. M, mesophyll cells; BS, bundle sheath cells. B. Isolated mesophyll protoplasts from corn leaves. C. Isolated bundle sheath strands from corn leaves.

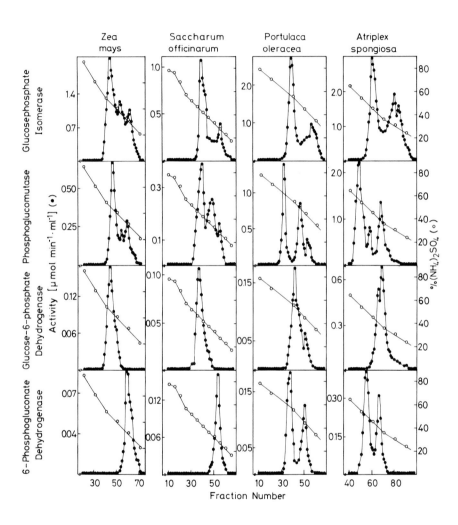

Fig. 5.   Separation of isoenzymes by $(NH_4)_2SO_4$ gradient solubilization for glucosephosphate isomerase, phosphoglucomutase, glucose-6-phosphate dehydrogenase, and 6-phosphogluconate dehydrogenase from leaves of corn, sugarcane, Portulaca oleracea, and Atriplex spongiosa [from Herbert et al, 1979].

and from Atriplex spongiosa leaves the activities of both phosphoglucomutase and glucosephosphate isomerase were found in both cell fractions, and glucose-6-phosphate dehydrogenase and 6-phosphogluconate dehydrogenase were found mainly in the mesophyll cell fraction, if compared with the distribution of the marker enzymes ribulosebisphosphate carboxylase and phosphoenolpyruvate carboxylase (Table III). This is consistent with previous reports on the intercellular distribution of these activities in C_4 plants [Hatch and Kagawa, 1973; Slack and Hatch, 1967]. Subjecting proteins from the two cell fractions of corn leaves to $(NH_4)_2SO_4$ gradient solubilization revealed one isozyme each of phosphoglucomutase and glucosephosphate isomerase in the mesophyll cells and the two other isozymes in the bundle sheath cells (Fig. 6). This means that in C_4 plants there are not only two isozymes which are specific for chloroplasts and for cytosol in bundle sheath cells, but there is

TABLE III. Intracellular Distribution of Phosphoglucomutase, Glucosephosphate Isomerase, Glucose-6-phosphate Dehydrogenase, and 6-Phosphogluconate Dehydrogenase and of the Two Marker Enzymes Ribulosebisphosphate (RuBP) Carboxylase and Phosphoenolpyruvate (PEP) Carboxylase in Bundle Sheath Strands and Mesophyll Protoplasts of Corn and Atriplex spongiosa

Plant species	Enzyme	Mesophyll protoplasts	Bundle sheath strands
Corn	Volume	3.8 ml	4.0 ml
	Protein	0.24 mg/ml^{-1}	0.18 mg/ml^{-1}
	RuBP carboxylase	30 mU/mg^{-1a}	389 mU/mg^{-1}
	PEP carboxylase	208 mU/mg^{-1}	11 mU/mg^{-1}
	Phosphoglucomutase	930 mU/mg^{-1}	844 mU/mg^{-1}
	Glucosephosphate isomerase	966 mU/mg^{-1}	422 mU/mg^{-1}
	Glucose-6-phosphate dehydrogenase	109 mU/mg^{-1}	17 mU/mg^{-1}
	6-Phosphogluconate dehydrogenase	46 mU/mg^{-1}	8 mU/mg^{-1}
Atriplex spongiosa	Volume	1.1 ml	0.85 ml
	Protein	0.9 mg	0.6 mg
	RuBP carboxylase	22 mU/mg^{-1}	142 mU/mg^{-1}
	PEP carboxylase	40 mU/mg^{-1}	10 mU/mg^{-1}
	Phosphoglucomutase	340 mU/mg^{-1}	304 mU/mg^{-1}
	Glucosephosphate isomerase	300 mU/mg^{-1}	192 mU/mg^{-1}
	Glucose-6-phosphate dehydrogenase	20 mU/mg^{-1}	20 mU/mg^{-1}
	6-Phosphogluconate dehydrogenase	36 mU/mg^{-1}	30 mU/mg^{-1}

[a]mU, 1 nmol min^{-1}.

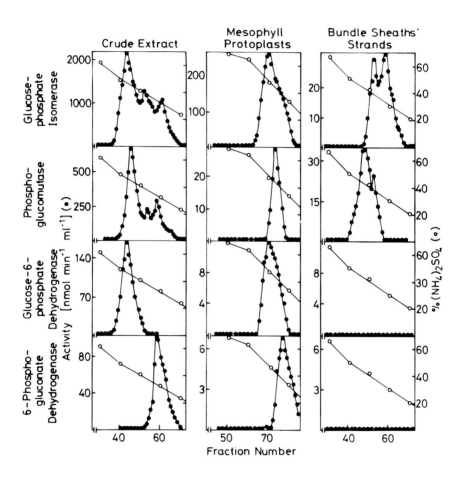

Fig. 6. Separation of isoenzymes from a crude extract, a mesophyll protoplast extract, and a bundle sheath strand extract of corn leaves by $(NH_4)_2SO_4$ gradient solubilization [from Herbert et al, 1979].

also another isozyme specific for another cell type, the mesophyll cells, with a yet unknown intracellular compartmentation.

3. Implications of cell-specific isozymes. Distinct isozymes of phosphoglucomutase and glucosephosphate isomerase in mesophyll and bundle sheath cells of C_4 plants manifest another principle for occurrence and compartmentation of isozymes in plants, ie, cell-specific isozymes. Prior to our findings, the presence of isozymes in the two cell types of C_4 plants had so far only been demonstrated for aspartate aminotransferase and alanine aminotransferase [Hatch and Mau, 1973; Hatch, 1973]. The functional significance of these isozymes is to be seen in a shuttle system between the two cell types. This scarcity of further information on isozymes in C_4 plants is mostly due to the difficulty of working with the rigid leaf tissue.

With respect to sugar phosphate metabolism there is much evidence that starch metabolism takes place in chloroplasts of plant leaf cells, and in those of the bundle sheath cells of C_4 plants in particular [Preiss and Levi, 1979] while sucrose metabolism is restricted to the cytosol of plant leaf cells and to the cytosol of both mesophyll and bundle sheath cells of C_4 plants [Whittingham et al, 1979]. It thus appears that the one isozyme of phosphoglucomutase and of glucosephosphate isomerase in the mesophyll cells is cytosolic and functions in sucrose metabolism, as does one of the two isozymes in the bundle sheath cells, while the third isozyme is a chloroplast enzyme and functions in starch metabolism of bundle sheath chloroplasts. There is a significant difference in the number of isozymes of glucose-6-phosphate dehydrogenase and 6-phosphogluconate dehydrogenase among the five species of C_4 plants. In corn, sugarcane, and Coix lacryma-jobi there is only one single enzyme for each, while in the two other species, Atriplex spongiosa and Portulaca oleracea, there are two isozymes for each. C_4 plants have been divided into three subgroups, which differ in the mode of CO_2 liberation [Hatch et al, 1975; Hattersley and Watson, 1976]. The number of enzymes of the two dehydrogenases correlates with the subgroups of plants in which they were found since the three species of corn, sugarcane, and Coix lacryma-jobi belong to the so-called NADP malic enzyme-type and the other two species to the NAD malic enzyme-type of C_4 plants. No plants of the phosphoenolpyruvate carboxykinase-type have been analyzed yet.

C. Immunochemical Comparison of Isozymes

1. Cross-reactivity of aldolases and glucosephosphate isomerases. Antisera have recently been used with great success for immunochemical comparisons of plant isozymes [Daussant, 1975]. Antigenic specificity can serve as a useful tool to determine differences and homologies between the organelle specific isozymes of sugar phosphate metabolism. We have recently produced antibodies against purified enzymes in guinea pigs and rabbits and looked for cross-reactivity between isozymes or the respective enzymes from other biological organisms.

The two isozymes of aldolase from spinach leaves and an aldolase from corn leaves have been purified to apparent homogeneity as judged from polyacrylamide gel electrophoresis in the presence of sodium dodecylsulfate (Fig. 7A–C). A guinea pig and a rabbit were immunized with the cytosolic and chloroplast aldolase from spinach leaves, respectively. Antisera were tested in the Ouchterlony double diffusion test for cross-reactivity. Only a single immunoprecipitin line formed between a given antiserum and the isozyme against which the antiserum had been raised; this antiserum did not recognize the other isozyme from spinach leaves (Fig. 8). This suggests that structural differences exist between the two isozymes from spinach leaves. Cross-reactivity was also observed between the antiserum against the chloroplast aldolase from spinach leaves and the aldolase from corn leaves, but antiserum against the cytosolic aldolase from spinach leaves did not cross-react with the corn leaf aldolase. These data imply a high degree of homology between the aldolase from spinach chloroplasts and the enzyme from corn

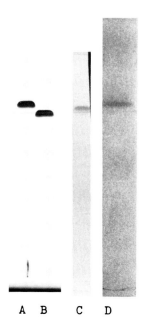

A B C D

Fig. 7. Protein pattern in polyacrylamide gels with 0.1% sodium dodecylsulfate after electrophoresis of purified chloroplast (A) and cytosolic (B) aldolase from spinach leaves, of a purified aldolase from corn leaves (C) and of purified glucosephosphate isomerase-2 (D) from spinach leaves. The gels were stained with Coomassie Blue R 250. The anode is at the top.

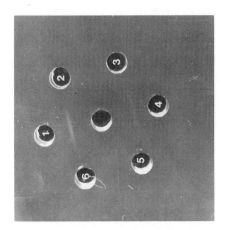

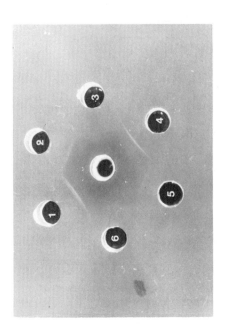

Fig. 8. Ouchterlony double diffusion test with antisera against the cytosolic (left) and chloroplast (right) fructose-bisphosphate aldolase from spinach leaves in the center wells. The left agar plate contained 2.5 μg (1) and 1.25 μg (4) cytosolic and 3.9 μg (2) and 2 μg (5) chloroplast aldolase from spinach leaves and 2.1 μg (3) and 1 μg (6) aldolase from corn leaves in the other wells. The right agar plate contained 2 μg (1) and 1 μg (4) cytosolic and 2 μg (2) and 1 μg (5) chloroplast aldolase from spinach leaves and 2.1 μg (3) and 1.05 μg (6) aldolase from corn leaves. The specific activities of the aldolases were 7.75 and 6.9 units per milligram protein for the cytosolic and chloroplast aldolase from spinach leaves, respectively, and 1.86 units per milligram protein for the aldolase from corn leaves.

leaves. Aldolase activity had previously been found exclusively in the bundle sheath cells of C_4 plants [Hatch and Kagawa, 1973]. It appears, therefore, that the predominant aldolase activity in corn leaves is due to a chloroplast enzyme in the bundle sheath cells. Attempts have thus far failed to demonstrate additional aldolases in corn leaves.

In another experiment we have purified glucosephosphate isomerase-2 from the cytosol of spinach leaves (Fig. 7D) and produced antiserum in guinea pigs. The antiserum was tested for cross-reactivity with glucosephosphate isomerase-1 from spinach leaves and the isomerases from rabbit muscle, yeast, and E coli *K12* (Fig. 9). No precipitation lines were observed except with glucosephosphate isomerase-2 from spinach leaves, suggesting structural differences between all these enzymes.

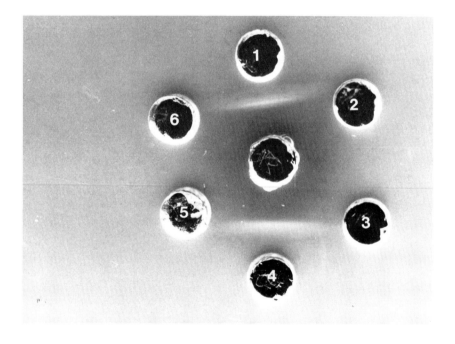

Fig. 9. Ouchterlony double diffusion test with antiserum against purified glucosephosphate isomerase-2 from spinach leaves in the center well and with 16 μg glucosephosphate isomerase-2 (1 and 4) and 150 μg isomerase 1 (2) from spinach leaves, 64 μg glucosephosphate isomerase from E coli K12 (3), 72 μg glucosephosphate isomerase from rabbit muscle (5), and 100 μg glucosephosphate isomerase from yeast (6) in the other wells. The specific activities of glucosephosphate isomerase-1 and -2 were 8 and 402 units per milligram protein, respectively [from Herbert and Schnarrenberger, 1982].

In an other set of experiments we produced antisera against glucosephosphate isomerases from rabbit muscle, yeast, and E coli *K12* (major form). For cross-reactivity, immune complexes were allowed to form, absorbed to protein A-coated Staphylococcus aureus Cowan I cells, and centrifuged. The activity remaining in the supernatant was determined and used as a measure for the lack of cross-reactivity. This method has the advantage over the Ouchterlony test in that the catalytic activity instead of nonspecific protein precipitation serves as a measure for cross-reactivity. From the results in Table IV it is apparent that enzymes are bound only by the respective antisera for which those enzymes were used for immunization. This means that besides a lack of cross-reactivity between glucosephosphate isomerase-2 and -1 there is also no cross-reactivity detectable between the isomerase-2 from spinach and the isomerases from rabbit muscle, yeast, or E coli *K12* (major form), and vice versa.

2. Implications for structural relationships. The lack of cross-reactivity between the organelle specific-isozymes of the chloroplast and cytosolic aldolase and glucosephosphate isomerase suggests that there are major differences in the primary structure of the two isozymes. Similar immunological results have also been reported for glyceraldehyde-phosphate dehydrogenases [Cerff and Chambers, 1979] and for glucosephosphate isomerases by Weeden and Gottlieb [1982].

Thus far analyses for isozymes have yielded only small differences in specific catalytic activities, which appear to be maintained unchanged as conservative markers during evolution. Small differences in molecular weight are significant in that there must be a different number of amino acids in each isozyme peptide chain, but it usually cannot be stated whether the

TABLE IV. Cross-reactivity Between Glucose-Phosphate Isomerases-2 and -1 (GPI) From Spinach and Glucosephosphate Isomerases From Rabbit Muscle, Yeast and E coli *L 12* (major form)[a]

Source of antigen	α GPI 2 spinach	α GPI rabbit muscle	α GPI yeast	α GPI E coli
GPI 2 (spinach)	0	100	98	100
GPI 1 (spinach)	100	96	100	100
GPI (rabbit muscle)	94	0	100	100
GPI (yeast)	100	81	0	100
GPI (E coli)	94	100	91	0

[a]100, no immune complexes formed; 0, immune complexes adsorbed to Staphyloccus aureus Cowan I cells and removed by centrifugation.

differences between isozymes are spread all over the molecule or are possibly confined to the end of a peptide chain. Amino acid sequencing of the two pea leaf aldolases yielded seven more aspartyl (asx) and four fewer leucine and isoleucine residues in the chloroplast than in the cytosolic enzyme [Anderson and Heinrikson, 1979]. The sequencing of terminal residues of the two pea leaf aldolases showed no differences [Anderson et al, 1975]. In this case it seems that the differences in the primary structure must be along the peptide chain. The immunochemical results imply that the differences are most likely spread over the molecules, particularly in view of the many different monoclonal antibodies against the 5-aminolevulinate dehydratase from spinach [Schneider and Liedgens, 1981].

In the case of the chloroplast and cytosolic isozymes of glyceraldehyde-phosphate dehydrogenase, the isozymes differ in cofactor specificity since the two chloroplast isozymes use $NADP^+$ and NAD^+ while the cytosolic isozyme uses NAD^+ only. Chloroplast and cytosolic isozymes do not cross-react immunologically and show, in addition, very different fingerprints. This also implies differences in the primary structure of the peptide chains [Cerff and Chambers, 1979].

It is also essential to know whether the organelle-specific isozymes of sugar phosphate metabolism are products of different genes or whether they originate from just one gene product by posttranslational modification. For long, the only evidence for two separate nuclear genes was a variety of pea which had a chloroplast aldolase with a different isoelectric point [Anderson and Levin, 1970].

More recent genetic and population genetic studies have shown that isozymes for the following activities are coded for by distinct nuclear genes: phosphoglucomutase from Clarkia [Weeden and Gottlieb, 1980b], date palms [Torres and Tisserat, 1980], and avocado [Torres et al, 1978], glucose-phosphate isomerase from Clarkia [Gottlieb, 1973; Gottlieb and Weeden, 1977], pea [Weeden and Gottlieb, 1980b], wheat [Hart, 1979b], and date palms [Torres and Tisserat, 1980], and aldolase from pea [Weeden and Gottlieb, 1980b].

IV. SUMMARY

The present paper has summarized evidence for the presence of two isozymes for many enzyme activities of sugar phosphate metabolism in plant leaves. These two isozymes are clearly compartmentalized in the chloroplasts and in the cytosol of plant leaf cells. In C_4 plants there exists an additional isozyme in the mesophyll cells of these leaves in addition to the two isozymes in the bundle sheath cells. Such cell-compartment-specific and cell-specific isozymes provide duplicate (and possibly triplicate) enzyme systems for complete or almost complete pathways (ie, glycolysis, gluconeogenesis, and the oxidative pentose phosphate pathway). They provide a basis for the understanding as to how many isozymes one may expect in plants. They also provide a challenge to determine what their function is particularly in the differential regulation of metabolic pathways in different cell compartments. Based on his genetic analyses Weeden [1981] has recently proposed a model for the evolution of chloroplast-specific isozymes of sugar phosphate metabolism. This model rests on the endosymbiotic theory for the origin of chloroplasts. It still is highly speculative. However, cell-compartment specific isozymes may eventually provide a means of studying plant evolution, especially if we succeed in analyzing their primary structure.

V. ACKNOWLEDGMENTS

The authors thank Prof. Dr. B. Vennesland (Max Planck Institut für molekulare Genetik, Berlin) for a critical reading of the manuscript. The authors also thank Dr. R. Schreyer and Prof. Dr. A. Böck, Lehrstuhl für Mikrobiologie, Universität München, for a gift of glucosephosphate isomerase-1 from E coli *K12* and the rabbit antibodies against this enzyme. The authors' work was supported by grants of the Deutsche Forschungsgemeinschaft.

VI. REFERENCES

Achenbach K (1980): "Charakterisierung and intrazelluläre Kompartimentierung der Phosphoglyceratmutase und der Enolase von Spinat (*Spinacia oleracea* L.) und *Bryophyllum calycinum* Salisb." Diplomarbeit, Freie Universität Berlin.

Anderson LE (1971a): Chloroplast and cytoplasmic enzymes. II. Pea leaf triose phosphate isomerases. Biochim Biophys Acta 235:237–244.

Anderson LE (1971b): Chloroplast and cytoplasmic enzymes. III. Pea leaf ribose 5-phosphate isomerases. Biochim Biophys Acta 235:245–249.

Anderson LE (1979): Interaction between photochemistry and activity of enzymes. In Gibbs M, Latzko E (eds): "Encyclopedia of Plant Physiology (New Series), Vol. 6: Photosynthesis II." Berlin: Springer-Verlag, pp 271–281.

Anderson LE, Advani VR (1970): Chloroplast and cytoplasmic enzymes. Three distinct isoenzymes associated with the reductive pentose phosphate cycle. Plant Physiol 45:583–585.

Anderson LE, Heinrikson RL (1979): Chloroplast and cytoplasmic enzymes. VIII. Amino acid composition of the pea leaf aldolases. Plant Physiol 64:404–405.

Anderson LE, Heinrikson RL, Noyes C (1975): Chloroplast and cytoplasmic enzymes. Subunit structure of pea leaf aldolases. Arch Biochem Biophys 169:262–268.

Anderson LE, Levin DA (1970): Chloroplast aldolase is controlled by a nuclear gene. Plant Physiol 46:819–820.

Anderson LE, Ng T-CL, Park K-EY (1974): Inactivation of pea leaf chloroplastic and cytoplasmic glucose 6-phosphate dehydrogenase by light and dithiothreitol. Plant Physiol 53:835–839.

Anderson LE, Pacold I (1972): Chloroplast and cytoplasmic enzymes. IV. Pea leaf fructose 1,6-diphosphate aldolases. Plant Physiol 49:393–397.

Arnon DI (1949): Copper enzymes in isolated chloroplasts. Polyphenoloxidase in *Beta vulgaris*. Plant Physiol 24:1–15.

Ben-Bassat D, Anderson LE (1981): Light-induced release of bound glucose-6-phosphate dehydrogenase to the stroma in pea chloroplasts. Plant Physiol 68:279–283.

Boyer CD, Preiss J (1981): Evidence for independent genetic control of the multiple forms of maize endosperm branching enzymes and starch synthases. Plant Physiol 67:1141–1145.

Boyer CD, Preiss J (1978): Multiple forms of starch branching enzyme of maize: Evidence for independent genetic control. Biochem Biophys Res Commun 80:169–175.

Bradford MM (1976): A rapid and sensitive method for the quantitation of microgram quantities of protein utilizing the principle of protein-dye binding. Anal Biochem 72:248–254.

Bukowiecki AC, Anderson LE (1974): Multiple forms of aldolase and triose phosphate isomerase in diverse plant species. Plant Sci Lett 3:381–386.

Cerff R, Chambers SE (1978): Glyceraldehyde-3-phosphate dehydrogenase (NADP$^+$) from Sinapis alba L. Isolation and electrophoretic characterization of isoenzymes. H-SZ Physiol Chem 359:769–772.

Cerff R, Chambers SE (1979): Subunit structure of higher plant glyceraldehyde-3-phosphate dehydrogenases (EC 1.2.1.12 and EC 1.2.1.13). J Biol Chem 254:6094–6098.

Daussant J (1975): Immunochemical investigations of plant proteins. In Harbone JB, van Sumere CF (eds): "The Chemistry and Biochemistry of Plant Proteins." New York: Academic Press, pp 31–69.

Davies DR, Plaskitt A (1971): Genetical and structural analyses of cell wall formation in *Chlamydomonas reinhardi*. Genet Res 17:33–43.

Fluri R, Ramasarma T, Horecker BL (1967): Purification and properties of fructose diphosphate aldolase from spinach leaves. Eur J Biochem 1:117–124.

Garland WJ, Dennis DT (1980): Plastid and cytosolic phosphofructokinases from the developing endosperm of *Ricinus communis*. I. Separation, purification, and initial characterization of the isoenzymes. Arch Biochem Biophys 204:302–309.

Gates P, Boulter D (1979): The use of seed isoenzymes as an aid to the breeding of field beans (*Vicia faba* L.). New Phytol 83:783–791.

Gottlieb LD (1977): Evidence for duplication and divergence of the structural gene for phosphoglucoisomerase in diploid species of *Clarkia*. Genetics 86:289–307.

Gottlieb LD (1973): Enzyme differentiation and phylogeny in *Clarkia franciscana, C. rubicunda,* and *C. amoena*. Evolution 27:205–214.

Gottlieb LD, Weeden NF (1979): Gene duplication and phylogeny in *Clarkia*. Evolution 33:1024–1039.

Haberlandt G (1881): "Vergleichende Anatomie des assimilatorischen Gewebesystems der Pflanzen." Berlin: Bernstein.

Hatch MD (1973): Separation of properties of leaf aspartate aminotransferase and alanine aminotransferase isoenzymes operative in the C_4 pathways of photosynthesis. Arch Biochem Biophys 156:202–214.

Hatch MD, Kagawa T (1973): Enzymes and functional capacities of mesophyll chloroplasts from plants with C_4-pathway photosynthesis. Arch Biochem Biophys 159:842–853.

Hatch MD, Kagawa T, Craig S (1975): Subdivision of C_4-pathway species based on differing C_4 acid decarboxylating systems and ultrastructural features. Aust J Plant Physiol 2:111–128.

Hatch MD, Mau S-L (1973): Activity, location, and role of aspartate aminotransferase isoenzymes in leaves with C_4 pathway photosynthesis. Arch Biochem Biophys 156:195–206.

Hatch MD, Osmond CB (1976): Compartmentation and transport in C_4 photosynthesis. In Stocking CR, Heber U (eds): "Encyclopedia of Plant Physiology (New Series), Vol 3: Transport in Plants III." Berlin: Springer-Verlag, pp 144–184.

Hart GE (1979a): "Genetical and Chromosomal Relationships Among the Wheats and Their Relatives." Stadler Symp Vol 11, Univ of Missouri: Columbia, pp 9–30.

Hart GE (1979b): Evidence for a triplicate set of glucosephosphate isomerase structural genes in hexaploid wheat. Biochem Genet 17:585–598.

Hattersley PW, Watson L (1976): C_4-grasses: An anatomical criterion for distinguishing between NADP-malic enzyme species and PCK or NAD-malic enzyme species. Aust J Bot 24:297–308.

Heil JA, Lebherz HG (1978): "Hybridization" between aldolase subunits derived from mammalian and plant origin. J Biol Chem 253:6599–6605.

Heldt HW (1976): Metabolic carriers of chloroplasts. In Stocking CR, Heber U (eds): "Encyclopedia of Plant Physiology (New Series), Vol 3: Transport in Plants III." Berlin: Springer-Verlag, pp 137–143.

Heber U, Pon NG, Heber M (1963): Localization of carboxydismutase and triosephosphate dehydrogenases in chloroplasts. Plant Physiol 38:355–360.

Herbert M, Burkhard C, Schnarrenberger C (1979): A survey for isoenzymes of glucosephosphate isomerase, phosphoglucomutase, glucose-6-phosphate dehydrogenase and 6-phosphogluconate dehydrogenase in C_3, C_4 and Crassulacean-acid-metabolism plants, and green algae. Planta 145:95–104.

Herbert M, Schnarrenberger C (1982): Purification and subunit structure of glucosephosphate isomerase 2 from spinach leaves and immunochemical comparison with other isomerases. Arch Biochem Biophys 217:452–459.

Hock B (1973): Kompartimentierung und Eigenschaften der MDH-Isoenzyme aus Wassermelonenkeimblättern. Planta 112:137–148.

Huber SC, Edwards GE (1975): Mesophyll protoplasts from C_3 and C_4 grasses. An evaluation of some parameters required for the enzymatic isolation of cells and protoplasts with CO_2 fixation capacity from C_3 and C_4 grasses. Physiol Plant 35:203–209.

Jaaska V (1976): Aspartate aminotransferase isoenzymes in the polyploid wheats and their diploid relatives. On the origin of tetraploid wheats. Biochem Physiol Pflanzen 170:159–171.

Kahl G, Lange H, Rosenstock G (1969): Regulation glykolytischen Umsatzes durch Synthese und Abbau von Enzymen. Z Naturforsch 24b:1544–1549.

Kanai L, Edwards GE (1973): Enzymatic separation of mesophyll protoplasts and bundle sheath cells from leaves of C_4 plants. Naturwiss. 60:157–158.

Kelly GJ, Gibbs M (1973): Nonreversible D-glyceraldehyde 3-phosphate dehydrogenase of plant tissues. Plant Physiol 52:111–118.

Kelly GJ, Latzko E (1977): Chloroplast phosphofructokinase. I. Proof of phosphofructokinase activity in chloroplasts. Plant Physiol 60:290–294.

Kessler SW (1975): Rapid isolation of antigens from cells with a staphylococcal protein A-antibody absorbent: parameters of the interaction of antibody-antigen complexes with protein A J Immunol 115:1617–1624.

Latzko E, Zimmermann G, Feller U (1974): Evidence for a hexosediphosphatase from the cytoplasm of spinach leaves. H-SZ Physiol Chem 355:321–326.

Longo GP, Scandalios JG (1969): Nuclear gene control of mitochondrial malic dehydrogenase in maize. Proc Natl Acad Sci USA 62:104–111.

Miernyk JA, Dennis DT (1982): Isoenzymes of the glycolytic enzymes in endosperm from developing castor oil seeds. Plant Physiol 69:825–828.

Mühlbach H, Schnarrenberger C (1978): Properties and intracellular distribution of two phosphoglucomutases from spinach leaves. Planta 141:65–70.

Nishimura M, Beevers H (1981): Isoenzymes of sugar phosphate metabolism in endosperm of germinating castor beans. Plant Physiol 67:1255–1258.

Ott LA, Scandalios JG (1978): Genetic control and linkage relationships among amino-peptidases in maize. Genetics 89:137–146.

Ouchterlony Ö (1949): Antigen-antibody reations in gels. Arkiv Kemi Mineralogi Geologi 26B(14):1–9.

Pacold I, Anderson LE (1975): Chloroplast and cytoplasmic enzymes. VI. Pea leaf 3-phosphoglycerate kinases. Plant Physiol 55:168–171.

Park WM, Stegemann H (1979): Rice protein patterns. Comparison by various PAGE-techniques in slabs. Z Acker- Pflanzenbau 148:446–454.

Preiss J, Levi C (1979): Metabolism of starch in leaves. In Gibbs M, Latzko E (eds): "Encyclopedia of Plant Physiology (New Series) Vol 6: Photosynthesis II." Berlin: Springer-Verlag, pp 282–312.

Rocha V, Ting IP (1970): Preparation of cellular plant organelles from spinach leaves. Arch Biochem Biophys 140:398–407.

Scandalios JG (1974): Isoenzymes in development and differentiation. Annu Rev Plant Physiol 25:225–258.

Schäfer G, Heber U (1977): Glucose transport into spinach chloroplasts. Plant Physiol 60:286–289.

Schnarrenberger C, Burkhard C (1977): In vitro interaction between chloroplasts and peroxisomes as controlled by inorganic phosphate. Planta 134:109–114.

Schnarrenberger C, Fock H (1976): Interactions among organelles involved in photorespiration. In Stocking CR, Heber U (eds): "Encyclopedia of Plant Physiology (New Series), Vol 3: Transport in Plants III." Berlin: Springer-Verlag, pp 185–234.

Schnarrenberger C, Oeser A (1974): Two isoenzymes of glucosephosphate isomerase from spinach leaves and their intracellular compartmentation. Eur J Biochem 45:77–82.

Schnarrenberger C, Oeser A, Tolbert NE (1973): Tow isoenzymes each of glucose-6-phosphate dehydrogenase and 6-phosphogluconate dehydrogenase in spinach leaves. Arch Biochem Biophys 154:438–448.

Schneider HAW, Liedgens W (1981): An evolutionary tree based on monoclonal antibody-recognized surface features of a plastid enzyme (5-aminolevulinate dehydratase). Z Naturforsch 36c:44–50.

Simcox PD, Dennis DT (1978): Isoenzymes of the glycolytic and pentose phosphate pathways in proplastids from the developing endosperm of Ricinus communis L. Plant Physiol 61:871–877.

Schreyer R, Böck A (1980): Phosphoglucose isomerase from Escherichia coli K12: Purification, properties and formation under aerobic and anaerobic conditions. Arch Microbiol 127:289–298.

Slack CR, Hatch MD (1967): Comparative studies on the activity of carboxylases and other enzymes in relation to the new pathway of photosynthetic carbon dioxide fixation in tropical grasses. Biochem J 103:660–665.

Stegemann H, Loeschcke V (1977): Das europäische Kartoffelsortiment und seine Indexierung. Potato Res 20:101–110.

Steup ME, Latzko E (1979): Intracellular localization of phosphorylases in spinach and pea leaves. Planta 145:69–75.

Steup M, Schächtele C, Latzko E (1980): Separation and partial characterization of chloroplast and non-chloroplast α-glucanphosphorylases from spinach leaves. Z Pflanzenphysiol 96:365–374.

Smillie RM (1963): Formation and function of soluble proteins in chloroplasts. Can J Bot 41:123–137.

Stitt M, ap Rees T (1979): Capacities of pea chloroplasts to catalyse the oxidative pentose phosphate pathway and glycolysis. Phytochemistry 18:1905–1911.

Torres AM. Bergh BO (1978): Isoenzymes of 'Duke' and its derivatives. California Avocado Soc Yearbook 62:111–117.

Torres AM, Diedenhofen U, Bergh BO, Knight RJ (1978): Enzyme polymorphism as genetic markers in the avocado. Am J Bot 65:134–139.

Torres AM, Tisserat B (1980): Leaf isoenzymes as genetic markers in date palms. Am J Bot 67:162–167.

Velick SF (1955): Glyceraldehyde-3-phosphate dehydrogenase from muscle. Methods Enzymol I:401–415.

Walker DA (1976): Interactions between cytoplasm and plastids. In Stocking CR, Heber U (eds): "Encyclopedia of Plant Physiology (New Series), Vol 3: Transport in Plants III." Berlin: Springer-Verlag, pp 85–136.

Weeden NF (1981): Genetic and biochemical implications of the endosymbiotic origin of the chloroplast. J Mol Evol 17:133–139.

Weeden NF, Gottlieb LD (1980a): Isolation of cytoplasmic enzymes from pollen. Plant Physiol 66:400–403.

Weeden NF, Gottlieb LD (1980b): The genetics of chloroplast enzymes. J Hered 71:392–396.

Weeden NF, Gottlieb LD (1979): Distinguishing alloenzymes and isoenzymes of phosphoglucoisomerase by isoelectric comparisons of pollen and somatic tissues. Biochem Genet 17:287–296.

Weeden NF, Gottlieb LD (1982): Dissociation, reassociation, and purification of plastid and cytosolic phosphoglucose isomerase isoenzymes. Plant Physiol 69:717–723.

Whittingham CP, Keys AJ, Bird IF (1979): The enzymology of sucrose synthesis in leaves. In Gibbs M, Latzko E (eds): "Encyclopedia of Plant Physiology (New Series), Vol 6: Photosynthesis II." Berlin: Springer-Verlag, pp 313–326.

Wu R, Racker E (1959): Regulatory mechanisms in carbohydrate metabolism. J Biol Chem 234:1029–1035.

Yamazaki RK, Tolbert NE (1969): Malate dehydrogenase in leaf peroxisomes. Biochim Biophys Acta 178:11–20.

Isozymes: Current Topics in Biological and Medical Research
Volume 8: Cellular Localization, Metabolism, and Physiology 53–66

Evolutionary Affinities of Plant Phosphoglucose Isomerase and Fructose-1,6-Bisphosphatase Isozymes

Norman F. Weeden

Department of Seed and Vegetable Sciences, Cornell University, Geneva, New York 14456

I. INTRODUCTION

The plant cell has been shown to be a remarkably rich source of isozymes [for reviews see Scandalios, 1974; Gottlieb, 1981]. Many of these isozymes are compartmentalized in organelles (Schnarrenberger; Scandalios; these Proceedings), the chloroplast contributing a unique form to the majority of isozyme systems in the plant cell. Although often referred to as chloroplast-specific isozymes, most of these isozymes are also found in leucoplasts, amyloplasts, proplastids, and chromoplasts and are more properly "plastid-specific" forms. Several studies [Anderson and Levin, 1970; Weeden and Gottlieb, 1980; Tanksley and Rick, 1980] have demonstrated that plastid-specific forms are not merely modified subsets of the cytosolic enzymes but are coded by nuclear genes distinct from those coding the cytosolic forms.

Plastid isozymes thus show biparental inheritance and assort independently of their cytosolic counterparts. The formation of the primitive plant cell must have involved, in part, the acquisition or development of these plastid-specific isozymes. Just how this occurred is an important consideration for studies on the evolution of the plant cell.

II. DEVELOPMENT OF ALTERNATIVE MODELS

Proteins exhibiting similarities in structure such as the various human hemoglobins [Ingram, 1961] or vertebrate lactate dehydrogenases [Markert et al, 1975] are believed to be coded by genes formed by a duplication of a common ancestral gene. Similar duplication events could have produced in the plant cell the nuclear genes that code for the plastid and cytosolic isozymes. However, the apparently random nature of chromosomal rearrangements and unequal crossovers would not be expected to generate the orderly set of chloroplast/cytosolic isozyme pairs observed in the plant cell [see Weeden, 1981, for a more detailed discussion]. Instead, a less structured assemblage of isozymes would be predicted, the number of forms present being dependent, to a certain extent, on how many times the respective coding sequence had been duplicated. The teleological explanation that many duplications have occurred, but that only those necessary for the efficient functioning of the cell have been retained, is a possible hypothesis but lacks a strong theoretical or experimental basis and allows for few testable predictions.

A second model, based on the endosymbiotic origin of the chloroplast, provides a rationale for not only the number but also the intracellular location of most enzymes in the plant cell [Weeden, 1981]. Assuming that the acquisition of a photosynthetic prokaryote by a eukaryotic "protoplant" cell was the first step in the evolution of modern plants, this initial assemblage would instantaneously have possessed "protoplastid" and cytosolic isozymes in a pattern similar to that observed in a typical plant cell. The major problem with this model as an explanation of the origin of plastid isozymes is that the protoplastid isozymes would have been coded on the endosymbiont's genome—not, as is the case in modern plants, on the nuclear genome.

It would appear that neither model successfully explains the origin of plastic-specifid isozymes without requiring additional evidence from, at present, such experimentally untestable subjects as selection pressures on or genomic rearrangements within the primitive plant cell. However, the two models make quite different predictions concerning relationships among the isozymes in plants and homologous enzymes in animals and prokaryotes. The development of plastid-specific isozymes by gene duplication events would have been initiated after the divergence of plant and animal lines, for animals generally possess only one (cytosolic) enzyme for those enzymes which exhibit plastid/cytosolic isozyme pairs in plants. The best estimate for the time of this divergence is between 1 billion and 700 million years ago [Schwartz and Dayhoff, 1978]. Assuming for the moment similar rates of evolution among the homologous enzymes, the gene duplication hypothesis predicts that the plastid-specific and plant cytosolic isozymes would exhibit the greatest amount of homology (Fig. 1). The enzyme isolated from animal tissues should be slightly more divergent, while that found in cyanobacteria would be expected to show three to five times the divergence observed between any of the eukaryotic enzymes.

By requiring that the plastid-specific isozyme is coded by a gene originally derived from a photosynthetic prokaryote, the second alternative shifts the evolutionary affinities of this isozyme to the prokaryotic side of the approximately 1.5–3-billion-year-old division between the eubacteria and the eukaryotes. Although the time of divergence between the cyanobacteria and the line leading to the hypothetical endosymbiote is difficult to ascertain from current evidence, it is presumably much shorter than the time of the eubacterial–eukaryotic split. Providing that evolutionary affinities of enzymes can be measured over such enormous periods of time, the plastid-specific isozyme and the cyanobacterial enzyme should cluster as one group while the plant

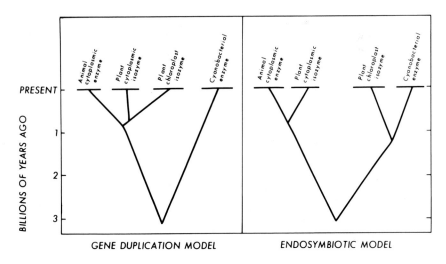

Fig. 1. Comparison of the relative times of divergence between homologous enzymes as predicted by the two alternative models presented in text. Divergence dates are best available approximations.

cytosolic isozyme and its animal homolog should form another. The following several sections will present results obtained in comparisons of homologous enzymes from plant, animal, and prokaryotic sources.

III. EXPERIMENTAL RESULTS

A. Comparison of Plant and Cyanobacterial Phosphoglucose Isomerases

Phosphoglucose isomerase (PGI, E.C. 5.3.1.9) is an enzyme of the Embden-Meyerhof pathway catalyzing the reversible reaction glucose-6-phosphate $\rightleftharpoons$ fructose-6-phosphate. Its distribution is nearly ubiquitous among living organisms and is usually found in activities sufficient to provide a rapid equilibrium between glucose-6-phosphate and fructose-6-phosphate. It does not show allosteric regulation, the only known natural regulators being the competitive inhibitors erythrose 4-phosphate, sedoheptulose-7-phosphate, and 6-phosphogluconate. The PGIs isolated from a wide variety of organisms exhibit very similar properties (Table I) and it would appear that the structure of this enzyme has undergone relatively minor modifications during evolution.

In spinach, the plastid and cytosolic isozymes, when first isolated, could be distinguished only on the basis of their ion-exchange properties, other biochemical parameters being nearly identical [Schnarrenberger and Oeser, 1974]. Even after more thorough investigations the relative evolutionary positions of the two isozymes with respect to other PGIs was difficult to ascertain [Weeden and Gottlieb, 1982]. The large size of the subunit makes sequencing of the molecule expensive and time-consuming and precludes a comparison of sequences among a variety of PGIs. Immunological techniques have often been used to investigate the evolutionary affinities among proteins, such results correlating well with amino acid sequence comparisons in proteins for which both sets of data are available [Champion et al, 1975]. Therefore, an immunological study was performed on plant and cyanobacterial PGIs to probe their evolutionary relationships.

Antisera against spinach plastid and cytosolic PGI isozymes were obtained by injecting New Zealand white rabbits with purified subunits as described previously [Weeden et al, 1982]. The antisera were further processed by affinity chromatography to obtain both plastid PGI-specific and cytosolic PGI-specific antibodies. These antibodies were used in an enzyme-linked immunosorbent assay (ELISA) [Engvall and Perlmann, 1971; as modified in Weeden et al, 1982] to determine the relative cross-reactivity between the antibodies and each of three PGI enzymes. ELISA rather than the more conventional techniques of immunodiffusion and microcomplement fixation was used to measure the cross-reactivity because of its high sensitivity, the

TABLE I. Physical and Kinetic Properties of Phosphoglucose Isomerase From Various Organisms[a]

	Human	Rabbit muscle	Brewer's yeast	Spinach cytosol	Spinach chloroplast	Synechococcus UTEX 625	E coli
Molecular weight	134,000	132,000	120,000	125,000	140,000	125,000	125,000
Quaternary structure	dimeric	dimeric	dimeric	dimeric	dimeric	dimeric	dimeric
Subunit molecular weight	61,000	ND[b]	60,000	63,000	63,000	60,000	59,000
Isoelectric point	9.3	8.5	5.2	6.0	4.8	4.8	ND
K_m (fructose-6-phosphate)	ND	70 μM	ND	300 μM	300 μM	ND	200 μM

[a]Data summarized from Carter and Yoshida [1969], Pon et al [1970], Kempe et al [1974], Schnarrenberger and Oeser, [1974], Weeden and Gottlieb [1982], Schreyer and Böck [1980], and Weeden [unpublished].
[b]ND, not determined.

advantages of quantitative rather than qualitative data, and the relative simplicity of the procedure.

Plastid PGI-specific antibodies gave significantly different cross-reactivities when tested against known quantities of purified PGI from spinach chloroplast, spinach cytosol, and Synechococcus sp *(UTEX 625)* (Table II). As expected, the greatest interaction was observed between the antibodies and their homologous antigen, the plastid PGI. However, the cyanobacterial PGI elicited a response one third that produced by the homologous antigen while the cytosolic isozyme cross-reacted at less than 2% of the control level. The cyanobacterial PGI thus exhibited an approximately 20-fold greater immunological similarity to the plastid PGI than did the cytosolic isozyme. This result is directly counter to the predictions of the gene duplication model in which the cytosolic isozyme should exhibit a much closer relationship. The observed immunological relationships support the hypothesis that the gene coding the chloroplast PGI subunits was derived from a prokaryotic genome.

When cytosolic PGI-specific antibodies were used in a parallel experiment the strongest cross-reactivity was again observed with the homologous antigen (Table III). The other two antigens, the plastid-specific and the cyanobacterial PGIs, gave low responses with the antibodies, indicating that these two proteins share relatively few antigenic sites with the cytosolic isozyme. The

TABLE II. Cross-Reactivities of Purified PGIs With Spinach Plastid PGI-Specific Antibodies

Amount of antigen plated (ng)	Source of antigen		
	Spinach chloroplast	Spinach cytosol	Synechococcus *UTEX 625*
1.2	0.009[a]	ND[b]	ND
3	0.017	ND	ND
6	0.022	ND	ND
9	0.030	ND	0.013
15	0.096	0.0	0.019
22	ND	0.0	0.035
45	ND	0.003	0.062
90	ND	0.011	0.173
135	ND	0.012	0.327
225	ND	0.023	0.507
Relative response[c]	100	1.7	36

[a]Figure represents average absorbance at 415 nm as determined on triplicate samples using enzyme-linked immunoabsorbant assay (ELISA).
[b]ND, not determined.
[c]Relative response, (cross-reactivity of antigen/cross-reactivity of spinach plastid PGI) × 100.

similarity of the response of the two heterologous antigens further suggests that the two are equally distantly related to the cytosolic isozyme. The results are consistent with the endosymbiotic model but contrary to the gene duplication hypothesis which predicts a fivefold stronger cross-reactivity between the antibodies and the plastid PGI than with the enzyme from the cyanobacterium.

The combined results of both experiments reveal an internal consistency which serves as a further check on the results. The relative cross-reactivity of the chloroplast PGI with cytosolic PGI-specific antibodies (2%) matches that of the cytosolic PGI with plastid PGI-specific antibodies. Whether this symmetry actually represents the proportion of antigenic sites with respect to the rabbit immune system the two isozymes share cannot be determined from the data available. The relative cross-reactivities observed for the spinach PGI isozymes were also seen when plastid and cytosolic PGIs from other vascular plant species were tested against the antibodies [Weeden et al, 1982], further supporting the interpretation that the plastid PGI is immunologically distant from the cytosolic form. The combined immunological data presented above demands the rejection of the hypothesis that the gene coding the plastid PGI subunits originated by a duplication of the gene coding cytosolic PGI subunits in the primitive plant cell. To maintain this hypothesis one would have to argue that the two plant isozymes have evolved at considerably

TABLE III. Cross-Reactivities of Purified PGIs With Cytosolic PGI-Specific Antibodies

Amount of antigen plated (ng)	Source of antigen		
	Spinach cytosol	Spinach chloroplast	Synechococcus UTEX 625
2.2	0.016[a]	0.0	0.0
4.5	0.027	0.0	0.0
11	0.086	0.0	0.0
22	0.229	0.003	0.0
32	—[b]	0.008	0.005
65	—	0.012	0.010
130	—	0.024	0.021
300	—	0.042	0.036
Relative response[c]	100	1.7	1.5

[a]Figures represent average absorbance at 415 nm as determined on quadruplicate samples using ELISA.
[b]Above linear range of assay.
[c]Relative response, (cross-reactivity of antigen/cross-reactivity of spinach cytosolic PGI) × 100.

different rates—different enough to mask the approximately 2.5 billion years of divergence between the eukaryotic and eubacterial lines.

B. Comparison of Plant, Animal, and Cyanobacterial Fructose-1,6-Bisphosphatases

Fructose-1,6-bisphosphatase (FBPase, E.C. 3.1.3.11) catalyzes the physiologically irreversible removal of a phosphate from fructose-1,6-bisphosphate in the pathway leading to the synthesis of glucose and more complex carbohydrates. FBPase, like PGI, is present in nearly all organisms, but in contrast to the previous enzyme, it is highly regulated, often functioning as the rate-determining step in glucose synthesis [Zimmermann et al, 1978]. The regulatory controls on this enzyme differ considerably depending on the source of the enzyme (Table IV). Comparison of these regulatory properties allows a partial structural comparison of the enzymes and may help elucidate their evolutionary relationships.

Soon after comparative studies of FBPases had begun, the grouping of these enzymes based on their pH optima was initiated. Eventually, two classes were accepted: alkaline FBPases with pH optima above 8 and neutral enzymes which exhibit greatest activity at pH 7.5 or below. The alkaline FBPases include the chloroplast isozyme [Smillie, 1960] and the enzyme from the cyanobacterium, Synechococcus [Udvardy et al, 1982]. FBPases isolated from the cytosol of eukaryotic organisms show neutral pH optima [Scala et

TABLE IV. Physical and Kinetic Properties of Fructose-1,6-bisphosphatase From Various Organisms[a]

	Rabbit muscle	Spinach cytosol	Spinach chloroplast	Synechococcus
Molecular weight	145,000	130,000	160,000	ND[b]
Quaternary structure	Tetrameric	Tetrameric	Tetrameric	Tetrameric
K_m (fructose-1,6-bisphosphate)	2.6 μM	2.5 μM	300 μM	88 μM
pH optimum	Neutral	Neutral	Alkaline	Alkaline
Activation				
DDT/thioredoxin	−	−	+	+
Ca^{++}/fructose-1,6-bisphosphate	−	−	+	ND
Inhibition				
AMP	+	+	−	−
High substrate	+	+	−	−
Fructose-2,6-bisphosphate ($I_{0.5}$)	1 μM	1 μM	100 μM	ND

[a]Data summarized from Pontremoli et al [1966], Zimmermann et al [1976, 1978], Udvardy et al [1981], Udvardy et al [1982], Czéke et al [1982], and Weeden and Buchanan [in preparation].
[b]ND, not determined.

al, 1968; Traniello et al, 1972]. A significant difference between the plastid and cytosolic isozymes also exists in their affinity for the substrate, fructose-1,6-bisphosphate (Table IV). The cytosolic form possesses a high affinity (low K_m) for the substrate while the plastid isozyme exhibits a much higher K_m. The low K_m found for the cytosolic isozyme is similar to that found for FBPases from mammalian tissues while the high K_m of the plastid isozyme mirrors that of the cyanobacterial enzyme. These differences are again paralleled by the susceptibility of a FBPase to competitive inhibition by fructose-2,6-bisphosphate, an important regulatory metabolite in the cytoplasm of both plants and animals [Cséke et al, 1982]. These two properties indicate that structural differences in the active site divide FBPases into at least two groups: animal and plant cytosolic enzymes in one and the chloroplast and cyanobacterial enzymes in another.

The enzymes may also be grouped on the basis of inhibition by adenosine monophosphate (AMP). The inhibition is allosteric, involving a portion of the enzyme distinct from the active site [Xu et al, 1981]. Mammalian and plant cytosolic forms are severely inhibited by 1 mM AMP (Table IV) while the plastid isozyme is relatively insensitive to AMP levels. Recent work [Udvardy et al, 1982] indicates that the FBPase from Synechococcus is also insensitive to AMP, in contrast to a previous finding by Bishop [1979]. It should be noted, however, that inhibition by AMP is not a universal feature of cytosolic FBPases; the enzyme isolated from bumblebee does not possess an AMP binding site [Leyton et al, 1980] nor, evidently, does the enzyme from slime mold [Rosen, 1966]. In addition, the AMP site is located on a labile portion of the molecule which apparently can be cleaved off by acid or proteases during extraction [Traniello et al, 1972; Youle and Huang, 1976]. Thus, AMP sensitivity may not be as useful as phylogenic marker as other properties of FBPases.

Two other properties which may reflect additional structural differences are pH stability and activitation by reducing compounds. It is known that low pH (< 4) will cause dissociation of the animal FBPase into dimeric subunits with a significant loss of activity [Pontremoli et al, 1966]. The plant cytosolic form also shows loss of activity when exposed to low pH, although such loss has yet to be linked to a dissociation of the enzyme [Weeden and Buchanan, submitted]. Both the plastid isozyme and the enzyme from Synechococcus are stable at relatively low pH, and at least the plastid enzyme undergoes a reversible dissociation a pHs greater than 8.5 with concomitant loss of activity [Buchanan et al, 1971].

The activation of the chloroplast isozyme by dithioerythritol (DTT) or reduced thioredoxin has been well documented [Buchanan, 1980]. The considerable cysteine content of this isozyme, especially in contrast to that of the animal FBPase, is probably an important factor in this enzyme's interaction with reducing agents [Zimmermann et al, 1976]. Neither rabbit muscle nor pea or spinach cytosolic FBPases show activation by DTT or reduced thioredoxin [Buchanan et al, 1971; Weeden and Buchanan, in preparation]. Although the amino acid compositions of the plant cytosolic isozyme and the enzyme from Synechococcus have yet to be determined the above results would suggest a modest half-cysteine content in the former and a relatively high content in the latter.

This comparison of several important properties of FBPase enzymes has revealed several parallels between the chloroplast isozyme and cyanobacterial enzyme on one hand and the plant and animal cytosolic enzymes on the other. The compared characteristics included conformation of the active site, presence of allosteric control regions on the enzyme, subunit binding properties, and control by reducing systems. These parameters would not be expected to be easily altered during evolution because of the important regulatory function this enzyme plays in cellular metabolism. Again, the data are more in concordance with the hypothesis that the gene coding the plastid isozyme was derived from a prokaryotic genome rather than from a duplication of the gene coding the cytosolic isozyme. Indeed, this latter possibility would require a remarkable case of rapid and convergent evolution.

C. Comparisons Performed on Other Proteins

The two enzymes examined in detail above both function in only a restricted portion of carbohydrate metabolism. Can these results be generalized to other isozyme systems, especially those in very different areas of metabolism? Several other plastid/cytosolic isozyme pairs have been compared both with each other and with homologous enzymes from prokaryotes or nonphotosynthetic eukaryotes. The plastid-specific isozymes of glyceraldehyde-3-phosphate dehydrogenase (E.C. 1.2.1.13), malate dehydrogenase (E.C. 1.1.1.37), and glutamate dehydrogenase (E.C. 1.4.1.3) share a pyridine nucleotide preference (NADP) similar to that exhibited by enzymes from cyanobacteria whereas those isolated from plant or animal cytoplasm generally are specific for NAD. Similarly, cyanobacteria and plastids contain an ADP-glucose phosphorylase while the cytosolic form in plants and animals uses UDP-glucose [Mares et al, 1978].

Perhaps the best-known comparisons are those performed on ribosomal proteins and aminoacyl-tRNA synthetases [Swamy and Pillay, 1982]. Many of the proteins incorporated into the 70S ribosomes in the chloroplast are coded in the nucleus; yet they are part of a structure which is very similar in size, arrangement, and inhibitor sensitivity to those found in prokaryotes. Comparative immunological studies using antiserum to chloroplast elongation factor G from Euglena demonstrated that this antiserum would partially inhibit the activity of Escherichia coli elongation factor G but not that isolated from Euglena cytosol or yeast [Breitenberger and Spremulli, 1980]. Chloroplast aminoacylation enzymes also appear to be nuclear coded; yet they recognize plastid or eubacterial tRNAs but not eukaryotic forms [Swamy and Pillay, 1982]. One could argue that because such proteins interact with RNAs of obvious prokaryotic affinities they would have been selected to show preference for or similarity to prokaryotic forms. The argument, though plausible, would again require an extraordinary case of convergent evolution. It should be noted that the argument does not apply to isozyme systems such as PGI or FBPase which use substrates identical in both eukaryotic and prokaryotic systems.

There are at least two cases in which the plastid form appears to be more similar to its cytosolic isozyme than to cyanobacterial homologs. The fructose-1,6-diphosphate aldolase isolated from spinach chloroplasts has been characterized as a class I (Schiff-base intermediate) enzyme [Brooks and Criddle, 1966; Jacobi, 1967]. The cytosolic isozyme and the typical mammalian form are also class I enzymes. The predominant eubacterial enzyme, and particularly that from cyanobacteria, is a class II metalloenzyme [Willard and Gibbs, 1968]. There appears to be significant variation within each class, preventing reliable evolutionary interpretation of the distribution of these two classes; however, at present, aldolase does not appear to conform to the plastid-eubacterial parallel.

Superoxide dismutase (SOD) is a conspicuous exception to the predictions of the endosymbiotic model. In the cytosol of eukaryotes the enzyme is cyanide sensitive, requiring both copper and zinc, while in many bacteria and in the mitochondrion of the eukaryotic cell it is a manganese-containing protein and is not inhibited by cyanide [Weisiger and Fridovich, 1973]. In cyanobacteria the form is similar to that in other eubacteria except that iron replaces the manganese as the metal cofactor [Fridovich, 1975]. Recently, an iron-containing SOD has been isolated from mustard leaf extracts [Salin and Bridges, 1980] but there is little doubt that the major chloroplast form is a cuprozinc enzyme very similar to the cytosolic isozyme. The plastid-specific cuprozinc SOD in corn is coded by a nuclear gene which assorts independently of the gene coding the cytosolic form [Baum and Scandalios, 1982]. Thus, chloroplast SOD represents the best candidate of a plastid-specific isozyme coded by a gene derived from a duplication event subsequent to the formation of the plant cell. This exceptional characteristic should make studies on the structure, control of expression, and processing of plastid SOD especially interesting.

IV. CONCLUSION

Comparisons of PGIs and FBPases indicate that the plastid-specific isozymes are more similar to homologous enzymes from cyanobacterial sources than they are to enzymes from the cytosol of the plant cell. Such results are consistent with a prokaryotic origin of the genes coding these isozymes, the coding sequences presumably being transferred to the nuclear genome after the acquisition of a photosynthetic prokaryote as an endosymbiote by the protoplant cell. Data from several other nuclear-coded plastid isozymes appear to support this model. Certain exceptions, most notably SOD, should provide interesting evolutionary comparisons.

It should be emphasized that the similarity between plastid isozymes and their cyanobacterial homologs cannot be taken as compelling evidence for the endosymbiotic origin of the plastid organelle. Such results are consistent with this hypothesis but are also compatible with the evolution of the eukaryotic plant cell directly from a photosynthetic prokaryotic ancestor, as suggested by several investigators [Allsop, 1969; Cavalier-Smith, 1975; Uzzell and Spolsky, 1974]. Animals would presumably have lost the plastid-specific isozymes when they separated from plants by "losing" the plastid organelle. However, other lines of evidence such as the presence of plastid DNA, the prokaryotic nature of the RNAs transcribed from this genome [Bonen and Doolittle, 1975; Zablen et al, 1975], and the lack of organisms which could be considered intermediate between photosynthetic prokaryotes and eukaryotes provide conclusive evidence for the endosymbiotic origin of the chloroplast.

V. REFERENCES

Allsop A (1969): Phylogenetic relationships of the procaryota and the origin of the eukaryotic cell. New Phytol 68:591–612.

Anderson LE, Levin D (1970): Chloroplast aldolase is controlled by a nuclear gene. Plant Physiol 46:819–820.

Baum JA, Scandalios JG (1982): Multiple genes controlling superoxide dismutase expression in maize. J Hered 73:93–100.

Bishop RH (1979): Regulatory characteristics of a fructose bisphosphatase from the blue-green bacterium *Anacystis nidulans*. Arch Biochem Biophys 196:295–300.

Bonen L, Doolittle WF (1975): On the prokaryotic nature of red algal chloroplasts. Proc Natl Acad Sci USA 72:2310–2314.

Breitenberger CA, Spremulli LL (1980): Purification of *Euglena gracilis* chloroplast elongation factor G and comparison with other prokaryotic and eukaryotic translocases. J Biol Chem 255:9814–9820.

Brooks K, Criddle RS (1966): Enzymes of the carbon cycle of photosynthesis. I. Isolation and properties of spinach chloroplast aldolase. Arch Biochem Biophys 117:650–659.

Buchanan BB (1980): Role of light in the regulation of chloroplast enzymes. Annu Rev Plant Physiol 31:341–374.

Buchanan BB, Schürmann P, Kalberer PP (1971): Ferredoxin-activated fructose diphosphatase of spinach chloroplasts. J Biol Chem 246:5952–5959.

Carter ND, Yoshida A (1969): Purification and characterization of human phosphoglucose isomerase. Biochim Biophys Acta 181:12–19.

Cavalier-Smith T (1975): The origin of nuclei and of eukaryotic cells. Nature 256:463–468.

Champion AB, Soderberg KL, Wilson AC, Ambler RP (1975): Immunological comparison of azurins of known amino acid sequence. J Mol Evol 5:291–305.

Cséke CS, Weeden NF, Buchanan BB, Uyeda K (1982): A special fructose bisphosphate functions as a cytoplasmic regulatory metabolite in green leaves. Proc Natl Acad Sci USA 79:4322–4326.

Engvall E, Perlmann P (1971): Enzyme-linked immunosorbent assay (ELISA), quantitative assay of immunoglobulin G. Immunochemistry 8:871–874.

Fridovich I (1975): Superoxide dismutases. Annu Rev Biochem 44:147–159.

Gottlieb LD (1981): Electrophoretic evidence and plant populations. Prog Phytochem 7:1–46.

Ingram VM (1961): Gene evolution and the haemoglobins. Nature 189:704–708.

Jacobi G (1967): Isolation and Eigenschaften von aldolase aus isolierten Spinatchloroplasten. Z Pflanzen Physiol 56:262–272.

Kempe TD, Gee DM, Hathaway GM, Noltmann EA (1974): Subunit and peptide compositions of yeast phosphoglucose isomerase isoenzymes. J Biol Chem 249:4625–4633.

Leyton JF, Chinelatto AM, El-Dorry HA, Bacila M (1980): Correlation of inhibition of fructose 1,6-bisphosphatase by AMP and the presence of the nucleotide-binding domain. Arch Biochem Biophys 202:168–171.

Mares D, Hawker J, Possingham J (1978): Starch synthesizing enzymes in chloroplasts of developing leaves of spinach (Spinacea oleracea L.). J Exp Bot 29:829–835.

Markert CL, Shaklee JB, Whitt GS (1975): Evolution of a gene. Science 189:102–114.

Pon NG, Schnackerz KD, Blackburn MN, Chatterjee GC, Noltmann EA (1970): Molecular weight and amino acid composition of five-times-crystallized phosphoglucose isomerase from rabbit skeletal muscle. Biochemistry 9:1506–1514.

Pontremoli S, Luppis B, Traniello S, Bargellesi A (1966): Fructose diphosphatase from rabbit liver. V. Subunit structure of the purified enzyme. Arch Biochem Biophys 114:24–30.

Rosen OM (1966): Purification and properties of fructose 1,6-diphosphatase from Polysphondylium pallidum. Arch Biochem Biophys 114:31–37.

Salin ML, Bridges SM (1980): Isolation and characterization of an iron-containing superoxide dismutase from a eucaryote, Brassica campestris. Arch Biochem Biophys 201:369–374.

Scala J, Patrick C, MacBeth G (1968): FDPases of the castor bean endosperm and leaf: Properties and partial purification. Arch Biochem Biophys 127:576–584.

Scandalios, JG (1974): Isozymes in development and differentiation. Annu Rev Plant Physiol 25:225–258.

Schnarrenberger C, Oeser A (1974): Two isoenzymes of glucose-phosphate isomerase from spinach leaves and their intracellular compartmentation. Eur J Biochem 45:77–82.

Schreyer R, Böck A (1980): Phosphoglucose isomerase from Escherischia coli K10: Purification, properties and formation under aerobic and anaerobic condition. Arch Microbiol 127:289–298.

Schwartz RM, Dayhoff MO (1978): Origins of prokaryotes, eukaryotes, mitochondria, and chloroplasts. Science 199:395–403.

Smillie R (1960): Alkaline C-1 fructose-1,6-diphosphatase: Evidence for its participation in photosynthesis. Nature 187:1024–1025.

Swamy GS, Pillay DTN (1982): Characterization of Glycine max cytoplasmic, chloroplastic and mitochondrial tRNAs and synthetases for phenylalanine, tryptophan and tyrosine. Plant Sci Lett 25:73–84.

Tanksley SD, Rick CD (1980): Isozymic gene linkage map of the tomato: Applications in genetics and breeding. Theor Appl Genet 57:161–170.

Traniello S, Melloni E, Pontremoli S, Sia CL, Horecker BL (1972): Rabbit liver fructose 1,6-diphosphatase. Properties of the native enzyme and their modification by subtilisin. Arch Biochem Biophys 149:222–231.

Udvardy J, Godeh M, Cséke Cs, Farkas GL (1981): Redox regulation of the fructose 1,6-bisphosphatase of the cyanobacterium Anacystis nidulans. International Conference on Thioredoxins, Berkeley, California, p 28.

Udvardy J, Godeh M, Farkas GL (1982): Regulatory properties of a fructose 1,6-bisphosphatase from the cyanobacterium *Anacystis nidulans*. J Bacteriol 151:203–208.

Uzzell T, Spolsky C (1974): Mitochondria and plastids as endosymbionts: A revival of special creation? Am Sci 62:334–343.

Weeden NF (1981): Genetic and biochemical implications of the endosymbiotic origin of the chloroplast. J Mol Evol 17:133–139.

Weeden NF, Gottlieb LD (1980): The genetics of chloroplast enzymes. J Hered 71:392–396.

Weeden NF, Gottlieb LD (1982): Dissociation, reassociation, and purification of plastid and cytosolic phosphoglucose isomerase isozymes. Plant Physiol 69:717–723.

Weeden, NF, Higgins RC, Gottlieb, LD (1982): Immunological similarity between a cyanobacterial enzyme and a nuclear coded plastid-specific isozyme from spinach. Proc Natl Acad Sci USA 79:5953–5955.

Weisiger RA, Fridovich I (1973): Superoxide dismutase. Organelle specificity. J Biol Chem 248:3582–3592.

Willard JM, Gibbs M (1968): Role of aldolase in photosynthesis. II Demonstration of aldolase types in photosynthetic organisms. Plant Physiol 43:793–798.

Xu G-J, Datta AG, Singh VN, Suda H, Pontremoli S, Horecker BL (1981): Rabbit liver fructose 1,6-biophosphatase: Labeling of the active and allosteric sites with pyridoxal 5-phosphate and sequence of a nonapeptide from the active site. Arch Biochem Biophys 210:93–103.

Youle RJ, Huang AHC (1976): Development and properties of fructose 1,6-bisphosphatase in the endosperm of castor-bean seedlings. Biochem J 154:647–652.

Zablen LB, Kissil MS, Woese CR, Buetow DE (1975): Phylogenetic origin of the chloroplast and prokaryotic nature of its ribosomal RNA. Proc Natl Acad Sci USA 72:2418–2422.

Zimmermann G, Kelly GJ, Latzko E (1976): Efficient purification and molecular properties of spinach chloroplast fructose 1,6-bisphosphatase. Eur J Biochem 70:361–367.

Zimmermann G, Kelly GJ, Latzko E (1978): Purification and properties of spinach leaf cytoplasmic fructose-1,6-bisphosphatase. J Biol Chem 253:5952–5956.

Isozymes: Current Topics in Biological and Medical Research
Volume 8: Cellular Localization, Metabolism, and Physiology 67–90

Genetic Analysis of the Duplicated Mitochondrial and Cytosolic Malate Dehydrogenase Isozymes in Maize

David E. McMillin and John G. Scandalios

Department of Biological Sciences, North Texas State University, Box 5318, Denton, Texas (D.E.M.), and Department of Genetics, North Carolina State University, Box 5487, Raleigh, North Carolina 27650 (J.G.S.)

I. INTRODUCTION

While there is a wealth of molecular information concerning gene regulation in many prokaryotic organisms, comparable information on the regulation of gene expression during development in eukaryotic organisms is sparse. Isozymes are particularly well suited as markers for studying gene expression during development [Scandalios, 1974]. For many developmental studies in plants Zea mays is the organism of choice since numerous genetic and cytogenetic studies have previously been conducted with this organism. The malate dehydrogenase system in Zea mays was chosen for study because multiple forms of the enzyme occur in mitochondria (mMDH), the cytosol (sMDH), and in glyoxysomes (gMDH) [Longo and Scandalios, 1969; Yang and Scandalios, 1974, 1975]. In addition, extensive biochemical analysis has been reported on five mMDH isozymes and two sMDH isozymes in Zea mays [Yang and Scandalios, 1974, 1975].

Each group of MDH is believed to have a unique function in metabolism. sMDH is involved in transporting NADH equivalents in the form of malate into the mitochondria, while mMDH is involved in the mitochondrial half of the malate shuttle and is an essential enzyme of the tricarboxylic acid cycle [Lehninger, 1975]. gMDH is thought to have a role in the glyoxylate cycle. Since sMDH and mMDH participate in the malate shuttle, both are important links between the cytoplasm and mitochondria. In addition, although mMDH is found primarily in the mitochondria, it is under nuclear gene control [Longo and Scandalios, 1969] and is coded for on cytoplasmic ribosomes [Yang and Scandalios, 1977]. Therefore, the sMDH and mMDH isozymes are excellent markers to probe the interaction between the nuclear genome and cytoplasmic organelles, as well as the processing of mMDH into the mitochondria.

In this report we present and discuss data on the mMDH and sMDH gene-enzyme systems using immunological, genetic, and cytogenetic approaches. Such approaches, we feel, may enhance our understanding of organelle interactions, the processing of enzymes into the organelles, and the basis for enzyme multiplicity and gene duplication.

II. sMDH ISOZYMES IN ZEA MAYS
A. Genetic Analysis

A large number of inbred lines from around the world were screened for cytosolic variants. The sMDH zymograms of variant phenotypes are shown (Fig. 1). Organelle isolation was used to confirm that these variants involved only cytosolic MDH [McMillin and Scandalios, 1980].

The most common sMDH zymogram phenotype observed is phenotype A (Fig. 1a), which is exhibited by inbred lines A215, W64A, and A187. Inbred line A188 exhibits two additional isozymes (sMDH3 and sMDH4) which migrate more anodally than sMDH1 and sMDH2 (phenotype B, Fig. 1a); while inbred lines A123 and A119 exhibit two isozymes (sMDH5 and sMDH6) which migrate more cathodally than sMDH1 and sMDH2 (phenotypes C and D, Fig. 1a). Since sMDH5 and sMDH6 overlap with mitochondrial isozymes, A123 extracts were subjected to sucrose gradient centrifugation to separate the mitochondria from the cytosol. sMDH5 and sMDH6 were recovered in the cytosolic fraction but were never observed in the mitochondrial fraction (Fig. 2a), confirming that they are cytosolic isozymes (Fig. 2a). Since superoxide dismutase (SOD-3) [Baum and Scandalios, 1979] and glutamate oxaloacetate transaminase (mGOT) [Scandalios et al, 1975]

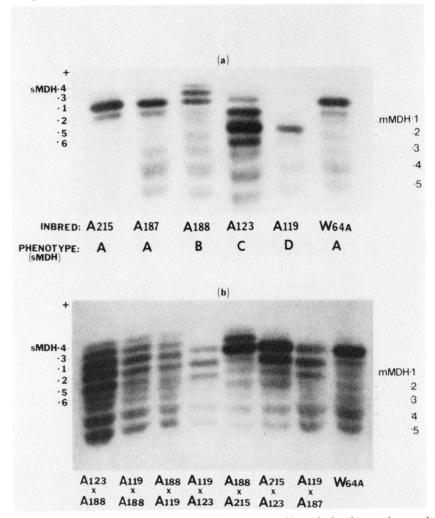

Fig. 1. Zymograms showing variant sMDH phenotypes used in analyzing the genetic control of sMDH isozymes (a) and the resulting F_1 sMDH phenotypes from the crosses (b). sMDH, cytosolic forms of MDH; mMDH, mitochondrial forms of MDH. Migration is anodal (from McMillin and Scandalios [1980], with permission).

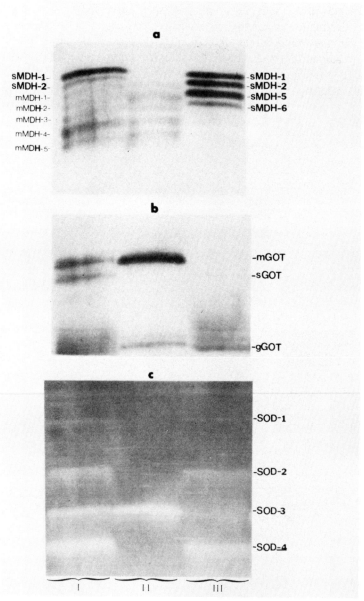

Fig. 2. Zymograms of mitochondrial and cytosolic fractions following cell fractionation. a. MDH. b. GOT. c. SOD. I, crude extract of W64A as marker; II, mitochondrial fraction from line A123; III, cytosolic fraction from line A123. Migration is anodal (from McMillin and Scandalios [1980], with permission).

have mitochondrial specific forms, they were used as markers to determine mitochondrial purity (Fig. 2b,c).

After all these variants were confirmed to involve only cytosolic MDH, crosses were made between the different phenotypes to determine the genetic control of sMDH. The F_1 phenotypes are shown (Fig. 1b). The results of the crosses demonstrated that the sMDH system in maize is coded by two unlinked duplicated genes [McMillin and Scandalios, 1980].

The results of a few of the crosses will be summarized in this review. Inbred line A123 expresses sMDH1, sMDH2, sMDH5, and sMDH6 (Fig. 1a, phenotype C); while inbred line A188 expresses sMDH1, sMDH2, sMDH3, and sMDH4 (Fig. 1a, phenotype B). The F_1 progeny of the cross A123 × A188 express six sMDH isozymes (Fig. 1b). The F_2 progeny express five distinct sMDH phenotypes (Table I, Fig. 3a). The phenotypes listed in Table I are based solely on the presence or absence of sMDH isozymes and not on the dosage differences expected in the F_2 progeny (Table IIA).

The appearance of five distinct phenotypes in the F_2 progeny of A123 × A188 cannot be explained by the assumption that one gene codes for sMDH. However, the assumption that two genes code for sMDH will explain the observed data (Table I). Furthermore, the appearance of F_2 progeny expressing phenotype A (sMDH1, sMDH2) is possible only if sMDH1 and sMDH2 in A123 are coded by a different locus than the counterparts are in line A188 (Table I).

Inbred line A119, which expresses only sMDH5, was also crossed to inbred line A188. The F_1 progeny exhibited phenotype E (Fig. 1b), while the F_2 progeny expressed six phenotypes (Fig. 3b). The six F_2 phenotypes and the frequencies observed can be explained by the assumption that two unlinked genes code for sMDH (Table I). Therefore, these data strongly suggest that two unlinked duplicated loci code for sMDH.

The two *sMdh* loci were designated *sMdh1* and *sMdh2* [McMillin and Scandalios, 1980]. Analysis of the crosses illustrated that isozyme sMDH1 could be coded for by the genes *sMdh1* and/or *sMdh2* (Table IIB). In addition, it was determined that sMDH5 was coded by the gene *sMdh1;* while sMDH4 was coded by the gene *sMdh2* (Table IIB). The results also indicated that sMDH3 was a heterodimer composed of sMDH1 and sMDH4 subunits; while the heterodimer between sMDH5 and sMDH1 migrated to the position of sMDH2, and the heterodimer between sMDH4 and sMDH5 migrated near sMDH1 [McMillin and Scandalios, 1980]. Since the expression of sMDH1 and sMDH2 as well as the expression of sMDH5 and sMDH6 appears to be coordinate and since sMDH2 and sMDH6 do not form detectable hybrids, the assumption was made that sMDH2 and sMDH6 may be products of secondary modification. The sMDH system is summarized in Table II.

TABLE I. Phenotypes and Frequencies Observed for F₂ Progeny of Crosses Involving sMDH Variants: chi-square and P Values of the F₂ Data Based on a Single sMDH Locus (a) or Duplicated sMDH Loci (b)[a]

Cross	Phenotype							Single gene (a)		Duplicated loci (b)	
	A	B	C	D	E	F	Total	χ^2	P value	χ^2	P value
1. (A123 × A188) selfed	14	28	41		76	12	171	—	0	5.2495	0.26
2. (A119 × A188) sib	13	21	15	7	42	28	126	—	0	4.421*	0.54
3. (A188 × A119) sib	14	52	32	15	85	53	251	—	0	2.375	0.80
4. (A119 × A123) sib	32		84	26			110	41.3136*	1×10^{-9}	0.0485*	0.83
5. (A188 × A215) sib		80					112	37.2533*	8×10^{-9}	0.5833*	0.45
6. (A215 × A123) sib	54		140				194	68.6418*	0	0.6873	0.41
7. (A119 × A187) sib	64		140	72			276	0.5217	0.77	187.1178	0

*Yates correction factor was used with 1 df or with sample sizes less than 140.

[a]Table from McMillin and Scandalios [1980], with permission.

TABLE II.[a] sMDH Nomenclature, Phenotypes, and Genotypes

(A) sMDH isozymes expressed						
Phenotype	sMDH-1	sMDH-2	sMDH-3	sMDH-4	sMDH-5	sMDH-6
A	+[c]	+				
B	+	+	+	+		
C	+	+			+	+
D					+	+
E	+	+	+	+	+	+
F[b]				+	+	+

Gene symbols and isozyme nomenclature (B)	
Gene	Isozyme coded
sMdh1-s1	sMDH-1
sMdh2-s1	sMDH-1
sMdh1-s5	sMDH-5
sMdh2-s4	sMDH-4
sMdh2-s8	sMDH-8

Inbred lines and respective genotypes used (C)	
Inbred lines	Genotype
A119	sMdh1-s5, sMdh2-s0
A123	sMdh1-s5, sMdh2-s1
A187	sMdh1-s1, sMdh2-s0
A188	sMdh1-s1, sMdh2-s4
A215	sMdh1,s1, sMdh2-s1
A205[d]	sMdh1-s1, sMdh2-s8

[a]Table from McMillin and Scandalios [1980], with permission.
[b]Phenotype F has an additional isozyme which migrates near sMDH-1.
[c]Indicates presence of particular sMDH isozyme.
[d]A205 possesses a new variant (sMDH-8) which is anodal to sMDH-4 and is allelic to sMDH-4 (data not shown).

In addition to crosses A123 × A188 and A119 × A188, other crosses (A119 × A123, A188 × A215, and A215 × A123) gave results consistent with two unlinked loci coding for sMDH (Table I). However, the cross A119 × A187 gave results consistent with a single gene coding for sMDH (Table I). The data indicated that not all lines of maize possess duplicated loci for sMDH. The significance of this finding will be considered later in the conclusions and comments.

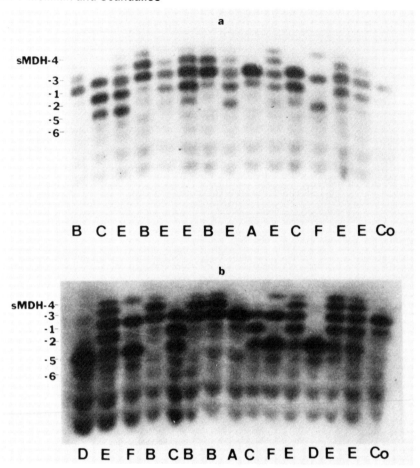

Fig. 3. Zymograms showing the five sMDH phenotypes (indicated by letters on horizontal axis) observed in F_2 progeny of A123 × A188 (a) and the six sMDH phenotypes observed in F_2 progeny of the cross A119 × A188 (b). Phenotypes are based on the presence or absence of sMDH isozymes and not on dosage intensities (see Table II). Co, control (W64A). Migration is anodal (from McMillin and Scandalios [1980], with permission).

B. Chromosome Location of the *sMdh* Loci

Crosses were made to determine if the *sMdh* loci were linked to other isozyme variants. *sMdh1* was found to be 7.59 ± 2.1 map units from *Amp1*, an aminopeptidase gene [McMillin and Scandalios, 1980, Table III]. *Amp1* had been shown previously to be on chromosome 1L, 17 map units from the marker gene *an1* (anther ear) and 15 map units from *Amp2* [Ott and Scandalios, 1978]. *sMdh2* was found to be 4.46 ± 1.9 map units from *Cat*

TABLE III. Linkage Analysis of *sMdh1* With *Amp1* and *sMdh2* with *Cat1*[a]

Linkage analysis of *sMdh1* and *Amp1*	Linkage analysis of *sMdh2* and *Cat1*
Cross: A188 × [A188 × A119]	Cross: $\dfrac{\text{A205} \times \text{D10}}{\text{A119}}$ selfed
Genotype: $\dfrac{sMdh1\text{-}s1,\ Amp1F}{sMdh1\text{-}s1,\ Amp1F} \times$ $\dfrac{sMdh1\text{-}s1,\ Amp1F}{sMdh1\text{-}s5,\ Amp1V}$	Genotype: $\dfrac{sMdh1\text{-}s8\ Cat1\text{-}F}{sMdh2\text{-}s0\ Cat1\text{-}V}$

Phenotypes observed	Number of progeny	Phenotypes observed	Number of progeny
sMDH1, AMP1F	68	sMDH8, CAT1F	31
sMDH1, AMP1F/V	6	sMDH8, CAT1F/V	68
sMDH1/5, AMP1F	6	sMDH8, CAT1V	4
sMDH1/5, AMP1F/V	78	sMDH0, CAT1F	0
		sMDH0, CAT1F/V	2
		sMDH0, CAT1V	30

1. Chi-square testing 1:1 segregation of sMDH1:sMDH5
   $\chi^2 = 0.51$ $P = 0.47$
2. Chi-square testing 1:1 segregation of AMP1F:AMP1-FV
   $\chi^2 = 0.51$ $P = 0.47$
3. Chi-square testing independence of *sMdh1* and *Amp1*
   $\chi^2 = 114.90$ $P = <0.001$
   Conclusion: *sMdh1* is linked with *Amp1*
4. Maximum likelihood estimation of linkage between *sMdh1* and *Amp1*
   7.59 ± 2.1 map units

1. Chi-square testing 3:1 segregation of sMDH8:sMDH0
   $\chi^2 = 0.12$ $P = 0.83$
2. Chi-square testing 1:2:1 segregation of CAT1
   $\chi^2 = 0.31$ $P = 0.86$
3. Chi-square testing independence of *sMdh2* and *Cat1*
   $\chi^2 = 101.81$ $P = <.001$
   Conclusion: *sMdh2* is linked with *Cat1*
4. Maximum likelihood estimation of linkage between *sMdh2* and *Cat1*
   4.46 ± 1.9 map units

[a]Table from McMillin and Scandalios 1980

1 (catalase 1) [McMillin and Scandalios, 1980, Table III]. *Cat 1* previously had been located on chromosome 5S, 9.1 map units from *bt* (brittle endosperm) [Roupakias et al, 1980].

III. mMDH ISOZYMES IN ZEA MAYS

A. Genetic Analysis

Yang et al [1977] demonstrated that mitochondrial malate dehydrogenase (mMDH) was coded by duplicated loci. They proposed a model that accounted for all the results available at the time. Their model can best be explained using the most common mMDH zymogram phenotype observed

214

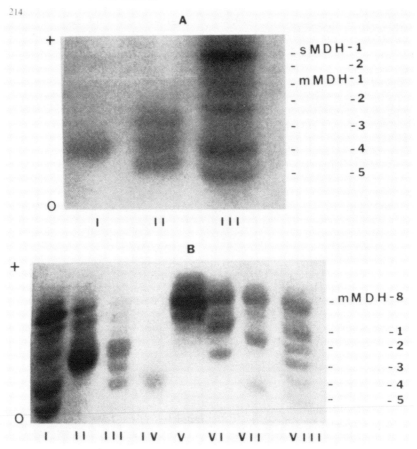

Fig. 4. Zymogram of freeze-thaw reversible denaturation experiments. AI, mMDH4 untreated control; AII, mMDH4 treated (note generation of mMDH3 and mMDH5); AIII, W64A crude extract. BI, W64A crude extract; BII, mMDH3 treated; BIII, mMDH3 + mMDH5 treated (note generation of mMDH4); BIV, mMDH5 treated; BV, mMDH8 treated; BVI, mMDH8 + mMDH3 treated (note generation of mMDH1); BVII, mMDH8 + mMDH5 treated (note generation of mMDH2). BVIII, mMDH8 + mMDH3 + mMDH5 treated (note generation of mMDH1 and mMDH2). The experiments illustrate that mMDH8, mMDH3, and mMDH5 are homeric in structure and that mMDH4 is a heterodimer of mMDH3 and mMDH5, mMDH1 is a heterodimer of mMDH8 and mMDH3, and that mMDH2 is a heterodimer of mMDH8 and mMDH5. Migration is anodal; 0 = point of sample insertion (from McMillin and Scandalios [1981], with permission).

among inbred lines of maize, phenotype III (Fig. 4A). Mitochondrial isolation on sucrose gradients had revealed five mMDH isozymes, mMDH1-5. Yang et al [1977] proposed that there were two gene sets: gene set *mMdh1, mMdh2* coded for mMDH2, mMDH5; and gene set *mMdh3, mMdh4* coded for the isozymes mMDH1 and mMDH3, respectively. Genetic analysis supported the conclusion that mMDH4 was a heterodimer composed of mMDH3 and mMDH5 subunits.

Denaturation experiments [Yang and Scandalios, 1974], two-dimensional gels [Newton and Schwartz, 1980], and organelle isolation [McMillin and Scandalios, 1980] suggested that mMDH1 and mMDH2 may be heterodimeric enzymes. This possibility led Goodman et al [1980] and Newton and Schwartz [1980] to propose a modification of the Yang et al model, which states that there are three *mMdh* genes, one coding for mMDH8 (a mitochondrial isozyme comigrating with sMDH1), one for mMDH3, and one for mMDH5.

Since it had not previously been unequivocally established which isozymes were homodimers and which were heterodimers, McMillin and Scandalios [1981] conducted a series of reversible denaturation experiments (Fig. 4) to resolve this question. The isozymes mMDH4, mMDH3, mMDH5, and mMDH8 were partially purified (Fig. 4AI, 4BII, IV and V, respectively). Reversible denaturation experiments conducted on mMDH3, mMDH5, and mMDH8 indicate that these isozymes are homodimers (Fig. 4B, II, IV and V, respectively). When mMDH4 was treated likewise, the isozymes mMDH3, mMDH4, and mMDH5 were generated (Fig. 4A). Also, when mMDH3 and mMDH5 were mixed together and subjected to the same treatment, the isozymes mMDH3, mMDH4, and mMDH5 were recovered (Fig. 4B, III). This suggests that mMDH4 is composed of mMDH3 and mMDH5 subunits. When mMDH8 and mMDH3 were reversibly denatured, mMDH1 was produced in addition to mMDH8 and mMDH3 (Fig. 4B, VI) confirming that mMDH1 is composed of subunits of mMDH8 and mMDH3. Reversible denaturation of mMDH8 and mMDH5 generated isozymes mMDH2, mMDH8, and mMDH5 (Fig. 4B, VIII), confirming that mMDH2 is composed of mMDH8 and mMDH5 subunits. Therefore, the model proposed by Yang et al [1977] would have to be modified to explain all the results. Since mMDH8 comigrates with sMDH1 in our Tris-citrate buffer system, organelle isolation was used to characterize a number of inbred lines for the presence of mMDH8 (Fig. 5). Another isozyme variant mMDH10, allelic to mMDH8, migrates more anodal than mMDH8 (Fig. 6). The heterodimers between mMDH10 and mMDH3 as well as mMDH10 and mMDH5 comigrate with sMDH1 and sMDH2 [McMillin and Scandalios, 1981]. Crosses were made [McMillin and Scandalios, 1981] between inbred lines possessing mMDH8 and lines possessing mMDH10 to determine if the isozyme mMDH8 was coded by a single *mMdh* locus as proposed by Goodman et al [1980]. If one gene codes for mMDH8 and if a line possessing mMDH10 is crossed to a line possessing mMDH8, the appearance of the heterodimeric enzymes mMDH1 and mMDH2 should follow a simple Mendelian ratio. The results overwhelmingly supported the conclusion that there are two genes which code for isozymes which comigrate to the position of mMDH8 in at least some maize lines (Fig. 6, Table IV). Thus, the results of our detailed genetic analyses suggest that

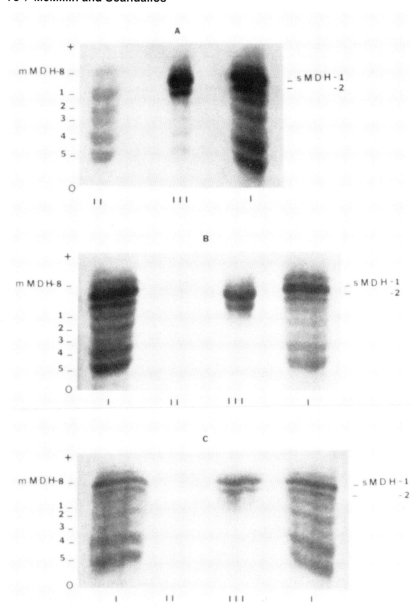

Fig. 5.   Zymograms of mitochondrial and cytosolic fractions following cell fractionation. A. MDH from cell fractionation of inbred W64A. B. MDH from inbred line D10. C. MDH from inbred A215. I, crude extract of W64A control; II, mitochondrial fraction; III, cytosolic fraction. Migration is anodal; 0 = point of sample insertion (from McMillin and Scandalios [1981], with permission).

TABLE IV. Phenotypes and Frequencies Observed for F_2 Progeny of Crosses Involving mMDH Variants[a]

Cross	Presence of mMDH1, mMDH2 and mMDH3a[b]	Absence of mMDH1, mMDH2 and mMDH3a[b]	Total	Duplicated[c] mMDH8 Loci		Single gene[d] coding for mMDH8	
				χ^2	P	χ^2	P
(A187 × A234) selfed	171	8	179	0.97	0.33	40.24	0
(A187 × A234) selfed	67	7	74	1.30	0.25	9.53	2.0×10^{-3}
(A187 × D10) selfed	157	25	182	0.26	0.61	22.19	2.4×10^{-6}
(A187 × D10) selfed	138	20	158	0.004	0.95	21.97	2.8×10^{-6}
(A215 × A193) selfed	155	24	179	0.39	0.82	22.73	1.9×10^{-6}
(A215 × A193) selfed	109	11	120	1.22	0.27	24.21	8.7×10^{-7}
(A193 × A215) selfed	63	12	75	0.84	0.36	6.73	9.5×10^{-3}

[a]Table from McMillin and Scandalios [1981], with permission.
[b]mMDH3 is observed only in crosses involving A234.
[c]Chi square and P values expected under the model proposed by McMillin and Scandalios.
[d]Chi square and P values expected under the model proposed by Goodman et al. (1980).

TABLE V. Summary of the mMDH System in Maize[a]

Gene	Isozyme coded
mMdh1	mMDH8 or mMDH10
mMdh2	mMDH5 or mMDH3
mMdh3	mMDH8
mMdh4	mMDH7 or mMDH3

Isozyme	Product of
mMDH10	*mMdh1-m10*
mMDH9	mMDH10/mMDH8 heterodimer
mMDH8	*mMdh1-m8* or *mMdh3-m8*
mMDH1	mMDH8/mMDH3 heterodimer
mMDH2	mMDH8/mMDH5 heterodimer
mMDH3	*mMdh2-m3, mMdh4-m3* or mMDH8/mMDH7 hybrid
mMDH4	mMDH3/mMDH5 heterodimer
mMDH5	*mMdh2-m5* or mMDH3/mMDH7 heterodimer
mMDH6	mMDH5/mMDH7 heterodimer
mMDH7	*mMdh4-m7*

mMDH Phenotypes of Figure 2	mMDH genotype			
	mMdh1	*mMdh2*	*mMdh3*	*mMdh4*
A	m8	m5	m8	m3
B	m8	m3	m8	m3
C	m8	m5	m8	m0
D	m8	m5	m8	m7
E	m8	m0	m8	m7
F	m10	m5	m0	m0 or m3
G	m10	m5	m0	m3
H	m8	m0	m8	m0
I	m8	m0	m8	m0
J	m10	m3	m0	m3
K	m8	m3	m8	m7

[a]Table from McMillin and Scandalios [1981], with permission.

there are four *mMdh* genes in maize: *mMdh3* and *mMdh4,* which are linked, and *mMdh1* and *mMdh2,* which are unlinked (Table V). In summary, the gene *mMdh1* codes for the isozymes mMDH8 and mMDH10; the gene *mMdh2* codes for the isozymes mMDH5 or mMDH3; the gene *mMdh3* codes for the isozyme mMDH8; and the gene *mMdh4* codes for the isozymes mMDH7 or mMDH3 (Table V).

B. Chromosomal Location of *mMdh2*

Nine of the possible ten trisomics are available for mapping studies in maize. In order to determine the chromosome location of *mMdh2,* female parent trisomic plants were crossed to male parent trisomic plants carrying a different mMDH variant. The F_1 trisomic progeny were then selected and backcrossed to the disomic parent or were self-fertilized. The critical chromosome (the chromosome where *mMdh2* resides) should show an altered Mendelian ratio. McMillin et al [1979] found that *mMdh2* resided on chromosome 6. These results were later confirmed by Goodman et al [1980].

Translocations between supernumerary chromosomes (B chromosomes) and the normal chromosome complement (A chromosomes) were obtained by irradiating pollen. The translocations obtained were characterized, and it was found that the translocated chromosome carrying the original B chromosome centromere often underwent mitotic nondisjunction during the second microspore division [Roman, 1947]. Such B-A translocations can be effectively utilized to locate maize genes on a particular chromosome segment (Fig. 7). Since nondisjunction occurs during the second microspore division, the resulting hypoploid and hyperploid sperm nuclei will fertilize the egg

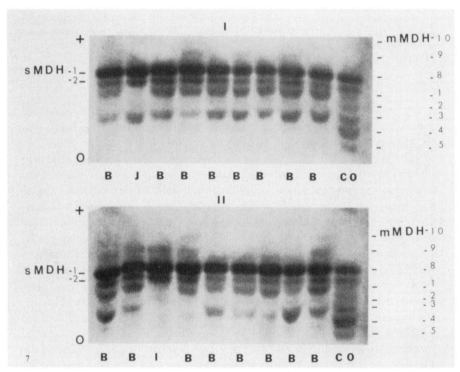

Fig. 6. Zymograms showing the mMDH phenotypes (indicated by letters on horizontal axis) observed in F_2 progeny of A193 × A215. Phenotypes are based on the presence or absence of mMDH isozymes and not on dosage intensities. Co, control (W64A). Migration is anodal; 0 = point of sample insertion (from McMillin and Scandalios [1981], with permission).

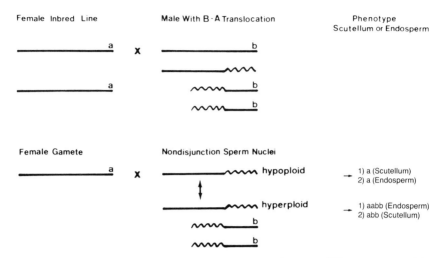

Fig. 7. Nondisjunction gametes in *B-A* translocations produce two different sperm nuclei. (1) When the hypoloid sperm nucleus fertilizes the egg cell, the scutellum will exhibit phenotype *a* and the endosperm will exhibit phenotype *aabb*. (2) When the hyperploid sperm nucleus fertilizes the egg cell, the scutellum will exhibit phenotype *abb* and the endosperm will exhibit phenotype *a* (from McMillin et al [1979], with permission).

cell or polar nucleus. When a B-A translocation line is crossed as a male to an inbred line carrying another isozyme variant, seed resulting from non-disjunction of the critical chromosome will exhibit different zymogram phenotypes in the scutellum and in the endosperm. A nondisjunction seed will exhibit only the maternal isozyme variant in the endosperm (results from fertilization of polar nuclei) or scutellum (embryonic tissue), depending upon which receives the hypoloid sperm nucleus (Fig. 7). Therefore, a nondisjunction seed will exhibit one phenotype in the scutellum and another in the endosperm, providing conclusive proof of their chromosomal locations. B-A translocations were used to determine that *mMdh2* resides on the long arm of chromosome 6 [McMillin et al 1979]. Crosses were made between a female inbred line (SD10) exhibiting phenotype B (Fig. 8) and a B-A translocation for chromosome 6L exhibiting zymogram phenotype A (Fig. 8). The progeny from this cross were examined and it was found that plant number 4 exhibited the F_1 phenotype in the scutellum (S4) and the maternal phenotype in the endosperm (E4) (Fig. 9) while plants 8 and 9 exhibited the maternal zymogram phenotype in the scutellum (S8 and S9) and the F_1 phenotype in the endosperm (E8 and E9) (Fig. 10). These zymogram phenotypes are possible only if non-disjunction of the critical chromosome arm has taken place. Furthermore, linkage analysis has shown that *mMdh2* is on the very distal end of chromosome 6L [McMillin et al, 1979].

The other *mMdh* genes also have been mapped. *mMdh1* is located on chromosome 3L [Newton and Schwartz, 1980], *mMdh3* is located on chromosome 8L [McMillin and Scandalios, 1982], and *mMdh4* is located on chromosome 8L [Newton and Schwartz, 1980].

IV. IMMUNOLOGICAL STUDIES OF sMDH AND mMDH

The mMDH and sMDH isozymes have been purified and injected into rabbits to produce monospecific antibodies. The technique of rocket immunoelectrophoresis, employing the monospecific sMDH and mMDH antibodies, was used to quantitate the amount of sMDH and mMDH protein in a number of inbred lines [McMillin and Scandalios, 1982]. It was found that sMDH antibodies only immunoprecipitate sMDH, and mMDH antibodies recognize only mMDH.

Genetic analysis has previously shown that not all lines possess both sMDH loci [McMillin and Scandalios, 1980, 1982] and all four *mMdh* loci [McMillin et al, 1979; McMillin and Scandalios, 1981].

When the total mMDH protein in lines lacking one or more *mMdh* genes was compared to lines possessing all *mMdh* genes (Table VI), it was found that lines lacking one or more of the *mMdh* loci had approximately 70% as much mMDH protein present, with the exception of line 59. These results suggest that the *mMdh* genes may show a dosage response.

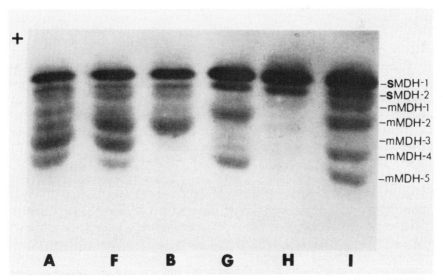

Fig. 8. mMDH zymogram phenotypes commonly observed (from McMillin et al [1979], with permission).

TABLE VI. Level of mMDH Protein (µg) in Different Lines of Zea mays

| Inbred line | MDH genotype | | | | µg mMDH protein |
	mMdh1	mMdh2	mMdh3	mMdh4	total µg protein
	Lack mMdh2 and/or mMdh4				
D10	m-8	m-0	m-8	m-0	0.0043
59[a]	m-8	m-5		m-0	0.0073
A215	m-8	m-0	m-8	m-0	0.0037
A234	m-8	m-0	m-8	m-7	0.0041
D15	m-8	m-0	m-8	m-3	0.0046
		$\overline{X}_1 = 0.0042 \pm 0.004*$			
	Possess mMdh1, mMdh2, and mMdh4				
A205[a]	m-8	m-5		m-3	0.0094
A187	m-10	m-5	m-0	m-3	0.0064
6[a]	m-8	m-5		m-7	0.0055
Tx303[a]	m-8	m-5		m-3	0.0053
W64A[a]	m-8	m-5		m-3	0.0081
W59[a]	m-8	m-3		m-3	0.0073
Tx325[a]	m-8	m-5		m-3	0.0074
A119[a]	m-8	m-5		m-3	0.0055
A123[a]	m-8	m-5		m-3	0.0063
Oh51A[a]	m-8	m-3		m-3	0.0072
A188[a]	m-8	m-5		m-3	0.0070
		$\overline{X}_2 = 0.0069 \pm 0.0012$			

*$\overline{X}_1 = 0.0042 \pm 0.004$ excluding 59, and 0.0048 ± 0.0014 including 59.
[a]The genotype of mMdh3 has not been genetically determined.

Rocket immunoelectrophoresis was also used to compare the total sMDH protein of lines with only one sMdh locus and lines possessing duplicated sMdh loci [McMillin and Scandalios, 1982]. The results indicate that lines possessing only one sMdh gene generally possess one-half the amount of sMDH protein (Table VII). One exception to this trend was inbred line W64A which has only one sMdh gene but possesses sMDH protein levels equal to lines with two sMdh genes.

In addition to gene mapping, B-A translocations were useful for gene-dosage studies [Tsaftaris et al, 1981; McMillin and Scandalios, 1982]. When crossing a disomic female to a male carrying a B-A translocation, progeny will be produced having one (meromonosomic), two (disomic), and three (merotrisomic) doses of a particular chromosome arm. When the hypoploid sperm nucleus fertilizes the female gamete a meromonosomic will be created, and when the hyperploid sperm nucleus fertilizes the female gamete a mer-

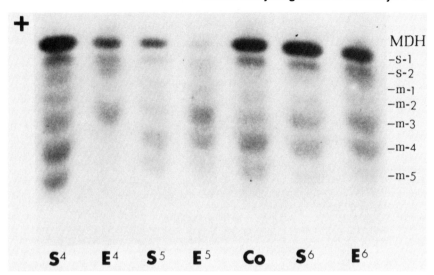

Fig. 9. Zymogram phenotypes of plants 4, 5, and 6 from the cross SD10 × Tb6Lc. S, scutella + embryo; E, endosperm; Co, W64A control (from McMillin et al [1979], with permission).

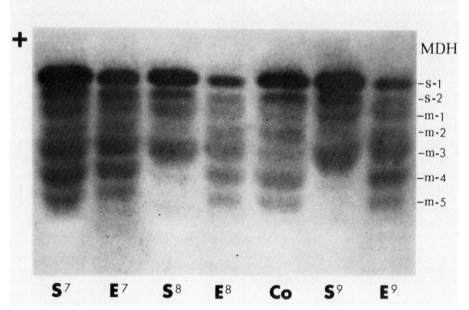

Fig. 10. Zymogram phenotypes of plants 7, 8, and 9 of the cross SD10 × Tb6Lc (from McMillin et al [1979], with permission).

TABLE VII. Level of *s*MDH Protein (μg) in
Different Lines of Zea mays

Inbred line	*s*MDH genotype		μg *s*MDH protein
	sMdh1	*sMdh2*	total μg protein
	Lack *sMdh1* or *sMdh2*		
A187	− s1	s0	0.0351
6	− s1	s0	0.0381
A119	s5	s0	0.0225
A117	s5	s0	0.0148
Tx325	s0	s4a	0.0264
W64A	s1	s0	0.0647
	X̄ = 0.0363 ± 0.0174		
	Possess *sMdh1* and *sMdh2*		
D10	s1	s1	0.0879
D15	s1	s1	0.0823
A215	s1	s1	0.0554
A205	s1	s8	0.0540
A123	s5	s1	0.0669
A188	s1	s4	0.0447
Tx303	s1	s4a	0.0550
	X̄ = 0.0637 ± 0.0160		

otrisomic will result. The fertilization of the female gamete by a normal male gamete will result in disomic progeny (Fig. 7).

Since *mMdh2* has been mapped to chromosome 6L using the B-A translocation cross SD10 × Tb6Lc, the same cross can also be used to conduct a gene-dosage study. Line SD10 exhibits phenotype B (Fig. 8). Plants that have one dose of chromosome 6L (meromonosomic) also will exhibit the maternal zymogram phenotype (phenotype B) and always will have 20 chromosomes, while plants disomic for chromosome 6L will exhibit phenotype A (Fig. 8) and have 20 or 21 chromosomes. Plants merotrisomic for chromosome 6L will exhibit phenotype F (Fig. 8) and always will possess 22 chromosomes. Therefore, zymogram analysis and chromosome counts were conducted on all progeny to determine the number of *mMdh2* genes each contained. The technique of rocket immunoelectrophoresis can be used to quantitate the amount of mMDH protein. The level of mMDH protein in disomic, meromonosomic, and merotrisomic plants were compared, and it was found that the ratio of meromonosomic to disomic was 0.62, while the ratio of meromonosomic to merotrisomic was 0.40 [McMillin and Scandalios, 1982; Fig. 11]. Since *mMdh2* is only one of four *mMdh* genes, the ratios obtained certainly suggest that *mMdh2* exhibits a gene-dosage response.

Gene-dosage experiments using B-A translocations did not indicate a gene dosage response for the *sMdh* genes [McMillin and Scandalios, 1982]. These results are discussed below.

V. CONCLUSIONS AND COMMENTS

A. Possible Origin of *mMdh* and *sMdh* Genes by Chromosome Segment Duplication

A number of maize genes show duplicate gene inheritance [Emerson et al, 1935; Rhoades, 1951; MacDonald and Brewbaker, 1974; Robertson, 1979; McMillin and Scandalios, 1980, 1981]. Some duplicate loci map to the same chromosome—*w5, w6,* [Demerec, 1923], *fr1, fr2* [Jenkins and Pope, in Emerson et al, 1935], and *au1, au2* [Eyster, in Emerson et al, 1935]—suggesting that intrachromosomal duplication may have been an important source of new maize genes.

In addition to intrachromosomal duplication, other genes map to different chromosomes such as cytosolic malate dehydrogenase (sMDH), which is coded by two unlinked duplicated loci, *sMdh1* and *sMdh2*. *sMdh1* has been mapped to chromosome 1L, 7.59 ± 2.1 map units from *Amp1* (aminopeptidase 1). *sMdh2* has been mapped to chromosome 5S, 4.46 ± 1.9 map units from *Cat1* (Catalase 1). *Cat1* previously has been shown to be 3 map

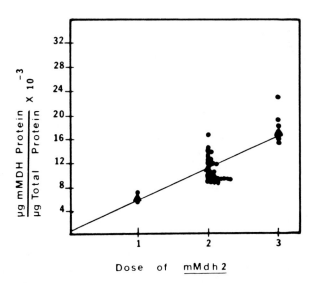

Fig. 11. Determination of the μg mMDH protein per total protein in progeny of SD10 × Tb6Lc carrying one, two, or three doses of *mMdh2*. Mean: meromonosomic plants = 0.0068; disomic plants = 0.0109 (from McMillin and Scandalios [1982], with permission).

units from another aminopeptidase gene, *Amp3*. Therefore, *sMdh1* and *Amp1* as well as *sMdh2* and *Amp3* could be approximately 8 map units apart, suggesting that the duplication event involved a chromosome segment, including *sMdh* and *Amp* loci. The genes *Pg 11, Pg 12* [Rhoades, 1951], *c1, c1m* [Robertson, 1979], *mMdh1, mMdh2, mMdh3,* and *mMdh4* [McMillin and Scandalios, 1981] also map to different chromosomes. The genes located thus far suggest the following chromosomes may have homologous regions: 6L and 9L [Rhoades, 1951], 3S and 8L [Robertson, 1979], 1L and 5S [McMillin and Scandalios, 1980], 6L and 8L, and 3L and 8L [McMillin and Scandalios, 1981]. The number of chromosomes with regions homologous to regions on chromosome 8 supports the proposal of Robertson [1979] that chromosome 8 had a number of intrachromosomal duplication events followed by interchromosomal events.

Chromosome segment duplication is an important mechanism for increasing the number of genes, or gene blocks [Metz, 1947]. Certainly the mammals appear to be an example where a high rate of anatomical evolution parallels the rate of chromosome rearrangements [Wilson et al, 1974]. The large number of duplicated maize loci found thus far suggests that maize would be an excellent choice for further studies on the importance of chromosome segment duplication on the evolution of a plant species.

In addition to providing data suggesting that chromosome segment duplications occurred in maize, the sMDH and mMDH systems are excellent choices for studying gene evolution. A number of inbred lines possess only one *sMdh* gene, while others possess two *sMdh* genes. In addition some inbred lines have two or three *mMdh* genes, while other lines have four *mMdh* genes. These lines may represent cases in which the duplication event occurred but in which one of the loci has evolved to the point that its temporal or spatial specificity is altered. Or, it is also possible that these lines originated from maize lines in which the duplication event did not occur.

B. Immunological Characterization of sMDH and mMDH Isozymes

Rocket immunoelectrophoresis was used to quantitate the amount of sMDH protein in lines with duplicated *sMdh* genes; lines with one *sMdh* gene had one-half the amount of sMDH protein with the exception of inbred line W64A [McMillin and Scandalios, 1982]. Line W64A must be characterized further to determine why the sMDH protein level is equal to lines possessing two *sMdh* genes (Table VII).

Gene dosage studies using B-A translocations were unable to confirm that sMDH exhibits a gene-dosage response. This may be due to the fact that a large portion of chromosome 1L and 5S was being varied. It is possible that there is a locus residing on either 1L or 5S that may influence the amount of sMDH produced; this is not without precedent [see Scandalios, these Proceedings].

Lines lacking one or more *mMdh* genes generally have lower mMDH protein levels. Inbred line 59 is an exception, because it lacks *mMdh4* and still has approximately normal levels of mMDH protein [McMillin and Scandalios, 1982]. Gene-dosage studies using B-A translocations demonstrated that *mMdh2* exhibits a gene-dosage response. Since *mMdh2* is one of four *mMdh* genes, the exact dosage response observed suggests that *mMdh2* must produce more mMDH protein than some of the other *mMdh* genes (Fig. 11). This is consistent with the zymogram patterns commonly observed. mMDH2 and mMDH4, both heterodimeric enzymes composed of mMDH5 subunits, as well as mMDH5 (coded by *mMdh2*), are the most intensely staining isozymes (Fig. 4A, III). Furthermore, inbred line 59 is null for *mMdh4* but possesses *mMdh2*. If *mMdh2* produced higher amounts of mMDH protein, line 59 may be expected to exhibit near-normal mMDH protein levels (Table VI). Other lines null for *mMdh2* have substantially lower mMDH protein levels (Table VI). These results may suggest that the production of the mMDH isozymes is differentially regulated.

C. Prospects for the Future

MDH is an excellent gene-enzyme system to use in the study of the process of chromosome segment duplication in maize. The *sMdh* and *mMdh* genes, along with other duplicated genes, can be used as probes in order to gain a better understanding of the origin and significance of chromosome segment duplication and may help in elucidating the evolution of maize.

The fact that there are mitochondrial, glyoxysomal, and cytosolic forms of MDH makes the MDH system one of the best systems for studying nuclear-cytoplasmic interactions and the mechanisms governing the processing of nuclear gene products into cytoplasmic organelles.

VI. ACKNOWLEDGMENTS

Research from the authors' laboratory was supported by research grants to J.G.S. from the NIH, NSF, and by the North Carolina Agricultural Foundation. The contributions to this study by Drs. G. P. Longo and N. S. Yang are gratefully acknowledged.

VII. REFERENCES

Baum JA, Scandalios JG (1979): Developmental expression and intracellular localization of superoxide dismutases in maize. Differentiation 13:133–140.

Demerec M (1923): Inheritance of white seedlings in maize. Genetics 8:561–593.

Emerson RA, Beadle GW, Fraser AC (1935): A summary of linkage studies in maize. Memoir 180 Cornell Univ Agric Exp Sta, pp 1–83.

Goodman MN, Stuber CW, Lee CN, Johnson FE (1980): Genetic control of malate dehydrogenase isozymes in maize. Genetics 94:153–168.

Lehninger AL (1975): Chap 19. In: "Biochemistry." 2nd ed. New York: Worth Publishers, p 535.

Longo GP, Scandalios JG (1969): Nuclear gene control of mitochondrial malic dehydrogenase in maize. Proc Natl Acad Sci USA 62:104–111.

MacDonald T, Brewbaker JL (1974): Isozyme polymorphism in flowering plants. J Hered 65:37–42.

McMillin DE, Scandalios JG (1980): Duplicated cytosolic malate dehydrogenase genes in *Zea mays*. Proc Natl Acad Sci USA 77:4866–4870.

McMillin DE, Scandalios JG (1981): Genetic analysis of the two groups of duplicated genes coding for mitochondrial malate dehydrogenase in *Zea mays:* Possible origin of *Mdh* genes by chromosome segment duplication. Mol Gen Genet 182:211–221.

McMillin DE, Scandalios JG (1982): Genetic, immunological, and gene dosage studies of mitochondrial and cytosolic MDH variants in maize. J Hered 73:177–182.

McMillin DE, Roupakias DG, Scandalios JG (1979): Chromosomal location of two mitochondrial malate dehydrogenase structural genes in *Zea mays* using trisomics and B-A translocations. Genetics 92:1241–1250.

Metz CW (1947): Duplication of chromosome parts as a factor in evolution. Am Nat 81:81–103.

Newton KJ, Schwartz D (1980): Genetic basis of the major malate dehydrogenase isozyme in maize. Genetics 95:425–442.

Ott LA, Scandalios JG (1978): Genetic control and linkage relationships among aminopeptidases in maize. Genetics 89:137–146.

Rhoades MM (1951): Duplicate genes in maize. Am Nat 85:105–110.

Robertson DS (1979): The location of *clm* in maize: A possible duplicate gene locus. J Hered 70:166–168.

Roman H (1947): Mitotic nondisjunction in the case of interchanges involving the B-type chromosome in maize. Genetics 32:391–409.

Roupakias DG, McMillin DE, Scandalios JG (1980): Chromosomal location of the catalase structural genes in *Zea Mays,* using B-A translocations. Theor Appl Genet 58:211–218.

Scandalios JG (1974): Isozymes in development and differentiation. Annu Rev Plant Physiol 25:225–258.

Scandalios JG, Sorenson JC, Ott LA (1975): Genetic control and intracellular localization of glutamate oxaloacetic transaminase in maize. Biochem Genet 13:759–769.

Tsaftaris AS, Scandalios JG, McMillin DE (1981): Gene dosage effects on catalase expression in maize. J Hered 72:11–14.

Wilson AC, Sarich VM, Maxson LR (1974): The importance of gene rearrangement in evolution: Evidence from studies on rates of chromosomal, protein, and anatomical evolution. Proc Natl Acad Sci USA 71:3028–3030.

Yang NS, Scandalios JG (1974): Purification and biochemical properties of genetically defined malate dehydrogenase in maize. Arch Biochem Biophys 161:335–353.

Yang NS, Scandalios JG (1975): *De novo* synthesis and developmental control of the multiple gene-controlled malate dehydrogenase isozymes in maize scutella. Biochem Biophys Acta 385:293–306.

Yang NS, Scandalios JG (1977): Effects of cycloheximide and chloramphenicol on the synthesis of polypeptides found in three subcellular fractions of maize scutellum. Plant Physiol 59:1067–1071.

Yang NS, Sorenson JC, Scandalios JG (1977): Genetic control of mitochondrial malate dehydrogenase: Evidence for duplicated chromosome segments. Proc Natl Acad Sci USA 74:310–314.

Isozymes: Current Topics in Biological and Medical Research
Volume 8: Cellular Localization, Metabolism, and Physiology 91–113

Role of Isozymes in Metabolic Regulation During Exercise: Insights From Comparative Studies

P.W. Hochachka, G.P. Dobson, and T.P. Mommsen

Department of Zoology, University of British Columbia, Vancouver, BC V6T 2A9, Canada

T.P. Mommsen's present address is Department of Biology, Dalhousie University, Halifax, N.S., Canada.

I. THE PROBLEM OF POWER OUTPUT AND FUEL SELECTION

Of all metabolic changes, the transition from rest to exercise work in most animals is one of the most extreme both in terms of the magnitude of change and in terms of absolute metabolic rates achieved. In metabolic terms, the first step in such transition involves activation of actomyosin ATPase-catalyzed hydrolysis of adenosine triphosphate (ATP) for driving muscle contraction; as this places a high demand upon a limited supply of endogenous ATP, there necessarily follows, in closely coordinated manner, the activation of ATP-replenishing metabolic pathways.

In mammals, the three main fuels available for muscle work are creatine phosphate (CrP), carbohydrate (glycogen plus glucose), and fat. The power output achievable with these different fuels, and the work duration, both vary (Table I). So it is not surprising that low-intensity work, sustainable for long time periods, is fueled by oxidative metabolism (burning either fat or carbohydrate); that intermediate intensities of work surpassing the power output capacities of oxidative metabolism are supported by anaerobic glycolysis; and that even higher intensity work can be sustained for short time periods on creatine phosphate hydrolysis. But what mechanisms assure that the cell mobilizes the correct fuel at the correct time at correct rates? And what roles do isozymes play in this process? Those are the central questions this chapter addresses. We shall proceed by considering aerobic and anaerobic ATP-synthesizing pathways separately; then an interpretative model will be discussed.

II. OXIDATIVE METABOLISM AND SUSTAINED MUSCLE WORK

Most mammals are capable of achieving about an order of magnitude increase in aerobic metabolic rate [Taylor et al, 1980], but there are many species that deviate from this average. Trained athletes can achieve about a 20-fold absolute activation, while maximum aerobic metabolism (V_{O_2} max) in horses can exceed basal metabolic rates by a full 40-fold [Thomas and Fregin, 1981]! At the level of muscle metabolism, this large activation requires a similarly large activation of flux through the Krebs cycle and through the electron transfer system.

TABLE I. Estimated Maximum Power Output for
Skeletal Muscle (of Man) Utilizing Different Substrates
and Metabolic Pathways[a]

Fuel/pathway	Power output μmoles ATP/gm wet weight/min
Fatty acid oxidation	20.4
Glycogen oxidation	30.0
Glycogen fermentation	60.0
CrP and ATP hydrolysis	96—360

[a]From McGilvery [1975] with modification.

A. Krebs Cycle Control Options

For the purposes of tuning up oxidative metabolism for sustained work organisms could in principle adjust both the amount and the isozyme type of enzyme present in muscle tissues. In fact, only the first alternative appears to be used in Krebs cycle adaptation. Thus, the levels of Krebs cycle enzymes are elevated (1) in muscles of species well adapted for sustained work [Marsh, 1981], (2) in red- vs white-type fibers [Guppy et al, 1979], and (3) in trained vs untrained individuals [Davies et al, 1981]. However, even if some of the Krebs cycle enzymes occur in mitochondrial vs cytosolic isozyme form (eg, malate dehydrogenases, transaminases, isocitrate dehydrogenases, fumarases) and some closely associated enzymes, such as pyruvate dehydrogenases [Laso and Sols, 1980; Prick et al, 1981], may occur in isozymic form, the mitochondrial enzymes of the Krebs cycle *per se typically do not occur as tissue-specific isozymes*. That is, the catalytic and regulatory properties of Krebs cycle enzymes in muscle are the same as they are in any other tissue, which means it is the unique compositional and content changes of muscle metabolites during transition from rest to exercise that must be at the heart of Krebs cycle regulation in muscle.

B. Krebs Cycle Control Sites

Singly, the most important feature of the Krebs cycle is that it is cyclic and catalytic, functioning with no net accumulation or depletion of intermediates. If for a moment one views the Krebs cycle in isolation, one can image it as a super-enzyme catalyzing the dissimilation of acetylcoenzyme A (CoA). Although of course this is an oversimplified view, it is useful because it clearly emphasizes that the simplest way of increasing flux is merely to increase the spinning rate of the Krebs cycle without any concomitant changes in cycle intermediates. This kind of control has two fundamental prerequisites. The first is that at least one (or more) enzymes in the process occur in "on" and "off" (low vs high activity) states. Within the cycle, three such enzymes are well known: citrate synthase (CS) and nicotinamide adenine dinucleotide (NAD)-linked isocitrate dehydrogenase in the first span of the cycle, and 2-oxoglutarate dehydrogenase in the second span. Citrate synthase is under close regulation by the adenylates and CoASH. Isocitrate dehydrogenase is regulated by the adenylates, Adenosine diphosphate (ADP) being essentially an absolute allosteric requirement for catalysis. And 2-oxoglutarate dehydrogenase is product inhibited by CoASH. Thus any changes in the mitochondrial redox state, in CoASH availability, or in the concentration ratios of ATP, ADP, Adenosine monophosphate (AMP), and P_i, as may be expected during transition from rest to work in muscle, may lead to concerted activation of all these enzymes, providing nothing else is limiting. Put another way, if substrate supply for any one of these enzymes were to be saturating under resting conditions, flux through the Krebs cycle could be activated by simply increasing spinning rate (ie, increasing the amounts of catalytically active enzymes at these key control sites). This condition, *that these enzymes be substrate saturated*, is a prerequisite for this simplest kind of control mechanism, but it cannot be met in muscle at rest. From the best evidence available, at least one of these enzymes (CS) is undoubtedly limited by vanishingly low concentrations of oxaloacetate; moreover, it is likely that the other two control points are also limited by isocitrate and 2-oxoglutarate availablity [Hochachka and Somero, 1983]. That is why, in order to increase the spinning rate of the Krebs cycle, it is also necessary to specifically augment the pool size of the cycle intermediates.

C. Augmentation of Krebs Cycle Intermediates

There are a variety of pathways by which intermediates can either be led from, or fed into, the Krebs cycle. In the powerfully energetic flight muscles of bees, pyruvate carboxylase channels pryuvate from mainline aerobic glycolysis into the mitochondrial oxaloacetate (OXA) pool from which carbon is "spread" throughout the cycle intermediates. In the flight muscle of the blowfly and the tsetse fly, and the mantle muscle of squid, proline serves as both a substrate for complete oxidation and as a means for augmenting the Krebs cycle [Hochachka and Guppy, 1978]. Whereas in principle these could work to a modest extent in mammalian muscle, they are far less important quantitatively than are aspartate and P-enolpyruvate (PEP). Aspartate is mobilized through the coupled operation of two transaminases (aspartate and alanine aminotransferases), to form oxaloacetate for the Krebs cycle [Hochachka and Storey, 1975]; alanine accumulates, and, in cases such as cardiac muscle, where this is the main means for augmenting the Krebs cycle, the alanine formed equals the summed increase in levels of all cycle intermediates. Skeletal muscle, in addition to this mechanism, contains significant levels of PEP carboxykinase, which is capable of channeling carbon from mainline glycolysis for purposes of Krebs cycle augmentation during activated fat catabolism. Indeed, as indicated in Table I, when glycogen is fully depleted, the rate of ATP formation from fat catabolism alone drops by about half; in part, this could be due to a gradual loss of Krebs cycle intermediates (due to a variety of side reactions), and hence a fall in its rate of spinning.

D. Mitochondrial Respiration and Phosphorylation

The end products of the Krebs cycle reactions are CO_2, H_2O, guanosine triphosphate, NADH, and reduced flavin adenine dinucleotide ($FADH_2$); the latter two both donate protons and electrons via the electron transfer system (ETS) to O_2, a process coupled to phosphorylation. As in the case of Krebs cycle, enzymes of the ETS appear to be conservative and there seem to be no reports of these occurring in isozymic forms. (Cytochrome oxidase has recently been reported to occur in isozymic forms [Kadenbach et al, 1983].) The situation with respect to ATP synthetase is not as clear, however.

The enzyme catalyzing this process, as first shown by Racker and his colleagues about 20 years ago, appears in electron micrographs as spherical projections; in intact mitochondria, these project on the matrix side of the inner mitochondrial membrane [Alfonso and Racker, 1979]. In vitro, these can be stripped by mechanical agitation to yield two kinds of preparations, submitochondrial particles (SMPs) and 85-Å spheres. The SMPs are able to transfer electrons but they can no longer synthesize ATP; the spheres are able to hydrolyze ATP. A critical insight is that the addition of these ATPase spheres back to the stripped SMPs restores their capacity to synthesize ATP. The spheres are referred to as coupling factor 1 or F_1 and it is now clear that the F_1 unit serves in vivo as an ATP synthetase [Alfonso and Racker, 1979].

The F_1 unit in heart muscle mitochondria is an oligomer of about 280,000 daltons, containing five kinds of polypeptide chains, but it is only part of the ATP-synthesizing machinery of mitochondria. The other major unit of this complex is F_0, a hydrophobic segment of four polypeptide chains that is anchored in the inner mitochondrial membrane. F_0 is the proton channel of the complex. The stalk between F_0 and F_1 includes several other proteins. One of them renders the complex sensitive to oligomycin, an antibiotic that blocks ATP synthesis by interfering with the flow of protons through the F_0 channel from the cytoplasmic to the matrix side of the membrane, which in the chemiosmotic theory is considered the driving force in ATP synthesis by F_1 [Alfonso and Racker, 1979].

Although the overall structure and composition of F_1 and other components of the ATP synthetase are similar in mitochondria from different tissues, with only modest adjustments in oligomeric composition, isozymic forms could be readily generated. The question of whether this occurs seems unsettled at this time, although there is some convincing physical-chemcial evidence that the liver ATP synthetase differs somewhat from that in heart and muscle: Overall molecular weight of heart F_1, for example, seems significantly smaller, and, while amino acid compositions show many similarities, they also display a number of quite notable differences [Catterall and Pederson, 1971]. Even subunit numbers of the whole complex in liver seem to differ from the system in heart muscle [see, for eg, Alfonso and Racker, 1979; Rott and Nelson, 1981]. Whether these structures turn out to display some tissue specificity must be clarified by further work; however, it is already clear that they do show quite different catalytic and regulatory properties.

E. Acceptor Control of Mitochondrial Function

In all aerobic cells, it is empirically observed that the rates of mitochondrial oxidative phosphorylation are rigorously coordinated with the ATP demands of the cytoplasm. How this phenomenon, called respiratory or acceptor control, is achieved in vivo is a central issue in the field of cellular bioenergetics. There are three prevalent theories [Jacobus et al, 1982]. The first and earliest theory proposes that rates of respiration are graded between state 3 and state 4 as a function of ADP availability. A second theory postulates that the extramitochondrial phosphorylation potential, [ATP]/[ADP] × [P_i], is the parameter which determines the immediate rates of oxygen consumption, a hypothesis that has received much recent attention. The third theory postulates that respiratory control is simply a function of the [ATP]/[ADP] ratio and is somewhat independent of [P_i].

Although the matter is not yet fully clarified, both the second and third theories above have been strongly undermined by recent data suggesting that the concentrations of free ADP in tissues are much lower than estimated from the values of ADP measured in cellular acid extracts. As a consequence, the phosphorylation potentials and [ATP]/[ADP] ratios may be at least an order of magnitude higher than previously estimated. In fact, the new values fall in ranges where only very low rates of mitochondrial respiration are usually measured. Thus, the new information creates a paradox as to how mitochondria can actively respire in tissues under the presumably inhibitory conditions of high phosphorylation potentials or high [ATP]/[ADP] ratios. This paradox appears to have been resolved in recent studies by Jacobus and his co-workers [1982], who experimentally managed to separate the two critical parameters: (1) availability of ADP to the F_1 enzyme and (2) the exogenous [ATP]/[ADP] ratio. Under such conditions, state 3 respiration rates correlate with absolute [ADP] and the most plausible *explanation of respiratory control is the availability of ADP to F_1* (and possibly the kinetics of its transport into the mitochondrion by the adenine nucleotide translocase). Thus Chance and Williams [1955] probably had it right over a quarter-century ago! From our point of view in this paper, it is particularly interesting that apparent K_m values for ADP of mitochondria from heart muscle and presumably skeletal muscle are in the 15 µM range if assessed by exogenous

ADP [Jacobus et al, 1982]. In contrast, apparent K_m values for ADP of liver mitochondria are about 50–70 μM [McGilvery, 1975; Jacobus et al, 1982]. Thus ATP synthetase of muscle mitochondria, in addition to showing some possible structural differences from that in liver mitochondria, also appears to show some critical functional specificities. One such seems intimately associated with the role of mitochondrial creatine phosphokinase (CPK_m) in oxidative metabolism of muscle cells.

F. Energy Transport Functions of Creatine Phosphate

It is now widely appreciated that creatine phosphate and CPK play important roles in aerobic energy metabolism of heart and muscle [Bessman and Geiger, 1981]. The MM-(muscle)type CPK is found in the cytosol (the so-called "soluble" form of the enzyme), but it is also localized within the thick filaments and on the sarcoplasmic reticulum (discussed further below). In contrast, a specific mitochondrial isozyme (CPK_m) is bound to the exterior aspect of the inner mitochondrial membrane. For over a decade, it has been considered plausible that the mitochondrial isozyme participates in the production of creatine phosphate in concert with oxidative phosphorylation, supplying creatine phosphate for cytoplasmic CPK to locally generate ATP required by the excitation-contraction-relaxation cycle. Much of the evidence for this scheme is reviewed elsewhere [Bessman and Geiger, 1981]. At this point it suffices to mention that one of the strongest bits of evidence supporting an energy transport function for creatine phosphate derives from tracer experiments showing that oxidative phosphorylation can supply ATP to cytoplasmic CPK without first mixing with the extramitochondrial pool of ATP. This result is in fact predictable from the shuttling models proposed [Bessman and Geiger, 1981] but otherwise is not easily explained.

G. Role of Mitochondrial Creatine Phosphokinase

Since the function of mitochondrial CPK may be the delivery of ADP via the adenylate translocase to F_1 ATP synthetase, the in vivo direction of net flux is

$$\text{Creatine (Cr)} + \text{ATP} \rightarrow \text{CrP} + \text{ADP}$$

Recent kinetic studies of CPK_m in situ (ie, in purified heart muscle mitochondria) indicate apparent K_m values for Cr and ATP of 5 mM and 0.7 mM, respectively, each being about an order of magnitude *higher* than the K_m values for Cr and ADP [Saks et al, 1975]. This suggests that CPK_m is usually saturated with ATP, while [Cr] may or may not be saturating. Equally important, the kinetic properties show that some provision must be made for rapidly removing the products, ADP and CrP, of the above reaction; for given the above relative affinities, *product inhibition is inevitable and would preclude CPK_m function in the direction written* [Saks et al, 1975].

Work from the laboratories of Saks and Jacobus supports they hypothesis that this kinetic problem is avoided by mitochondrial CPK being strategically positioned so as to supply a preferred pathway for ADP from CPK to the adenine dinucleotide translocase. For example, in one set of studies [Moreadith and Jacobus, 1982], state 3 respiration was initiated either with exogenous ADP (readily inhibitable with a competitive inhibitor, atractyloside) or with ATP in the presence of 20 mM creatine (ie, *utilizing mitochondrial CPK to generate ADP endogenously*). In the latter case, four to fivefold higher amounts of inhibitor were required to block respiration, even though the actual concentrations of ADP sparking respiration were *less* than in the control experiments. The possibility that this endogenous effect with heart mitochondria was simply explainable by intermembrane ADP generation was ruled out by parallel studies using liver mitochondria and nucleoside diphosphokinase for endogenous ADP generation (CPK could not be used since liver mitochondria do not contain CPK); state 3 respiration in this case showed normal behavior. Taken together, these data therefore suggest that in heart muscle mitochondria, the ADP generated by mitochondrial CPK is formed in such close proximity to the adenine nucleotide translocase that it effectively overcomes the atractyloside inhibition of respiration; ie, there is a functional coupling between the two systems (a preferential access for CPK-generated ADP to the translocase). Aside from obvious functional implications, these experiments allow more accurate estimates of ADP affinity and establish (1) that the apparent K_m for state 3 respiration of heart muscle mitochondria is as low as 2 μM ADP [Moreadith and Jacobus, 1982], a value close to the 0.5–1.0-μM values observed by direct measurements of F_1-ADP binding [Wielders et al, 1980], and (2) that the *apparent affinity of heart muscle F_1 for ADP is not three to fourfold, but rather may be some 30-fold, higher than in the case of the liver homolog*.

H. Significance of High Mitochondrial ADP Affinities

Two important implications arise. First, in the case of muscle or heart cells working under aerobic conditions, the high apparent affinity for ADP assures that mitochondrial respiration can respond sensitively to even modest changes in free ADP concentration. A second implication of the very low K_m (ADP) values plus the key role played by ADP in respiratory control is that in vivo heart and muscle mitochondria operate *at below saturating levels of this key substrate*. As with other metabolic enzymes, small changes in substrate (ADP) availability would thus lead to changes in flux. Conversely, in view of studies of isolated F_1 demonstrating catalytic properties typically found for regulatory enzymes [Grubmeyer and Penefsky, 1981], small changes in the ADP affinity of F_1 ATP synthetase may lead to large changes in catalytic rate.

III. ADP CONTROL OF MITOCHONDRIAL RESPIRATION DURING EXERCISE AND TRAINING

To properly place the above mechanisms into the context of exercise metabolism, three series of critical experiments must be emphasized:

(1) Sustained muscle work, supported by aerobic metabolism, is associated with only modest drops in ATP [Sutton et al, 1981] and therefore with even smaller increases in available ADP (since a significant fraction of the latter is protein bound). From the above model and from direct measurements [Mahler and Homsher, 1982], the cytosolic ADP "pulse" appears be reflected in a (creatine) change to which heart and muscle mitochondria can respond via membrane-bound CPK.

(2) During endurance training, the oxidative capacity of skeletal muscle approximately doubles even in a relatively glycolytic muscle such as the gastrocnemius [Oscai and Holloszy, 1971]. In principle, two strategies could be utilized for achieving this end: adjustments in enzyme amount or in isozyme kind. Currently, it appears that although both mechanisms are utilized, the dependence upon isozyme adjustments is minimal, CPK isozyme MB constituting the only good example of this that we could find. This isozyme increases in activity/gm tissue by about two to fourfold during endurance training and in a constant proportion manner with citrate synthase [Sylven and Jansson, 1982]. Other enzyme adaptations of muscle mitochondria are known to involve change in activity/gm tissue, but isozymic forms are either not known (eg, most ETS components) or have not been looked for during training (eg, cytochrome oxidase). Included in this category of adjustment are citrate synthase and other Krebs cycle enzymes, various ETS enzymes in a constant proportion manner [Davies et al, 1981], and F_1 ATP synthetase [Oscai and Holloszy, 1971].

(3) Many comparable enzyme adaptations occur during high-altitude adaptation, which at the level of muscle metabolism may involve adjustments similar to those in endurance training. In this case, in addition to enzyme content and composition adjustments, the K_m (ADP) of mitochondria may be even further reduced, although mechanisms for this effect are thus far unknown [Reynafarje, 1971].

When all these observations are integrated with the new developments in acceptor control of mitochondrial metabolism, several unexpected and previously overlooked features of metabolism during exercise derive. First, for a given level of work, muscle mitochondria from endurance-trained (and high-altitude-adapted) individuals sustain one half the flux rate/ETS unit that mitochondria do from muscle of untrained individes (because they have twice the enzyme capacity). Second, the ADP saturation curves for muscle mitochondria from high-altitude-adapted (and from trained?) individuals are left-shifted (ie, display lower K_m values for ADP). Third, because of the first two features above, for a given level of work, muscle mitochondria from trained (and high-altitude-adapted) individuals operate at substantially *lower ADP concentration range and therefore can respond more sensitively to change in [ADP]*. And fourth, the mitochondrial catalytic potentials (*amounts* of oxidative enzymes/gm tissue) are elevated during adaptations to strenuous conditions such as endurance performance or high altitude not simply to elevate maximum flux rates attainable, *but rather to maintain and indeed improve control of mitochondrial respiration*. This is particularly true of CPK_m, for its strategic mitochondrial positioning assures that these mitochondria are elegantly designed to sense even the smallest, micromolar pulses of [ADP]; i.e. to operate effectively at low [ADP].

In addition, increasing ADP affinity while lowering the concentration range over which F_1 operates should buffer mitochondrial function against falling O_2 concentrations, which are to be expected during strenous muscle work or during chronic hypoxia (as at high altitude). It is pointed out by Wilson et al [1979] that one way of adjusting to falling O_2 concentrations involves increasing the [ADP] and the [ADP]/[ATP] ratios so as to maintain appropriate (ie, unaltered) rates of ATP synthesis. Indeed, this is one mechanism (along with adjustments in the redox state of cytochrome c) that is proposed to explain why mitochondrial respiration can be so apparently insensitive to changing O_2 concentrations (down to less than 1 μM levels). What this means is that at any given level of work, mitochondria from trained individuals should be able to maintain ATP synthesis rates independent of O_2 down to lower O_2 concentrations than in untrained individuals, and this can be viewed as a final benefit of the above enzyme adaptations. However, if power demands exceed about 0.5 μmoles ATP/gm/sec (Table I), they surpass the ATP generating capacity of aerobic metabolism, and even these elegent adaptations are now not enough. Under such conditions, muscle work must become supplanted by anaerobic metabolism, to which we will now turn our attention.

IV. ISOZYME FOUNDATION OF MUSCLE GLYCOLYTIC PATHWAY

While all muscle fibers possess some capacity for anaerobic fermentation of glycogen (a process which shall term anaerobic glycolysis in this paper; it is more correctly called glycogenolysis), in all vertebrates the catalytic potential of this pathway is exaggerated in so-called white fibers; this relationship is so widespread these are often termed fast-twitch glycolytic muscles. Animals adapted for burst performance typically retain higher proportions of white fibers in their muscles, store more glycogen in their white fibers, and retain higher *amounts* of glycolytic enzymes [Guppy et al, 1979]. Overall glycolytic capacity of white muscle is therefore particularly high.

Although effective, these simple mechanisms cannot account for one of the most dramatic features of muscle glycolysis: its capacity for sustaining very large flux changes on transition from rest to burst work. Newsholme [1982] and McGilvery [1975] have argued that in the leg muscle of well-trained sprint runners glycolysis may be activated by over 1,000-fold; ie, an absolute flux change of over three orders of magnitude! This characteristic depends less on the amounts of each enzyme present than *upon the isozyme kinds retained in muscle,* particularly upon their catalytic and regulatory properties. It is now well established that essentially every step in the glycogen → lactate conversion occurs in muscle-specific isozyme form or forms (some of the enzymes occur in more than one form/cell). It is beyond the scope of this essay to review these in detail; however, it is clear that glycolytic support of burst muscle work is dependent upon the coordinated regulation of this pathway, which we must therefore briefly review.

A. Turning On Muscle Glycogen Phosphorylase

In mammals, glycogen phosphorylase occurs in at least three isozyme forms, one of which is characteristic of skeletal and cardiac muscle [Cohen, 1978]. Two classes of signals, endocrine and neuronal, act indirectly to activate glycogen phosphorolysis. Various endocrines (epinephrine being one of the most potent) serve to activate membrane-bound adenyl cyclase, which initiates a cascade control system.

The neuronal mechanism for activating glycogen breakdown involves membrane depolarization and Ca^{++} release from sarcoplasmic reticulum (SR). Ca^{++} control cuts in at the level of inactive phosphorylase b-kinase by binding to its smallest subunit; calmodulin. Calmodulin in muscle, unlike other tissues, is incorporated into the integral oligomeric structure of phosphorylase b-kinase; as in calmodulin from other tissues, it has two Ca^{++} binding sites. The binding of Ca^{++} causes a large (about 15-fold) increase in affinity for substrate which under physiological conditions leads to an ATP-dependent phosphororylation of b-kinase and thus its activation. Phosphorylase b-kinase in turn leads to the polymerization of phosphorylase-b to phosphorylase-a. In this cascade system in liver, the degree of amplification of the incoming epinephrine signal is about 10^6 [Hochachka and Somero, 1983]. The molar ratio [Cohen, 1978] of the cascade enzyme in muscle (1:10:240), compared to 1:0.25:14 in liver, indicates that the amplification capacity is higher in the former than in the latter, and is easily adequate to account for the 10^3 change in glycolytic flux.

In this capacity to function over such large absolute ranges of flux the pathway of glycogenolysis is unique in metabolism; no other pathway ever achieves the same degree of activation. All intermediates along the pathway have been monitored through these kinds of transitions and although many if not all of these increase in concentration during activated flux, none change nearly as much as can the actual flux through the system [Hintz et al, 1982]. That is why amplification mechanisms must exist for the large activation of catalytic machinery in muscle during burst work. And that is why strategic significance is attached to the cascade control of glycogen phosphorylase, for it would otherwise be difficult to understand how flux changes of 10^3 could be achieved concomitant with less than tenfold changes in the levels of key pathway intermediates. But even if it is probably the most important single mechanism for turning on muscle glycolysis, the glycogen phosphorylase system in turn must be integrated with at least one additional control site in the pathway: the step catalyzed by phosphofructokinase (PFK).

B. Regulatory Functions of Muscle Phosphofructokinase

Phosphofructokinase (PFK) catalyzes the first committed step in glycolysis and as such has long been reconized as an important locus of control. As in the case of phosphorylase, muscle PFK occurs as a tissue-specific isozyme form, displaying unique catalytic and regulatory properties that tailor it for burst-type work in muscle. In all mammals [Tsai et al, 1975] and most other animals that have been studied in this regard [Storey and Hochachka, 1974], PFK control is based upon its interactions with both substrates, Fructose-6-phosphate (F6P) and ATP: the F6P saturation curve is typically sigmoidal (at physiological pH) with the $S_{(0.5)}$ in the 0.1-mM range, similar to physiological levels of F6P. The saturation curve of ATP, in sharp contrast, is hyperbolic and through physiological concentrations of ATP (above 1 mM), the enzyme displays a kinetic order less than one. This is as it should be for an enzyme in a pathway whose function is to make ATP: The lower the in vivo level of ATP, the less inhibited by ATP the enzyme becomes, the greater its catalytic potential.

toward appropriate control of PFK: during burst work, for example, F6P levels rise as flux is activated, and increasing F6P availability would serve to increase its rate of utilization by PFK (positive cooperativity) while reversing ATP substrate inhibition. At the same time, falling ATP levels simultaneously lead to reduced substrate (ATP) inhibition and to an increased affinity for F6P, in effect increasing reaction velocity. These are synergistic regulatory properties that help in integrating PFK function with that of glycogen phosphorylase and, indeed, with myosin ATPase. But built upon this control foundation are other inputs that add even more versatility to the control of this locus in glycolysis: the most important of these are activation by fructose-2,6-bisphosphate (F2,6BP), F1,6BP, AMP, ADP, P_i, and NH_4^+ as well as inhibition by citrate and fatty acylCoA. Much of the older information is reviewed by Tsai et al [1975].

In metabolic terms, an exciting new development in our understanding of how PFK may be regulated in vivo is the discovery of F2,6BP as the most potent activator of PFK thus far known [see Furuya and Uyeda, 1980]. The modulator is formed from F6P by the action of a specific enzyme and has several critical effects on PFK: (1) It increases enzyme-F6P affinity substantially, while reducing the strength of F6P site-site cooperative interactions (in effect, saturation curves for F6P are moved to the left and become less sigmoidal), (2) it increases the affinity for the cosubstrate, ATP; (3) it reverses inhibition by high levels of ATP; (4) it reverses inhibition by citrate; and (5) it is synergistic in its effects with other potent positive modulators, in particular AMP and P_i [see Uyeda et al, 1981]. Recent metabolic measurements indicate that [F2,6BP] rises by two to fourfold during insulin or epinephrine activation of glycolysis in perfused rat hindlimb muscle [Blackmore et al, 1982], thus providing in situ support for a novel control situation:

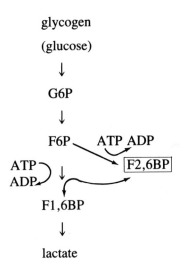

ADP and F1,6BP effects on muscle PFK can be viewed as adding an autocatalytic component to PFK control: These are the immediate products of the reaction and they in effect stimulate their own further rate of formation. At least in part for this reason, PFK catalytic rate is not a linear function of time, but increases exponentially with time, making an important contribution to the flare-up of glycolysis that is characteristic of burst work.

C. Role of ADP in Integrating PFK and Glycolytic ATP-Forming Reactions

ADP plays another most critical function: as a substrate for P-glycerate kinase (PGK) and pyruvate kinase (PK), it serves to integrate these activities with PFK catalysis. Muscle PGK is a high-activity enzyme with kinetic properties suited for glycolytic function. In particular, it displays very high affinity for 1,3-diphosphoglycerate (micromolar range) and under most (especially working) conditions, the enzyme should be saturated with this substrate. Its affinity for ADP, however, is not so high and the apparent Michaelis constant clearly falls in the physiological range [Hochachka and Guderley, 1975]. Thus, PGK activity in vivo is probably paced by ADP availability.

The situation at the PK locus is more complex. In lower vertebrates and invertebrates, F1,6BP is a feedforward activator of PK and serves as a coupling signal between PFK and PK, a mechanism potentiated as glycolysis proceeds and pH drops [see Hochachka, 1980; Storey and Hochachka, 1974]. In mammalian muscle PK, this control is lost and PFK-PK integration depends solely upon ADP (being the product of one, and the substrate of the other). The kinetic properties of muscle PK (particularly its marked positive cooperativity in binding of substrates) admirably suits this isozyme for glycolytic function in muscle. The dissociation constant for ADP binding to the free enzyme is lowered from a nonphysiological range (>2 mM ADP) down to about 0.2–0.3 mM by addition of PEP; ie, the binding of PEP leads to a very large (approximately an order of magnitude) increase in the affinity of the enzyme for its cosubstrate, ADP [Dann and Britton, 1978]. In metabolic terms, this means that two signals are needed to integrate muscle PK and muscle PFK activities: The first one is PEP, formed (via several reaction steps) from F1,6BP, a product of the PFK reaction; the second is ADP, supplied directly by the PFK reaction. The first (PEP) is needed to make PK competitive for the second (ADP).

D. Role of ADP in Coupling Anaerobic Glycolysis with ATPases

The end products of anaerobic glycolysis (considered at about pH 8 to avoid the problem of H^+ stoichiometry [Hochachka and Mommsen, 1982], are lactate, ATP, and water:

$$\text{glycogen(glucosyl)} + 3\ ADP^{3-} + 3\ P_i^{2-} \rightarrow 2\ \text{lactate}^{1-} + 3\ ATP^{4-} + 2H_2O$$

The cytosolic pool size in muscle of vertebrates ranges between 6 and 9 μmoles/gm, so even if all endogenous ADP were phosphorylated to ATP, maximum levels of lactate produced by this reaction pathway as written would be two thirds the adenylate pool size or a maximum of about 6 μmoles lactate/gm muscle (in fact it would have to be less, since ADP can never account for the total adenylate pool). In contrast, in vivo, mammalian muscle can readily accumulate 20–40 μmoles lactate/gm; tuna white muscle can accumulate over 100 μmoles/gm [Guppy et al, 1979]; and diving turtles can achieve up to 200 μmoles/gm [Ultsch and Jackson, 1982]. That is, more lactate is observed than can be produced by the above fermentation pathway as written. This apparent paradox does not mean that the glycogen → lactate conversion is dissociated from ADP phosphorylation but rather that glycolysis and myosin ATPase are coupled in vivo and that the continuous hydrolysis of ATP serves as a mechanism for *generating ADP and driving the above glycolytic reaction to the right*. This aspect of glycolytic regulation is little discussed in reviews of this field, although it is clear from reconstituted glycolytic systems that glycolytic flux can be effectively activated by addition of ATPases [Wu and Davis, 1981].

E. Redox Regulation

For sustained anaerobic glycolysis, a final provision must be made for redox balance, which is usually achieved by the coupling between glyceraldehyde-3-phosphate dehydrogenase and lactate dehydrogenase (LDH). LDH isozymes and the especial role of M_4 LDH in muscle glycolysis need not be emphasized to this audience. It suffices to mention that the importance of having M_4 LDH during anaerobic muscle work is nowhere better illustrated than in a recently described myopathy: Individuals lacking M_4 LDH in skeletal muscle are found to display abnormally low capacities for lactate production and reduced capacity for anaerobic muscle work [Kanno et al, 1980].

F. Costs and Benefits of Anaerobic Glycolysis

In summary, it may be useful to consider the advantages and the risks of dependence on anaerobic glycolysis. On the cost side, there appear to be three overriding disadvantages: (1) noxious end products such as H^+, (2) merely a short-term solution to the problem of ATP needs, and (3) an energetically inefficient system, therefore expressing a high-glucose demand.

On the benefit side, there are two notable advantages of anaerobic glycolysis as a means for powering muscle work. First, the system works without O_2, and second, it is a high-power output system; these are considerable advantages when O_2 is lacking or when the power output requirements cannot be met by O_2-based metabolism. On this latter criterion, the power output of muscle working on anaerobic glycolysis can only be surpassed by phosphagen hydrolysis or by direct ATP hydrolysis.

V. ROLE OF CREATINE PHOSPHATE AS A STORAGE ENERGY FORM

For highest rates of power output (up to 6 μmoles ATP/gm/sec for mammalian muscle (Table I)), ATP can be utilized directly for a second or two, but because these reserves are modest (6–9 μmoles/gm) and are preserved to maintain [ATP]/[ADP] ratios (or adequate chemical potentials), they are immediately augmented from larger phosphagen reserves. In vertebrate muscles, creatine phosphate is the high-energy phosphate reservoir; in many invertebrates, arginine phosphate is utilized. Creatine phosphate is most abundant in white muscles, occurring at about 30 μmoles/gm wet weight. Although stored generally in the cytosol, there is evidence that it is locally concentrated near myosin ATPase, where myosin-bound CPK is found [Bessman and Geiger, 1981] and where ATP supplies must be sustained if high rates of work are to continue. As already mentioned, CPK occurs in two main isozyme forms in mammalian muscles, a so-called soluble, or cytosolic CPK-I (MM), and a mitochondrial (CPK$_m$, or CPK-II. Since the fractional volume of white muscle fiber occupied by mitochondria is very small in most vertebrates, from less than 0.2% to about 2% [Guppy et al, 1979], most of the CPK activity in white fibers is represented by CPK-I.

Not only is the positioning of CPK-I appropriate to its function; so also are some of its catalytic and regulatory properties. Under highest intensity anaerobic work, the direction of net flux for this reaction is

$$CrP \ + \ ADP \rightarrow Cr \ + \ ATP$$

Thus, the relative affinities for CrP and ADP are of particular interest. Recent kinetic studies of the human muscle CPK [Jacobs and Kuby, 1980] indicate that the dissociation constants of CrP from both the binary and ternary complexes are high (72 and 32 mM, respectively), implying that under most in vivo concentration ranges *CrP is not saturating and the enzyme is maximally responsive to [CrP] changes*. Although the enzyme shows a low affinity for CrP, its affinity for ADP is high (dissociation constants of ADP from the binary and ternary complex, respectively, are about 0.2 mM and 0.06 mM), thus making it very competitive for ADP; this means that under highest-intensity work conditions, when ADP concentrations may rise to values above the enzyme-CrP affinity for ADP, the enzyme may become saturated with this substrate and its activity would then be largely determined by changing concentrations of CrP.

Finally, since the total adenylate pool in muscle is only 6–9 μmoles/gm even if all available ADP were converted to ATP, the reaction

$$CrP \ + \ ADP \rightarrow ATP \ + \ Cr$$

could lead to a CrP change of substantially less than 6–9 μmoles/gm; yet nearly a total depletion of CrP (about 30 μmoles/gm) is commonly observed during highest-intensity muscle work. As with the paradox of lactate accumulation (much more being found that could be accounted for by the adenylate pool), this is only possible because the above reaction is coupled with (in fact is *initiated* by) myosin ATPase. As with glycolysis, the significance of this interaction is usually overlooked in discussions of anaerobic muscle work.

VI. ROLE OF ADP DURING ANAEROBIC MUSCLE WORK

Before putting the above theoretical information in the context of exercise metabolism, two critical experimental observations must be emphasized:

(1) During burst work (involving power output of 1.6–6 μmoles/ATP/ gm/sec), there usually is observed a very significant drop in ATP. In mammalian systems, both in vitro and in vivo, a drop of over 1 μmoles/gm in ATP concentration is not all unusual [Sutton et al, 1981]. Consequently the rise in [ADP] must be much higher than during aerobic work. In trout swimming against a current to absolute fatigue, white muscle concentrations of ATP can drop to as low as 1 μmole/gm [Mommsen, Dobson, and Hochachka, unpublished data]. In such cases again, the rise in [ADP] is large relative to that observed during sustained work, reaching values as high as 1 μmole/gm!

(2) Often there is a clear-cut separation in time between CPK activation and glycolytic activation; ie, CrP reserves may become largely depleted before there occurs any significant lactate accumulation [Danforth, 1965]. This is also often seen in anaerobic work supported by arginine phosphate in molluscs [Hochachka and Mommsen, 1983, review this literature].

When the theoretical data on glycolytic and CPK functions are integrated with such empirical data from working muscles, a number of insights again arise. First, under anaerobic conditions, there are at least two cytosolic pathways potentially competitive for the ADP being released upon myosin ATPase activation; CPK and glycolysis. (To our knowledge, the competitive interaction between these two pathways has not been explored.) Second, when myosin ATPase is activated maximally (under conditions calling for highest power output), CPK appears to outcompete anaerobic glycolysis for the ADP being released; this may be due to kinetic or structural reasons (favored positioning of key enzymes). The main signals for subsequent activation of glycolysis appear to be dropping ATP levels (deinhibiting PFK), rising P_i, AMP, and F2,6BP levels serving to activate PFK, and rising ADP levels, serving (1) to activate PFK and (2) when PEP availability is assured, to increase the flux rate through pyruvate kinase.

VII. INTERPRETIVE MODEL OF FUEL (PATHWAY) SELECTION AND POWER OUTPUT

We are now in a position to return to our initial question: What determines which ATP-yielding pathways are utilized during muscle work of varying intensity? From our analysis, and for heuristic reasons, we propose a model at the heart of which lies a functional competition for ADP. We envisage the system to operate as follows:

(1) During work of highest power output (up to 6 μmoles ATP/gm/sec), myosin ATPases are activated to approximately their physiological maximum. Since the myosin isozymes of white muscle display higher turnover numbers than do their homologs in any other fiber types, this may involve their specific activation (but this is not a necessary part of our model). Despite the near-maximum activation of myosin ATPase, its catalytic potential apparently cannot exceed that of CPK-I, which responds to changing [adenylate]. During early stages of phosphagen-powered work, change in [ATP] cannot be easily detected, probably because its fractional decrease (100–300 nmoles/gm) is small compared to the total (5 μmoles/gm) pool size available. In contrast, the change in concentration of free ADP is more readily estimated [Gadian et al, 1981] because its fractional increase is large compared to its starting pool size. If CPK and myosin ATPase behave under these conditions as a closed system the change in [ATP] must be the same as that in [ADP]; if the reactants for these two enzymes are also in equilibrium with adenylate kinase, then the drop in [ATP] may by only about one half that in [ADP]. In either case it is the latter that is important, for CPK-I, a high-activity enzyme, displays in the presence of CrP an avid affinity for ADP; *by out-competing PGK and PK for ADP, a preferential mobilization of CrP is assured at the appropriate time.* Since ADP may gradually become saturating for CPK-I at such times, this process can continue until phosphagen is depleted, *but at decreasing rates,* since CPK flux becomes proportional to falling [CrP]. In fact, this is why the highest power output achievable by CrP hydrolysis cannot be sustained for more than a few seconds.

(2) During sustained muscle work (power output of about 0.25–0.5 μmole ATP/gm/sec) myosin ATPases are activated to only about one sixth to one tenth of their physiological maximum (different myosin isozymes may in fact be powering this level of work, but again this is not a necessary part of our interpretation). Changes in [ATP] and [ADP] at this level of work are smallest of all; nevertheless, [ATP] changes usually are observed often in the range of about 0.2–0.5 μmoles ATP/gm [Sutton et al, 1981], and the changes in [ADP] are accordingly even smaller. As in paragraph 1 above, CPK-I is catalytically and kinetically tailored to outcompete glycolysis for small amounts of ADP, and, the change in [ADP] is expressed as an increase

in [Cr], which serves to activate CPK_m (ie, to complete the CrP-Cr shuttle). In essence, the CrP-Cr shuttle serves to transmit a small [ADP] signal from cytosol to F_1 ATP synthetases in the mitochondria. Because of the very high ADP affinity of F_1 ATP synthetases, this assures that oxidative phosphorylation is the only pathway that can respond to the modest (μM) changes in [ADP] that way be expected during sustained work of low power output.

(3) During work of intermediate power output (about 1 μmole ATP/gm/sec), when CrP supplies are depleted, myosin ATPases are activated to only about one third of their physiological maximum rate (this is an empirical statement and is assumed to be the explanation for why power output (Table I) is reduced when CrP reserves are depleted). Falling [ATP] and rising [ADP] are always reported when phosphagen supplies are depleted and these changes are larger than during higher or lower power output periods. At these intermediate power outputs, dropping [ATP] may be large enough to deinhibit PFK allowing glycolytic carbon flow to increase PEP availability; at this point, and as dropping [CrP] becomes limiting to CPK (while [ADP] may be saturating), *muscle PK becomes ever more competitive for ADP, thus completing the preferential glycolytic activation and mobilization of glycogen at intermediate power output.* The overall system is set up so as to give CPK-I preferential access to the ADP liberated by myosin ATPase hydrolysis of ATP. At highest power output, this system in essence precludes significant glycolytic contribution (unitl and unless ADP becomes saturating or CrP becomes limiting, at which time glycolysis may phase in). At lower power outputs, indefinitely sustainable, the [ADP] pulse released by myosin ATPase function is transmitted via the CrP-Cr shuttle to F1,ATP synthetase. In this view, the CrP-Cr shuttle serves as a means for precluding significant glycolytic consumption of ADP under aerobic condition and thus helps to assure that it is not untilized inappropriately.

This model is useful for making predictions and for explaining earlier and sometimes perplexing data:

(1) Rates of glycolysis should be higher in the presence of an active ATPase, because of the cycling of ADP between the latter and the former, as in fact has been experimentally observed [Wu and Davis, 1981].

(2) CPK-I can outcompete glycolysis for ADP in the 0.1 μmoles/gm range through all [CrP] changes (ie, until CrP is depleted). This prediction is based on kinetic properties of CPK (MM isozyme) and PK (muscle isozyme), and empirically is often observed [for example, see Gadian et al, 1981], which is why, under highest work rates, phosphagen depletion may be virtually complete *prior* to any significant glycolytic activity [Danforth, 1965]. An important enzyme basis for this observation is that PK is not an effective competitor for ADP until PEP is available. And even then, it has a lower affinity for ADP then does CPK. That is why, while accepting usually em-

phasized glycolytic control mechanisms (focused on PFK and glycogen phosphorylase) our model places *additional emphasis on ADP regulation of the lower half of the glycolytic path*. In fact, our model would predict that in reconstituted glycolytic systems, exogenous addition of CPK and CrP would strongly *inhibit* glycolysis by out-competing PK for limiting ADP (experiments are in progress to test this prediction).

(3) Our model also predicts that at [ADP] of about 0.1 μmole/gm, exogenous CPK and CrP should potently inhibit mitochondrial respiration, which indeed has been observed [Gatt and Racker, 1959].

(4) Another prediction is that at about 0.1 μmole ADP/gm, glycolysis should potently inhibit mitochondrial respiration (if CrP is low or CPK is absent). This too has been experimentally observed [Gatt and Racker, 1959]. Moreover, this inhibition (a) is dependent upon a competition for ADP and (b) is *abolished* if PGK and PK are deleted [Gatt and Racker, 1959]—results entirely consistent with our model.

(5) Although experimentally it is already known that the competition for ADP between glycolysis and mitochondrial metabolism can lead to respiratory inhibition, the ADP concentration dependence of this process has not been clarified. If our model is correct, the above inhibitory interaction should be abolished at low ADP (in the μM range), where only mitochondrial metabolism appears competitive.

(6) If our model is correct, it suggests that activation of ATP-yielding pathways could follow either the temporal sequence CrP hydrolysis $\rightarrow$ glycolysis $\rightarrow$ oxidative metabolism or oxidative metabolism $\rightarrow$ CrP hydrolysis $\rightarrow$ glycolysis, depending upon sequential changes in power output requirements. Furthermore, it should be possible to show CrP depletion or glycolytic activation *before* O_2 supplies of working muscle are depleted; the latter has in fact been observed but never properly explained [Jöbsis and Stainsby, 1968].

(7) Finally, this interpretive model supplies a biological rationale and explanation for why, of the three pathways for generating ATP, mitochondrial metabolism displays by far the highest ADP affinity: this assures the organism that whenever O_2 availability is adequate, oxidative metabolism will outcompete the anaerobic pathways for limiting ADP, thus gaining efficiency advantages while avoiding the undesirable problems of fermentation.

VIII. REFERENCES

Alfonso M, Racker E (1979): Components and mechanism of action of ATP-driven proton pumps. Can J Biochem 57:1351–1358.

Bessman SP, Geiger PJ (1981): Transport of energy in muscle: The phosphorylcreatine shuttle. Science 211:448–452.

Blackmore PF, Hue L, Shikama H, Robinson-Steiner A, Exton JH (1982): Regulation of fructose 2,6-bisphosphate content in rat hepatocytes, perfused hearts, and perfused hindlimbs. Fed Proc 41:8234.

Catterall WA, Pederson PL (1971): Adenosine triphosphatase from rat liver mitochondria. J Biol Chem 246:4987–4994.

Chance B, Williams GR (1955): Respiratory enzymes in oxidative phosphorylation. J Biol Chem 217:383–393.

Cohen P (1978): The role of cyclic-AMP-dependent protein kinase in the regulation of glycogen metabolism in mammalian skeletal muscle. Curr Topics Cell Reg 14:117–196.

Danforth WH (1965): Activation of glycolytic pathway in muscle. In Chance B, Estabrook RW, Williamson JR (eds): "Control of Energy Metabolism." New York: Academic Press, pp 287–297.

Dann LG, Britton HG (1978): Kinetics and mechanism of action of muscle pyruvate kinase. Biochem J 169:39–54.

Davies KJA, Packer L, Brooks GA (1981): Biochemical adaptation of mitochondria, muscle, and whole-animal respiration to endurance training. Arch Biochem Biophys 209:539–554.

Furuya E, Uyeda K (1980): Regulation of phosphofructokinase by a new mechanism. An 'activation factor' binding to the phosphorylated enzyme. J Biol Chem 255:11656–11659.

Gadian DG, Radda GK, Brown TK, Chance EM, Dawson MJ, Wilkie DR (1981): The activity of creatine kinase in frog skeletal muscle studied by saturation-transfer nuclear magnetic resouance. Biochem J 194:215–228.

Gatt: S, Racker E (1959): Regulatory mechanisms in carbohydrate metabolism. I. Crabtree effect in reconstructed systems. J Biol Chem 234:1015–1023.

Grubmeyer C, Penefsky HS (1981): Cooperativity between catalytic sites in the mechanism of action of beef heart mitochondrial adenosine triphosphatase. J Biol Chem 256:3728–3734.

Guppy M, Hulbert WC, Hochachka PW (1979): Metabolic sources of heat and power in tuna muscles. II. Enzyme and metabolite profiles. J Exp Biol 82:303–320.

Hintz CS, Chi MMY, Fell RD, Ivy JL, Kaiser KK, Lowry CV, Lowry OH (1982): Metabolite changes in individual rat muscle fibers during stimulation. Am J Physiol 242:C218–C228.

Hochachka PW (1980): "Living Without Oxygen." Cambridge: Harvard University Press, pp 1–181.

Hochachka, PW, Guderley HE (1975): Forms and functions of gluconeogenic enzymes in arthropods. In Markert CL (ed): "Isozymes II: Physiological Function." New York: Academic Press, pp 519–537.

Hochachka PW, Guppy M (1978): Variation on a theme by Embden, Meyerhof, and Parnas. In Jobsis FF (ed): "Oxygen and Physiological Function." Dallas, Texas: Prof. Information Library, pp 292–310.

Hochachka, PW, Mommsen TP (1982): Protons and anaerobiosis. Science (in press).

Hochachka PW, Mommsen TP (1983): Metabolic and enzyme regulation during rest-to-work transition: A mammal vs mollusc comparison. In Wilbur KM, Hochachka PW (eds): "The Biochemistry and Physiology of Mollusca." New York: Academic Press, in press.

Hochachka, PW, Somero GN (1983): "Biochemical Adaptation." Princeton: Princeton University Press, in press.

Hochachka, PW, Storey KB (1975): Metabolic consequences of diving in animals and man. Science 187:613–621.

Jacobs HK, Kuby SA (1980): Studies on muscular dystrophy. A comparison of the steady-state kinetics of the normal human ATP-creatine transphosphorylase isoenzymes (creatine kinases) with those from tissues of Duchenne muscular dystrophy. J Biol Chem 255:8477–8482.

Jacobus WE, Moreadith RW, Vandegaer KM (1982): Mitochondrial respiratory control. Evidence against the regulation of respiration by extramitochondrial phosphorylation potentials or by [ATP]/[ADP] ratios. J Biol Chem 257:2397–2402.

Jöbsis FF, Stainsby WN (1968): Oxidation of NADH during contractions of circulated mammalian skeletal muscle. Resp Physiol 4:292–300.

Kadenbach B (1983): Tissue-specific isozymes of cytochrome C oxidase. This Issue.

Kanno T, Sudo K, Takeuchi I, Kanda S, Honda N, Nishimura Y, Oyama K (1980): Hereditary deficiency of lactate dehydrogenase M-subunit. Clinica Chim Acta 108:267–276.

Laso PA, Sols A (1980): Identification of an AMP-activatable pyruvate dehydrogenase isozyme in embryos and tumors. FEBS Lett 120:287–288.

Mahler M, Homsher E (1982): Metabolic rate changes in parallel with creatine level during non-steady states in frog skeletal muscle. Fed Proc 41:4145.

Marsh RL (1981): Catabolic enzyme activities in relation to premigratory fattening muscle hypertrophy in the gray catbird (Dumatella carolinensis). J Comp Physiol 141:417–423.

McGilvery RW (1975): The use of fuels for muscular work. In Howald H, Poortmans JR (eds): "Metabolic Adaptation to Prolonged Physical Exercise." Basel: Birkhauser Verlag, pp 12–30.

Moreadith RW, Jacobus WE (1982): Creatine kinase of heart mitochondria. Functional coupling of ADP transfer to the adenine nucleotide translocase. J Biol Chem 257:899–905.

Newsholme E (1982): Control of fuel supply and fatigue in sprinting and endurance exercise. In: "Proc Hypoxia Symp Banff, Alberta." In press.

Oscai LB, Holloszy JO (1971): Biochemical adaptations in muscle. II. Response of mitochondrial adenosine triphosphatase, creatine phosphokinase, and adenylate kinase activities in skeletal muscle to exercise. J Biol Chem 246:6968–6972.

Prick M, Gabreels F, Renier W, Trijbels F, Jaspar H, Lamers K, Kok J (1981): Pyruvate dehydrogenase deficiency restricted to brain. Neurology 31:398–404.

Reynafarje B (1971): Effect of chronic hypoxia on the kinetics of energy transformation in heart mitochondria. Cardiology 56:206–208.

Rott R, Nelson N (1981): Purification and immunological properties of proton-ATPase complexes from yeast and rat liver mitochondria. J Biol Chem 256:9224–9228.

Saks VA, Chernousova GB, Gukovsky DE, Smirnov VN, Chazov EI (1975): Studies of energy transport in heart cells. Mitochondrial isoenzyme of creatine phosphokinase: Kinetic properties and regulatory action of Mg^{2+} ions. Eur J Biochem 57:273–290.

Storey KB, Hochachka PW (1974): Enzymes of energy metabolism in a vertebrate facultative anaerobe, Pseudemys scripta. Turtle heart pyruvate kinase. J Biol Chem 249:1423–1427.

Sutton JR, Jones NL, Toews CJ (1981): The effect of pH on muscle glycolysis during exercise. Clin Sci 61:331–337.

Sylven C, Jansson E (1982): Myocardial and skeletal muscle enzyme activities: Creatine kinase and its isozyme MB as related to oxidative enzymes and fiber types. Fed Proc 41:4150.

Taylor CR, Maloiy GMO, Weibel ER, Langman VA, Kamau JMZ, Seeherman HJ, Heglund NC (1980): Design of the mammalian respiratory system. III. Scaling maximum aerobic capacity to body mass: Wild and domestic mammals. Resp Physiol 44:25–37.

Thomas DP, Fregin GF, (1981): Cardiorespiratory and metabolic responses to treadmill exercise in the horse. J Appl Physiol 50:864–868.

Tsai MY, Gonzalez F, Kemp RG (1975): Physiological significance of phosphofructokinase isozymes. In Markert CL (eds): "Isozymes II. Physiological Function." New York: Academic Press, pp 819–835.

Ultsch GR, Jackson DC (1982): Long-term submergence at 3°C of the turtle, *Chrysemys picta bellii,* in normoxic and severely hypoxic water. J Exp Biol 96:11–28.

Uyeda K, Furuya E, Luby LJ (1981): The effect of natural and synthetic D-fructose 2,6-bisphosphate on the regulatory kinetic properties of liver and muscle phosphofructokinase. J Biol Chem 256:8394–8399.

Wielders JPM, Slater EC, Muller JLM (1980): Binding of ADP to beef heart mitochondrial ATPase (F_1). Biochem Biophys Acta 589:231–240.

Wilson DF, Erecinska M, Drown C, Silver IA (1979): The oxygen dependence of cellular energy metabolism. Arch Biochem Biophys 195:485–493.

Wu TFL, Davis EJ (1981): Regulation of glycolytic flux in an energetically controlled cell-free system: The effects of adenine nucleotide ratios, inorganic phosphate, pH, and citrate. Arch Biochem Biophys 209:85–99.

Isozymes: Current Topics in Biological and Medical Research
Volume 8: Cellular Localization, Metabolism, and Physiology 115–140

Impact of Isozymes Upon Partitioning of Carbon Flow and Regulation of Aromatic Biosynthesis in Prokaryotes

Graham S. Byng and Roy A. Jensen

Center for Somatic-cell Genetics and Biochemistry, State University of New York at Binghamton, Binghamton, New York 13901

I. INTRODUCTION

The multibranched shikimate pathway of aromatic amino acid biosynthesis is a complex biochemical network of central metabolic importance. The major endproducts are the three aromatic amino acids: L-phenylalanine, L-tyrosine, and L-tryptophan (Fig. 1). In addition, the shikimate pathway supplies a quantitatively minor but crucial output of beginning substrates needed for biosynthesis of folate, vitamin K, and ubiquinones [Weiss and Edwards, 1980]. Points of departure for metabolic steps of catabolism or of secondary metabolism also originate from numerous pathway intermediates or end-products and are highly variable from organism to organism. Within the shikimate pathway, different regulatory arrangements and protein-protein organizations of isozymes may contribute to alternative mechanisms for suitable partitioning of carbon flow to individual amino acid endproducts. Such mechanisms also exist to deal with the challenge of separating biosynthetic flow routes from connecting catabolic or secondary metabolite pathways. In many instances isozymes that are found to catalyze a given step of aromatic biosynthesis equate with seemingly obvious physiological interpretations. In other cases the differential in vivo roles of isozymes, if any, are more mysterious. It is likely that some of the latter isozyme systems represent intermediate stages of enzyme evolution [Jensen and Byng, 1981] that intervene between gene duplication and eventual differential specialization [Jensen, 1976].

Fig. 1. Divergent, multibranched pathway of aromatic amino acid biosynthesis. Enzymes [1–7] catalyze steps within the common shikimate branch; enzyme [13] catalyzes the single reaction of the midbranch; enzymes [8–12] and [14–20] catalyze terminal branchlet reactions culminating with L-tryptophan (TRP), L-phenylalanine (PHE), or L-tyrosine (TYR) synthesis. Only some organisms possess the entire array of dual branchlets to PHE and TYR, ie, enzymes [14–20]. The dotted arrows show the arogenate branchlets of PHE and TYR biosynthesis. Enzymes [16] or [17] may be NAD-linked, NADP-linked, or both—depending on the organism. The pathway begins (upper left) with the condensation of erythrose-4-phosphate and phosphoenolypyruvate (PEP) to form 3-deoxy-D-arabino-heptulosonate 7-phosphate (DAHP). Other abbreviations: DHQ, dehydroquinate; DHS, dehydroshikimate; SHK, shikimate; S-3-P, shikimate-3-phosphate; EPS, 5-enolpyruvylshikimate-3-phosphate; CHA, chorismate; ANT, anthranilate; GLN, glutamine; PPA, prephenate; AGN, L-arogenate; PPY, phenylpyruvate; HPP, 4-hydroxyphenylpyruvate; and PLP, pyridoxal-5'phosphate. Enzymes: [1], DAHP synthase; [2], dehydroquinate synthase; [3], dehydroquinase; [4], dehydroshikimate reductase; [5], shikimate kinase; [6], 5-enolypyruvylshikimate-3-phosphate synthase; [7], chorismate synthase; [8], anthranilate synthase; [9], anthranilate phosphoribosylpyrophosphate transferase; [10], phosphoribosyl anthranilate isomerase; [11], indoleglycerol phosphate synthase; [12], tryptophan synthase; [13], chorismate mutase; [14], prephenate aminotransferase; [15], arogenate dehydratase; [16], arogenate dehydrogenase; [17], prephenate dehydrogenase; [18], 4-hydroxyphenylpyruvate aminotransferase; [19], prephenate dehydratase; and [20], phenylpyruvate aminotransferase.

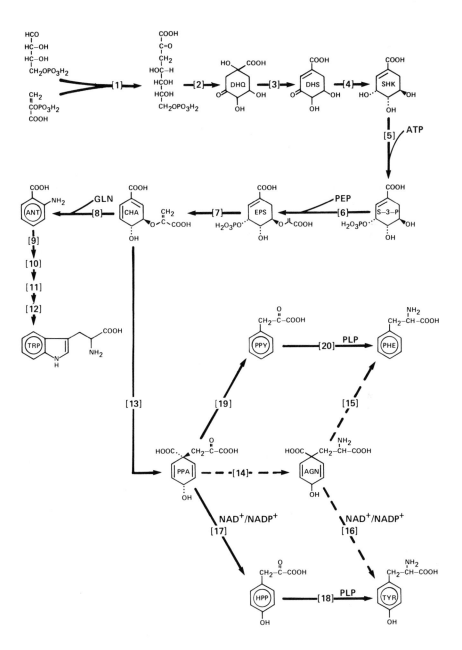

Fig. 1.

II. DAHP SYNTHASE ISOZYMES AND EARLY COMMITMENT OF CARBON TO AROMATIC FLOWTHROUGH

The initial flow of carbon into the shikimate pathway is mediated by 3-deoxy-D-arabino-heptulosonate 7-phosphate (DAHP) synthase. A diversity of allosteric patterns of control have been observed for this enzyme in nature, including the presence of differentially controlled isozyme species [Jensen and Rebello, 1970; Byng et al, 1982]. Some of these isozyme systems which illustrate the diversity of individual arrangements are shown in Figure 2.

A. Three Isozymes of DAHP Synthase in Enteric Bacteria

Isozymes of DAHP synthase are characteristic traits of enteric bacteria [Jensen et al, 1967; Jensen and Byng, 1981; Byng et al, 1982]. In Escherichia coli each of the three aromatic amino acids is a specific feedback inhibitor of one isozyme species [Smith et al, 1962; Brown and Doy, 1963; Wallace and Pittard, 1967; Staub and Denes, 1969a,b; Schoner and Herrmann, 1976; Zurawski et al, 1981; Davis and Davidson, 1982]. Differential transcriptional control of each isozyme-encoded gene *(aroF, aroG, aroH)* involves a common apo-repressor moiety *(tyrR)* [Brown, 1968] which yields three selectively acting holo-repressors by binding: (1) L-tyrosine, (2) L-tryptophan, or (3) L-phenylalanine in multivalent combination with L-tryptophan. An appealing expectation would be for each isozyme to generate a fraction of total DAHP that is about equivalent to the fraction of total endproduct comprised by the cognate regulatory amino acid. Although this regulatory relationship is often at least implied to operate, an unequal relationship between isozyme and cognate aromatic endproduct is, in fact, found in E coli. Thus, in crude extracts obtained from cells grown on defined minimal salts-glucose medium, the retro-phenylalanine isozyme comprises 75% of the total DAHP synthase activity, whereas the retro-tryptophan isozyme at the other extreme contributes a mere 1% of total activity [Jensen and Nasser, 1968]. Hence, in E coli the retro-phenylalanine isozyme ordinarily generates most DAHP molecules that traverse the aromatic pathway. The retro-tyrosine isozyme seems to exist largely as a reserve catalytic resource available under conditions of increased demand upon total output of the pathway. Although details vary between various species, enteric bacteria generally express a "dominant" isozyme during growth in minimal salts medium [Jensen and Nasser, 1968].

Fig. 2. Variable patterns of isozyme regulation for DAHP synthase in diverse genera of prokaryotes. The leftward arrows represent regulatory isozymes of DAHP synthase, each drawn with a pattern matching the pattern of the metabolite(s) circled. Consult Figure 1 for structures, details of full pathway arrangement, and abbreviations. For clarity of presentation the arogenate branchlets to L-phenylalanine and L-tyrosine (shown with dotted lines in Fig. 1) which exist in P aeruginosa are not shown.

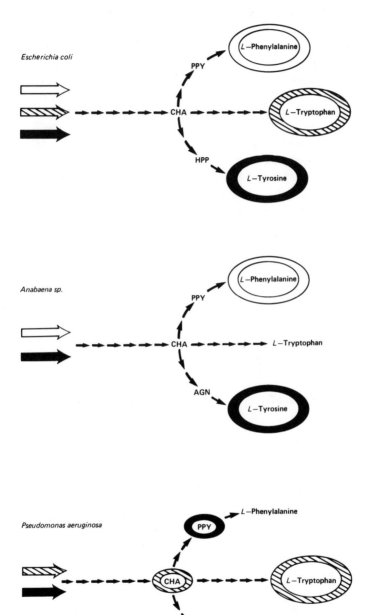

Fig. 2.

B. Major and Minor Allosteric Isozymes of DAHP Synthase in Pseudomonas Species

In organisms which lack significant transcriptional control of DAHP synthase, an unequal relationship between endproduct and cognate allosteric isozyme (as seen in E coli) is even more dramatic. The presence of quantitatively minor isozymes of DAHP synthase is now becoming apparent in some microorganisms originally thought to possess a single enzyme. In Pseudomonas aeruginosa, DAHP synthase was reported to be feedback inhibited by L-tryptophan and phenylpyruvate [Jensen et al, 1973] in additon to the earlier-known feedback inhibition by L-tyrosine [Jensen et al, 1967]. This control was interpreted to reflect a balanced allosteric pattern in which a single metabolite within each terminal branchlet of the shikimate pathway provides a feedback signal to DAHP synthase. Two distinct regulatory isozymes of DAHP synthase from P aeruginosa have now been resolved [Whitaker et al, 1982a]. The major (>90%) species (DAHP synthase-tyr) recognizes L-tyrosine as a potent feedback inhibitor, while phenylpyruvate is a relatively weak feedback inhibitor. The minor (<10%) isozyme (DAHP synthase-trp) is feedback inhibited strongly by L-tryptophan, while chorismate is a relatively weak competitive inhibitor. Each isozyme is therefore strongly inhibited by an amino acid endproduct and weakly inhibited by an intermediary metabolite. In P aeruginosa, the feedback pattern can be regarded as not only isozymic but also cumulative and sequential in that (1) each isozyme is controlled by two effectors which inhibit cumulatively in combination, and (2) each isozyme is also regulated by an intermediary metabolite which indirectly reflects the levels of one or more endproducts. In contrast to the isozymic species of DAHP synthase in E coli, the synthesis of these isozymes in P aeruginosa is not repressible by endproducts. This pattern of isozymic DAHP synthases in P acruginosa evidently extends to a large group of pseudomonad bacteria [Whitaker et al, 1981a.].

C. Two Isozymes of DAHP Synthase in a Cyanobacterium

In cyanobacteria the focal point of regulation is centered on allosteric control of DAHP synthase [Jensen and Hall, 1982]. From the additive nature of inhibition patterns in crude extracts, isozyme species of DAHP synthase have been inferred to exist in some species of cyanobacteria, predominantly members of the genera, Anabaena and Nostoc [Hall et al, 1982]. Indeed, two isozymes of DAHP synthase (retro-phenylalanine and retro-tyrosine) were resolved from one species of Anabaena [Hall and Jensen, 1981a]. The tyrosine-sensitive and phenylalanine-sensitive isozymes comprise about 60% and 40% of total enzyme activity, respectively. The DAHP synthases are subject to only very modest transcriptional control (<threefold). This isozyme system is perhaps the nearest of those described to having a symmetrical relationship of endproduct and cognate isozyme. Since L-tryptophan is a

minor amino acid with respect to quantitative input into protein synthesis, sufficient chorismate presumably would be available to satisfy L-tryptophan biosynthesis during maximal inhibition of DAHP synthase isozymes because inhibition is incomplete (residual, uninhibited activity being about 15%).

III. MIDPATHWAY ISOZYMES OF AROMATIC BIOSYNTHESIS

Isozymes can bring about spatial compartmentalization of metabolite flow if one or both are covalently associated with enzymes that mark a point of metabolic divergence. This type of fused system offers the advantages of restricting wasteful diffusion of intermediates within the cell in addition to enhancing the efficiency of multistep catalysis through spatial proximity of catalytic sites [Welch and Gaertner, 1975]. Catalytic isozyme units arising through gene duplication also have the potential to fuse with other enzymes, such that new allosteric binding sites are recruited from the original catalytic binding sites.

A. Isozymic Components of Channeling Proteins in Enteric Bacteria

Divergent, multienzyme channels to L-phenylalanine and to L-tyrosine begin with chorismate mutase isozymes in enteric bacteria (Fig. 3). One isozyme is synonymous with the protein catalyzing the reaction of prephenate dehydratase for phenylalanine biosynthesis (P-protein); the other isozyme is in synonymy with prephenate dehydrogenase for tyrosine biosynthesis (T-protein). These have been found in E coli, Salmonella typhimurium, and Aerobacter aerogenes (Klebsiella pneumoniae) [Cotton and Gibson, 1965, 1967, 1968; Koch et al, 1970; Schmidt et al, 1970; Schmidt and Zalkin, 1969]. Note that such an arrangement essentially pushes the true branchpoint back one step, chorismate rather than prephenate becoming the functional site of divergence. In effect, the one-step midbranch of the aromatic pathway as it is usually drawn is eliminated. A feasible evolutionary scenario invoking gene duplication followed by gene fusion as discussed by Jensen [1976] is shown in Figure 4.

One possible role of the multifunctional channels that leads away from chorismate in enteric bacteria is the in vivo isolation of prephenate from highly active aminotransferase enzymes. E coli and Klebsiella are capable of transaminating prephenate to L-arogenate quite well in vitro [Jensen, upublished data]. L-arogenate is not a normal intermediate of aromatic bio-synthesis in enteric bacteria (see Figs. 1, 2). Although prephenate molecules are undoubtedly enzyme-bound nearly always in wild type, at least one case is known where prephenate is freed from the sequestered state. Mutants of E coli lacking the chorismate mutase activity of the P-protein cannot be selected directly. Loss of chorismate mutase activity (P-activity) is a silent mutation in the presence of an operative T-protein (chorismate mutase-pre-

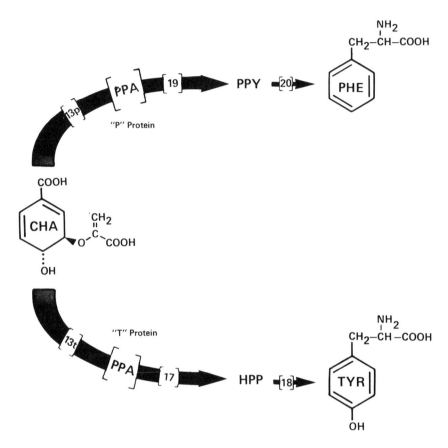

Fig. 3. Channeling isozymes of chorismate mutase in E coli. Enzymes are numbered according to the generalized pathway shown in Figure 1, the legend of which may be consulted for abbrevations. Chorismate mutase isozymes [13p] and [13t] direct their common product (PPA) to separate fates since each coordinates with a different multifunctional activity, ie, activity [17] or activity [19].

phenate dehydrogenase). Partial starvation for L-phenylalanine would promote increased intracellular chorismate, and hence increased prephenate since chroismate mutase-T is hardly inhibited by L-tyrosine while prephenate dehydrogenase is exceedingly sensitive to inhibition by L-tyrosine [Cotton and Gibson, 1965]. If a strain defective in T-protein activity is first isolated (lacking both chorismate mutase and prephenate dehydrogenase activities), it is then possible to isolate phenylalaninine auxotrophs lacking chorismate mutase (P-activity) in this genetic background [Baldwin and Davidson, 1981]. Mutants lacking prephenate dehydratase activity of the P-protein [Simmonds,

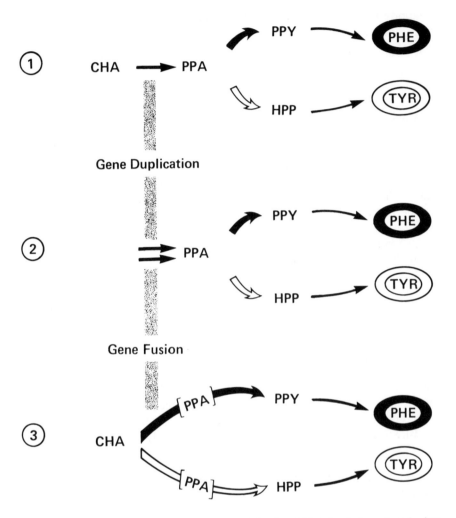

Fig. 4. Evolutionary scenario accounting for origin of multifunctional channels to L-phenylalanine and to L-tyrosine in E coli. The ancestral state envisioned at the top portrays a single chorismate mutase. The two branchpoint enzymes following prephenate are feedback inhibited by endproducts according to the symbolic patterns shown. Gene duplication yields chorismate mutase isozymes (middle panel). The final steps of gene fusion yield (bottom panel) the arrangement to be found in contemporary E coli. See Figure 1 for abbreviations.

1950; Davis, 1953; Katagiri and Sato, 1953; Baldwin and Davidson, 1981], and pleiotropic auxotrophs lacking both chorismate mutase and prephenate dehydratase activities of the P-protein [Cotton and Gibson, 1965; Baldwin and Davidson, 1981] can be selected directly.

B. Monofunctional/Bifunctional Isozymes of Chorismate Mutase in Pseudomonas

A bifunctional protein catalyzing the overall conversion of chorismate to phenylpyruvate, similar to the aforementioned P-protein of E coli, appears to be common in nature. It is present [see Byng et al, 1982; Whitaker et al, 1981b] in two large groups of pseudomonad organisms (group I and group V) which form a phylogenetic cluster with enteric bacteria at a suprafamilial level [Stackebrandt and Woese, 1982]. In contrast to the P-protein, the latter organisms lack the equivalent of the E coli multifunctional T-protein. Instead a second monofunctional chorismate mutase is physically separate from any aromatic-pathway dehydrogenase activity. Considering the apparent hierarchical relationships of phylogeny, the ancestral fusion event in the phenylalanine branchlet appears to be more ancient that the fusion event in the tyrosine branchlet.

Among pseudomonad genera, the most detailed studies have been carried out in P aeruginosa. Calhoun et al [1973] reported a bifunctional protein catalyzing the overall conversion of chorismate to prephenate. Like the P-protein of E coli, the chorismate mutase component is partially inhibited by phenylalanine and is also competitively inhibited by prephenate. The monofunctional chorismate mutase of P aeruginosa is insensitive to allosteric control [Patel et al, 1977]. In enzyme arrangements typified by P aeruginosa, a multifunctional channel leads to phenylalanine which is regulated with great sensitivity. Here the fate of prephenate is fixed, always forming L-phenylalanine from phenylpyruvate. On the other hand, the monofunctional mutase generates prephenate molecules having three possible molecular fates: (1) formation of L-phenylalanine via L-arogenate, (2) formation of L-tyrosine via 4-hydroxyphenylpyruvate, and (3) formation of L-tyrosine via L-arogenate.

C. Monofunctional/Bifunctional Chorismate Mutase Isozymes of Bacillus

In species of Bacillus one isozyme of chorismate mutase is a multifunctional protein, but the role of this is totally different from the aforementioned P-protein type (or T-protein type) arrangements. In Bacillus the significance of fused proteins relates to a mechanism of allosteric control rather than to a mechanism for channeling intermediates. The most comprehensive studies have been done in B subtilis. B subtilis strain 23 possesses two widely spaced genes that specify chorismate mutase isozymes, one of which is synonymous with the sole gene for chorismate mutase in B subtilis strain 168 [Lorence and Nester, 1967; Kane et al, 1971]. The latter gene specifies a bifunctional enzyme bearing catalytic centers for chorismate mutase and DAHP synthase [Huang et al, 1974a]. In addition shikimate kinase is only active when bound to the bifunctional protein [Nakatsukasa and Nester, 1972; Huang et al, 1974b]. Chorismate and prephenate (substrate and product of chorismate mutase) feedback inhibit the activities of DAHP synthase and shikimate kinase. The active site of chorismate mutase is the regulatory site for DAHP synthase [Huang et al, 1974b]. In this instance the protein-protein interactions of the molecular organization provide a physical basis for the regulatory pattern (sequential feedback inhibition), rather than serving as a basis for carbon channeling. In strains of B subtilis which possess both isozymes of chorismate mutase, loss of the monofunctional isozyme constitutes a silent mutation. Loss of the chorismate mutase component of the bifunctional protein may also be suppressed by the monofunctional isozyme, but all mutants so far isolated in strain 168 simultaneously lack both catalytic activities of the bifunctional protein [Nester et al, 1967].

IV. UNUSUAL ISOZYME REPRESENTATION WITHIN DISTAL PATHWAY BRANCHLETS

The branchlets extending to L-phenylalanine and to L-tyrosine are rich examples of biochemical diversity in nature [Byng et al, 1982]. Two separate biochemical routes to each amino acid exist. Thus, L-phenylalanine may be formed from L-arogenate or from phenylpyruvate, while L-tyrosine synthesis may proceed from either L-arogenate or 4-hydroxyphenylpyruvate (Fig. 1). L-arogenate is formed by transamination of prephenate [Stenmark et al, 1974; Jensen et al, 1977]. B subtilis and Euglena gracilis represent two extreme cases where isozymic arrangements play no role within the terminal branchlets. B subtilis possesses nonisozymic prephenate dehydratase and prephenate dehydrogenase proteins. E gracilis exemplifies a most interesting metabolic extreme in its reliance upon L-arogenate as a precursor of both L-phenylalanine and L-tyrosine [Byng et al, 1981], thus effectively repositioning the metabolic branchpoint and elongating the midbranch portion of the pathway. Between these extremes are a large and growing list of organisms which possess coexisting dehydratase and/or dehydrogenase proteins that can be regarded as isozymes.

A. Aromatic Pathway Dehydratases

1. Enteric bacteria. Cotton and Gibson [1965] originally described a second species of prephenate dehydratase (denoted prephenate dehydratase A) which separated from prephenate dehydratase P of the multifunctional P-protein of Klebsiella pneumoniae. Prephenate dehydratase P was found to be very sensitive to L-phenylalanine-mediated feedback inhibition, while prephenate dehydratase A was totally unaffected by L-phenylalanine. Prephenate dehydratase A is encoded by a gene separate from pheA which encodes the P-protein since mutants which lack the P-protein retain prephenate dehydratase A. We have found that prephenate dehydratase A also carries out the arogenate dehydratase reaction [Jensen, unpublished data]. E coli W was found [Cotton and Gibson, 1965] to lack prephenate dehydratase A (arogenate dehydratase), and presumably other E coli strains also lack arogenate dehydratase. Since prephenate is ordinarily enzyme-bound within the P-protein and T-protein channels, the monofunctional dehydratase of Klebsiella is apparently never able to function as a prephenate dehydratase or as an arogenate dehydratase. It seems likely that this activity is an evolutionary remnant fated to be discarded (as in E coli) because the evolutionary event of gene fusion created the P-protein channel which then isolated the dehydratase from its substrate(s). The substrate ambiguity of prephenate dehydratase A/arogenate dehydratase is consistent with speculations about the nature of ancient enzymes [Jensen, 1976]. Gene duplication, specialization for prephenate as substrate, and fusion with the gene encoding the chorismate mutase-P isozyme would then yield the contemporary P-protein. It would be interesting to see whether such intermediate evolutionary stages or other evolutionary relics might be found in other genera within Enterobactereaceae.

2. Group I/group V pseudomonads. Pseudomonad bacteria fall into five distinct phylogenetic groups [Palleroni et al, 1973]. Group V consists mainly of Xanthomonas species. Group I consists of a small cluster (four species to date) of nonfluorescent species and a very large number of fluorescent species such as P aeruginosa, P fluorescens, P putida, and the phytopathogenic P syringae. All group I and group V pseudomonads studied to date possess the phenylalanine-regulated P-protein. Except for the nonfluorescent subgroup of group I, all species possess an unregulated "arogenate dehydratase" which also catalyzes the reaction of prephenate dehydratase [Whitaker et al, 1981b]. Thus, these prephenate dehydratase isozymes are remarkably similar to the prephenate dehydratase P and prephenate dehydratase A isozymes aforementioned in Klebsiella. It is further suggestive that pseudomonad groups I and V share a common genealogical lineage with enteric bacteria within a grouping denoted as "purple-sulphur bacteria" by Stackebrandt and Woese [1982].

The nonfluorescent members of group I pseudomonads lack the monofunctional prephenate dehydratase (arogenate dehydratase), which thus eliminates the arogenate route to L-phenylalanine. In addition, the monofunctional, unregulated chorismate mutase that is characteristic of other group I and group V pseudomonads is also absent, an arrangement which implicates a "channel-shuttle" mechanism [Calhoun et al, 1973] in order for some prephenate molecules formed in the first half-reaction catalyzed by the P-protein to be diverted to L-tyrosine biosynthesis. Overall, the nonfluorescent subgroup of group I pseudomonads seems to have evolved in the direction of isozyme reduction (ie, loss of a chorismate mutase and loss of a prephenate/ arogenate dehydratase).

B. Aromatic Pathway Dehydrogenases

The presence of coexisting dehydrogenases which would fulfill the definition of isozymes has not been rigorously established in any system thus far. However, it seems likely that group I/group V pseudomonads will prove to possess isozymic prephenate dehydrogenases, one isozyme also capable of catalyzing the reaction of arogenate dehydrogenase [Byng et al, 1980]. In P aeruginosa (group I) neither phenylalanine nor tyrosine auxotrophs are recovered following routine mutant screenings. The dual pathways to phenylalanine in concert with two separable dehydratases explain the "reluctant auxotrophy" [Patel et al, 1978] for L-phenylalanine. It seems likely that the dual pathways to L-tyrosine [Patel et al, 1977] also involve separate dehydrogenase enzymes, although these have not yet been resolved from one another following chromatographic fractionation. However, Xanthomonas campestris (group V) has recently been studied and shown to yield two separate dehydrogenases [Whitaker et al, in preparation]. One is a prephenate dehydrogenase, while the second is a prephenate/arogenate dehydrogenase.

C. Aromatic Aminotransferases

Multiple species of aminotransferases exist which are capable of catalyzing transamination reactions required to synthesize L-tyrosine and L-phenylalanine. These multiple aminotransferases typically have distinctly different, but highly overlapping substrate specificities. They commonly overlap even different amino acid pathways, as demonstrated by detailed mutant studies in some systems (see Jensen and Calhoun [1981] for a recent review). These aminotransferases can be fairly denoted as isozymes, although this is not the usual convention.

In B subtilis [Weigent and Fester, 1976] the transaminations of phenylpyruvate and 4-hydroxyphenylpyruvate are catalyzed by aminotransferase "isozymes" encoded by aroJ and hisH. In E coli the same transamination reactions are catalyzed by gene products of tyrB, aspC, and ilvE [Gelfand and Steinberg, 1977]. In coryneform species of bacteria prephenate and phenylpyruvate transaminations are carried out by two separable aminotransferases having broadly overlapping specificities [Fazel and Jensen, 1979]. In P aeruginosa transamination reactions with prephenate, phenylpyruvate, and 4-hydroxyphenylpyruvate are all physiologically significant (see Fig. 1) and five aminotransferase proteins have been described [Whitaker et al, 1982b], each capable of catalyzing any of the three reactions. Special strategies are usually required to obtain aminotransferase-deficient mutants [Jensen and Calhoun, 1981; Whitaker et al, 1982b] because of the common ability of remaining aminotransferase enzymes to substitute for the deficient enzyme in vivo.

V. ANALOGS AND MUTATIONS AS PROBES OF ISOZYME IMPACT UPON CARBON FLOW

It has been firmly established in the general discipline of biochemical genetics that regulatory mutants and structural-gene mutants offer a powerful basis for gaining insight into the nature of gene-enzyme relationships in wild type. Endproduct analogs cannot only be used as selective agents for regulatory mutants, but can be used advantageously to manipulate or stress the physiology of both wild type and various derivative mutants. These approaches are all the more valuable in complicated pathway systems in which isozymes play a heavy role in the metabolic complexity observed. Aromatic biosynthesis in P aeruginosa perhaps exemplifies the epitome of such complexity. Figure 5 illustrates the overall pathway arrangement and regulation

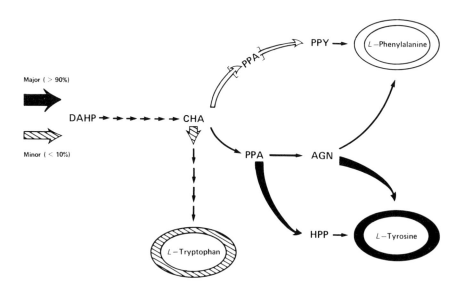

Fig. 5. Aromatic pathway isozymes in P aeruginosa. Isozymes exist for DAHP synthase, chorismate mutase, dehydratase, dehydrogenase, and aminotransferase reactions as explained in the text. Allosteric regulation is indicated symbolically: solid shading, striped patterning, and no shading identify enzymes subject to control by L-tyrosine, L-tryptophan, or L-phenylalanine, respectively. Note the presence of a P-protein similar to that shown for E coli in Figure 3.

in wild-type P aeruginosa. Isozymes are found throughout the pathway: (1) two differentially regulated DAHP synthase isozymes, (2) two chorismate mutase isozymes, (3) prephenate dehydratase and arogenate dehydratase (as discussed before) may be regarded as isozymes, (4) prephenate dehydrogenase and arogenate dehydrogenase are probably isozymes, and (5) five aminotransferase "isozymes" exist, each capable of catalyzing the three pathway transamination steps.

A. Pseudomonas Aeruginosa

When P aeruginosa is grown at the expense of glucose as the carbon source, analogs of L-phenylalanine or L-tyrosine are not inhibitory to growth. Unlike E coli or B subtilis the internal pools of L-phenylalanine and L-tyrosine on glucose-based medium are adequate to reverse potential anti-metabolite effects of endproduct analogs. However, initial carbon flow into the aromatic pathway is highly variable, depending upon the carbon source. Calhoun and Jensen [1972] showed that aromatic amino acid synthesis is actually rate-limiting during growth on fructose as the sole carbon source. Since the synthesis of each aromatic amino acid molecule requires two molecules of phosphoenolpyruvate (PEP) (see Fig. 1), a likely explanation for the fructose carbon-flow effect is the depletion of PEP required in the PEP-dependent phosphotransferase system of transport for fructose [Durham and Phibbs, 1982]. Thus, the use of fructose as carbon source is a crucial aid in the isolation of regulatory mutants since analogs of L-phenylalanine and L-tyrosine become effective growth inhibitors (ie, selective agents) under these conditions.

the distal portion of the pathway since mutant blockage of one of two flow routes to endproduct may retard the growth rate. If the latter effect is too subtle to accommodate convenient selection, such bradytrophs may be more readily detected by screening for a phenotype of analog hypersensitivity. Thus, technical roadblocks that previously thwarted the isolation of regulatory and structural-gene mutants have been largely overcome, and a mutant collection is now being developed.

1. Regulatory mutants. m-fluorophenylalanine (MFP) was used as a selective agent (on fructose-based medium) to isolate analog-resistant mutants, and these yielded a fraction of regulatory mutants which excreted L-phenylalanine sparingly on fructose-based medium but heavily on glucose-based medium [Fiske et al, unpublished data]. One class of mutant lacked the normal sensitivity of prephenate dehydratase (P-protein) to feedback inhibition. Overproduction of L-phenylalanine was curbed dramatically on glucose-based medium in the presence of L-tyrosine. Exogenous L-tyrosine must act through feedback inhibition of DAHP synthase-tyr, the major isozyme species. This in turn would greatly reduce substrate availability for prephenate dehydratase).

The second class of mutant is unusual (in the literature but perhaps not in nature). This mutant lacks the allosteric sensitivity of DAHP synthase-tyr to L-tyrosine. On glucose-based medium, excretion of L-phenylalanine is unchanged or slightly increased in the presence of L-tyrosine. This is because DAHP synthase-tyr is invulnerable to L-tyrosine inhibition under conditions where inhibition of L-tyrosine spares the total demand for endproducts. Since in the latter mutant, the P-protein and both dehydrogenases within the two flow routes to L-tyrosine retain stringent regulation by feedback inhibition, excreted L-phenylalanine must arise from the arogenate flow route. This includes the monofunctional chorismate mutase, prephenate aminotrans-ferase, and arogenate dehydratase—none of which are regulated in wild type. This overflow pathway to L-phenylalanine is illustrated in Figure 6.

This overflow pathway must be dependent upon high substrate levels for its operation. In wild type growing on fructose-based medium, carbon flow to L-phenylalanine and L-tyrosine may be limited to the phenylpyruvate and 4-hydroxyphenylpyruvate routes. The elevated internal pool sizes of end-products on glucose-based medium may reflect the additional flow routes via L-arogenate. It is clear from the mutant studies that the overflow route of wild type is indirectly kept in check by potent L-tyrosine control of the major isozyme of DAHP synthase. All three enzymes of the overflow route can be regarded as isozyme counterparts of other pathway enzymes, and the carbon flow through the overflow route is highly dependent upon the catalytic output of the key early pathway isozyme, DAHP synthase-tyr.

2. Structural-gene mutants. Conventional mutant screening yields nei-ther L-phenylalanine nor L-tyrosine auxotrophs in P aeruginosa. The basis for such reluctant auxotrophy has been related to the joint presence of four separate pathway branchlets linking prephenate to L-phenylalanine or to L-tyrosine [Patel et al, 1977, 1978]. A successful strategy for mutant isolation employs limitation of carbon flow into the pathway through use of fructose as sole carbon source. Even with this nutritional stress, elimination by mu-tation of an aromatic aminotransferase is the only distal-pathway deficiency found to exhibit a selectable phenotype. This mutant was initially selected as a slow-growing clone, but reconstruction experiments indicate equal fea-sibility for selection of this bradytroph type on the basis of analog (m-fluorophenylalanine) hypersensitivity [Patel et al, 1978]. The wild-type growth rate is fully restored by L-phenylalanine and is partially restored by L-tyrosine. This suggests that the deficient aminotransferase normally functions in both phenylalanine and tyrosine biosynthesis. L-tyrosine may be less effective than L-phenylalanine in satisfying the auxotrophic requirement of the mutant because of the potent inhibitory effect of L-tyrosine upon DAHP synthase-tyr, an effect which would cause diminution of precursors needed for L-phenylalanine biosynthesis.

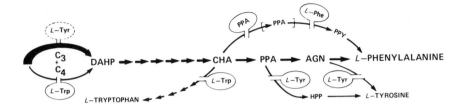

Fig. 6. Overflow pathway funneling aromatic intermediates to L-phenylalanine in a DAHP synthase-tyr-deregulated mutant of P aeruginosa. Compare with the wild-type arrangement as shown in Figure 5. Biochemical details of pathway construction and abbreviations are shown fully in Figure 1. C_3 and C_4 denote phosphoenolpyruvate and erythrose-4-phosphate. The two dehydrogenase (reactions [16] and [17] in Fig. 1) are NAD$^+$-linked. Allosteric specificities of inhibition remaining in the mutant are marked by gapped arrows. The overflow route to L-phenylalanine in the mutant is indicated by the stream of heavy, solid arrows.

In the strategy of sequential mutagenesis, the crucial step is to obtain an initial mutant phenotype. This can then be used as a new genetic background for selection of a second mutant deficiency. The double mutant can than be used as a genetic background for selection of a third deficiency. Ultimately, these mutations can be separated from one another for individual study by recombination. To date a double mutant has been isolated [Whitaker et al, 1982b] which lacks a second aminotransferase. The double mutant has an absolute requirement for L-phenylalanine and also has additional requirements for L-glutamate and L-aspartate. Because these two aminotransferase mutations eliminate L-phenylalanine synthesis, both of the dual routes to L-phenylalanine must be blocked. It follows that L-arogenate formation by transamination is blocked in the double mutant. Hence, only the 4-hydroxyphenylpyruvate route to L-tyrosine can be operative, and tyrosine auxotrophs should be readily isolated in this genetic background.

B. Enteric Bacteria

In E coli and S typhimurium regulatory mutants which are selected by analog resistance are inevitably deregulated within the terminal branchlets of aromatic biosynthesis (eg, constitutive mutants that excrete L-tryptophan or feedback-resistant prephenate dehydrogenase mutants which excrete L-tyrosine). Although excreted L-tyrosine, for example, will maximally repress and feedback-inhibit DAHP synthase-tyr, the unrestrained flow of precursors into the tyrosine branchlet will tend to promote phenylalanine and perhaps tryptophan starvation, leading to maximally derepressed DAHP synthase-phe and DAHP synthase-trp. Unlike P aeruginosa, deregulated isozymes of DAHP synthase are never selected as analog-resistant mutants. For example, a mutation conferring loss of allostery for DAHP synthase-phe would be offset by a compensatory increase in the level of feedback inhibition of DAHP synthase-trp and DAHP synthase-tyr. Furthermore all three isozymes, including DAHP synthase-phe, would be maximally repressed. E coli best typifies those microorganisms which are heavily oriented to the exogenous supply of amino acids. The "feast and famine" nature of the E coli econiche in the mammalian gut demands exaggerated contrasts of efficient biosynthesis during famine (between meals) coupled with tight shutoff controls during feast (at mealtime). Such regular transitions between extremes of turnoff and turnon regulation have selected for (1) more dramatic transcriptional control than is usually seen in biosynthetic pathways, and (2) the leverage promoted by highly developed regulatory mechanisms controlling each terminal branchlet in conjuction with the virtually universal control to be found for DAHP synthase. E coli-like systems exemplify what have been termed exo-oriented systems [Jensen and Hall, 1982]. In contrast, endo-oriented organisms such as the cyanobacteria need only to gear their control pattern to the endogenous synthesis of amino acids, since scavenging of amino acids is not a cyanobacterial specialization. These endo-oriented organisms [Jensen and Hall, 1982] thus find it appropriate to maintain a primary emphasis upon DAHP synthase as the major focal point of endproduct regulation.

In E coli loss of individual DAHP synthase activities via mutation constitutes a silent phenotype, ie, no obvious auxotrophy. However, such a loss confers sensitivity to growth inhibition by paired combinations of aromatic amino acids. For example, aroF mutants (lacking the retro-tyrosine isozyme of DAHP synthase) are growth inhibited in the joint presence of L-phenylalanine and L-tryptophan. This is due to the feedback inhibition and repression of the two remaining isozymes, the consequences being starvation for precursors needed for L-tyrosine biosynthesis [Wallace and Pittard, 1967].

C. Bacillus subtilis

As previously mentioned, some species of B subtilis possess isozymes of chorismate mutase: (1) a low-level activity borne on the same protein as DAHP synthase and denoted chorismate mutase-L, and (2) a high-level monofunctional activity denoted as chorismate mutase-H. As chorismate is the branchpoint for tryptophan biosynthesis, the presence or absence of chorismate mutase-H distinctly influences the distribution of carbon flow through alteration of the balance between anthranilate synthase and chorismate mutase (which compete with one another for chorismate). For B subtilis the analogs of choice to probe relative endproduct levels have been D-tyrosine (for tyrosine), β-2-thienylalanine (for phenylalanine), and 5-methyltryptophan (for tryptophan). Derivatives of two B subtilis strains have been studied in detail. Strain 23 has both chorismate mutase-H and chorismate mutase-L activities, while strain 168 has only chorismate mutase-L. The presence of both chorismate mutase isozymes (strain 23) confers elevated resistance to growth inhibition by D-tyrosine and hypersensitivity to 5-methyltryptophan, thus demonstrating increased carbon flow toward phenylalanine and tyrosine and away from tryptophan. Strain 168, which only possesses chorismate mutase-L, is hypersensitive to D-tyrosine [Champney and Jensen, 1969], and exhibits elevated resistance to growth inhibition by 5-methyltryptophan, ie, relative carbon flow toward L-tryptophan is favored [Kane et al, 1971]. In wild type these differences are relatively subtle because of the compensatory effects of stringent regulation present in each terminal branchlet. In regulatory mutants, however, exaggerated effects are seen. For example, the presence or absence of chorismate mutase-H has a significant impact on tryptophan excretion in *trpR* regulatory mutants, in which all of the tryptophan biosynthetic enzymes are synthesized constitutively [Kane and Jensen, 1970a,b; Hoch et al, 1971]. In a strain lacking chorismate mutase-H and possessing the *trpR* mutation, anthranilate synthase overcompetes for chorismate, actually resulting in a partial requirement for phenylalanine in addition to overproduction of tryptophan (50 mg L-tryptophan excreted/mg dry weight/hr). On the other hand, the presence of chorismate mutase-H (in the *trpR* background) allows prototrophy to be retained, and tryptophan excretion is more modest (5 mg L-tryptophan/mg dry weight/hr).

B subtilis strain 168 is thought to be deleted in all or part of the gene for chorismate mutase-H [Kane et al, 1971]. Llewellyn et al [1980] found that the type strain of B subtilis (ATCC 6051) differs from B subtilis 23 and B subtilis 168 in having a monofunctional DAHP synthase (ie, no chorismate mutase). Like strain 23, ATCC 6051 possesses chorismate mutase-H. The monofunctional DAHP synthase of ATCC 6051 is feedback inhibited by prephenate but differs from the bifunctional DAHP synthases in its insensitivity to feedback inhibition by chorismate. Strain 23 seems to be representative of Bacillus species on two counts: (1) strain 168 (having only chorismate mutase-L) is hypersensitive to the antimetabolic action of D-tyrosine, ATCC 6051 (having only chorismate mutase-H) is moderately sensitive to D-tyrosine, while strain 23 (having both chorismate mutase-H and chorismate mutase-L) together with over 30 strains of Bacillus is totally resistant to D-tyrosine, and (2) 33 of 33 strains which possessed a DAHP synthase sensitive to prephenate also exhibited sensitivity to chorismate [Jensen et al, 1967]. If chorismate mutase-L evolved from the allosteric site for prephenate on a DAHP synthase similar to that of comtemporary ATCC 6051, as suggested by Llewellyn et al [1980], this must have occurred in the ancestral progenitor of all contemporary Bacillus. In this case strain 168 has evolved in the direction of discarding the monofunctional chorismate mutase, while ATCC 6051 could be an evolutionary relic (or have mutated back to the ancestral condition). We favor an evolutionary scenario [Jensen and Pierson, 1975; Jensen, 1976; Jensen and Byng, 1981] involving gene duplication of an ancestral chorismate mutase, followed by fusion of the gene encoding one newly arisen isozyme with the gene specifying DAHP synthase. In this case ATCC 6051 would be a derivative mutant in which loss of the chorismate binding site on the bifunctional protein simultaneously eliminated chorismate-mediated inhibition and the activity of chorismate mutase-L.

D. Cyanobacteria

In sharp contrast to organisms such as E coli and B subtilis, cyanobacterial genera exemplify a relatively simple pattern of aromatic control in nature which is oriented to endogenous carbon flow. This endo-oriented mode of regulation [Jensen and Hall, 1982] centers about DAHP synthase as the focal point of regulation. Thus, mutants from various species of cyanobacteria which possess deregulated DAHP synthase enzymes tend to excrete all three endproducts, especially L-tyrosine and L-phenylalanine [Hall et al, 1980; Hall and Jensen, 1980]. In cases where regulation is found in a terminal branchlet, mutants lacking regulation of the terminal branchlet enzyme produced only a fraction of the endproduct output seen in mutants having a desensitized DAHP synthase [Jensen and Hall, 1982]. In Anabaena sp there is a superficial resemblance to an organism like E coli in that isozymes of DAHP synthase exist which are subject to differential allosteric control. However, unlike E coli, deregulation of the retro-tyrosine isozyme of DAHP synthase in Anabaena sp led to excretion of all three aromatic amino acids [Hall et al, 1980; Hall and Jensen, 1981a]. In large part, it is probable that this difference between organisms is due to the lack in Anabaena of a compensatory repression of isozyme synthesis which operates in E coli in response to increased flux to endproducts following release of allosteric control.

In wild-type Anabaena sp a delicate balance is struck between chorismate mutase and anthranilate synthase activities which compete for a common substrate (chorismate) at the branchpoint (Fig. 7). Even though anthranilate synthase is subject to feedback inhibition by L-tryptophan, loss of feedback inhibition apparently does not lead to significant tryptophan excretion. Thus, 6-fluorotryptophan-resistant mutants were not found to possess feedback-resistant anthranilate synthases. Instead they either (1) possessed a deregulated DAHP synthase isozyme, or (2) lost a part of the total chorismate mutase activity (apparently a loss of one of two isozymes). In both cases the indirect effect is to deliver elevated substrate levels to anthranilate synthase. It appears that DAHP synthase is such an effective regulator of the entire pathway because entry substrates for all terminal branchlets are highly limiting to endproduct formation [Jensen and Hall, 1982]. The second class

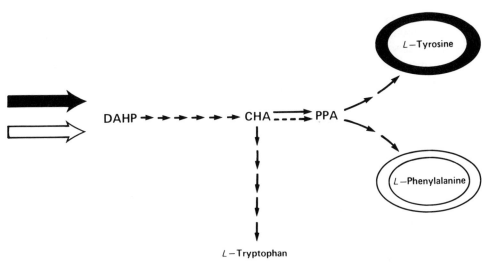

Fig. 7. Endo-oriented regulation in Anabaena sp (ATCC 29151). Consult Figure 1 for abbreviations and for biochemical details. The major focus of allosteric regulation is at two isozymes of DAHP synthase, controlled by L-phenylalanine and L-tyrosine as shown symbolically. Two unregulated isozymes of chorismate mutase also exist for conversion of CHA to PPA. Anabaena possesses steps [14] and [16] of Figure 1 (using NADP$^+$) as the sole route of L-tyrosine biosynthesis and steps [19] and [20] of Figure 1 as the sole route of L-phenylalanine biosynthesis.

of mutant above (loss of one chorismate mutase isozyme) is the most dramatic of tryptophan excretors. The chorismate mutase defect has two effects that increase chorismate availability. First, chorismate is accumulated behind the partial blockade. Second, limitation of phenylalanine and tyrosine biosynthesis (the mutant is bradytrophic) relieves both DAHP synthase isozymes from all restraining influences of regulation otherwise in effect. The overall result is forced excretion of L-tryptophan, whereby a relatively weak competitive inhibition of anthranilate synthase is overwhelmed.

Cyanobacteria exemplify an extreme case where elevation of L-tryptophan production is virtually 100% dependent upon mechanisms that supply additional beginning substrate for the pathway. Less extreme cases of similarity can be cited. For example, recall the aforementioned case in B subtilis where elimination of one chorismate mutase isozyme increases the L-tryptophan pool to a modest extent. When an additional background eliminating transcriptional control *(trpR)* is also present, the effect of presence or absence of chorismate mutase-H was dramatic—more nearly reminiscent of cyanobacteria. A roughly similar situation probably exists in the yeast, Hansenula polymorpha. A phenylalanine plus tyrosine bradytroph was isolated as part of a strategy of sequential mutagenesis for obtaining elevated production of L-tryptophan [Denenu and Demain, 1981]. Tightly blocked auxotrophs that completely lack chorismate mutase activity have not been obtained in this organism [Sanchez and Demain, 1977]. Hence, it is probable that chorismate mutase in this yeast exists as two or more isozymes, as is observed in Saccharomyces cerevisiae [Lingens et al, 1966, 1967].

VI. PERSPECTIVE

Isozymes may be found throughout the multibranched pathway of aromatic biosynthesis in arrangements which vary widely in different microbial groupings. The diverse array of examples already known reveals isozymes to be very important components in the evolution of regulatory mechanisms that ensure the efficient partitioning of carbon to the outlying endproducts of the pathway. Differentially regulated isozymes of DAHP synthase (which dictates the rate of carbon flow into the pathway) offer an apt mechanism for each of the divergently formed endproducts to signal the feedback control of an appropriate fraction of total DAHP synthase activity. A similar rationale for differentially regulated isozymes of chorismate mutase located at a midpathway branchpoint can readily be appreciated.

Isozymes may provide a basis for channeling mechanisms whereby gene fusion creates multifunctional proteins that channel intermediates efficiently to a given endproduct. In E coli, the channeling of prephenate prevents it from being transaminated to L-arogenate, a metabolite which is of no use to E coli. Isozymes can also be recruited during evolution for development of new regulatory function. Given the existence of two isozyme catalysts, one can be modified to become a regulatory subunit whose former substrate binding site(s) becomes an allosteric effector site(s), eg, DAHP synthase in B subtilis. As exemplified in the latter case, the catalytic activity need not be lost (in which case a multifunctional enzyme is also created).

Arogenate dehydrogenase and prephenate dehydrogenase catalyze analogous reactions of L-tyrosine biosynthesis, as do arogenate dehydratase and prephenate dehydratase in L-phenylalanine biosynthesis. It seems likely that these are homologous sets of enzymes which originated by gene duplication of a substrate-ambigous dehydrogenase or dehydratase, followed by differential substrate specialization. Indeed, examples exist of contemporary dehydrogenases and dehydratases that exhibit substrate ambiguity for either L-arogenate or prephenate. In some organisms, eg, Pseudomonas aeruginosa, two dehydratases and two dehydrogenases coexist and can be regarded as isozymes. This complex arrangement within the terminal branchlets of P aeruginosa influences the level of endproduct formation in ways which vary significantly depending upon overall carbon-flow conditions.

The nature of isozymes at one catalytic step of the pathway cannot be fully appreciated in isolation from isozyme arrangements elsewhere in the pathway. For example, E coli, P aeruginosa, and Anabaena sp all possess isozymic DAHP synthases. In each of these cases, the pattern of early pathway control by allosteric isozymes is crucially important, but in each system the isozyme control is uniquely integrated with the remainder of the pathway. Each system possesses a tyrosine-inhibited isozyme of DAHP synthase. What happens in each system if a mutation abolishes allosteric control of DAHP synthase-tyr by L-tyrosine? (1) In E coli there is almost no net effect upon endproduct levels due to offsetting increases in endproduct-mediated repression control of DAHP synthase isozymes and because of sensitive feedback control of the terminal branchlets. (2) In P aeruginosa a similar outcome is prevented by the presence of an unregulated isozyme of chorismate mutase and an unregulated arogenate dehydratase, resulting in heavy excretion of L-phenylalanine. Thus, in wild type this overflow pathway to L-phenylalanine is least preferred at low flux levels of substrate, and DAHP synthase-tyr plays a critical role in curbing carbon flow to keep substrate levels below the threshold required by the overflow pathway to L-phenylalanine. (3) In Anabaena, the mutant loss of feedback sensitivity of DAHP synthase-tyr leads to excretion of all three aromatic amino acids (L-tryptophan, L-tyrosine, and L-phenylalanine).

At one extreme in the cyanobacteria, DAHP synthase-tyr is an all-important focal point of regulation which restrains total endproduct formation. At the other extreme in E coli, DAHP synthase-tyr allostery is important but is an integral part of a complex network of feedback units that all interplay as a larger unit of regulation. Thus, E coli can compensate for a regulatory flaw in DAHP synthase-tyr almost entirely, while Anabaena compensates very little. P aeruginosa can be regarded as an interesting intermediate in the sense that the effect of the deregulation upon phenylalanine excretion is reminiscent of cyanobacteria, while the compensatory controls existing for L-tryptophan and L-tyrosine synthesis, on the other hand, are reminiscent of E coli.

VII. REFERENCES

Baldwin GS, Davidson BE (1981): A kinetic and structural comparison of chorismate mutase/prephenate dehydratase from mutant strains of *Escherichia coli* K12 defective in the *pheA* gene. Arch Biochem Biophys 211:66–75.

Brown KD (1968): Regulation of aromatic amino acid biosynthesis in *Escherichia coli* K12. Genetics 60:31–48.

Brown KD, Doy CH (1963): End-product regulation of the general aromatic pathway in *Escherichia coli*. Biochim Biophys Acta 77:170–172.

Byng GS, Kane JF, Jensen RA (1982): Diversity in the routing and regulation of complex biochemical pathways as indicators of microbial relatedness. Crit Rev Microbiol 9:227–252.

Byng GS, Whitaker RJ, Gherna RL, Jensen RA (1980): Variable enzymological patterning in tyrosine biosynthesis as a means of determining natural relatedness among the *Psudomonadaceae*. J Bacteriol 144:247–257.

Byng GS, Whitaker RJ, Shapiro CL, Jensen RA (1981): The aromatic amino acid pathway branches at *L*-arogenate in *Euglena gracilis*. Mol Cell Biol 1:426–438.

Calhoun DH, Jensen RA (1972): Significance of altered carbon flow in aromatic amino acid synthesis: An approach to the isolation of regulatory mutants in *Pseudomonas aeruginosa*. J Bacteriol 109:369–372.

Calhoun DH, Pierson DL, Jensen RA (1973): A channel-shuttle mechanism for the regulation of phenylalanine and tyrosine synthesis at a metabolic branchpoint in *Pseudomonas aeruginosa*. J Bacteriol 113:241–251.

Champney WS, Jensen RA (1969): *D*-tyrosine as a metabolic inhibitor of *Bacillus subtilis*. J Bacteriol 98:205–214.

Cotton RGH, Gibson F (1965): The biosynthesis of phenylalanine and tyrosine: Enzymes converting chorismic acid into prephenic acid and their relationship to prephenate dehydratase and prephenate dehydrogenase. Biochim Biophys Acta 100:76–88.

Cotton RGH, Gibson F (1967): The biosynthesis of tyrosine in *Aerobacter aerogenes:* Partial purification of T-protein. Biochim Biophys Acta 147:222–237.

Cotton RGH, Gibson F (1968): The biosynthesis of tyrosine in *Aerobacter aerogenes:* Evidence for a subunit structure of the protein converting chorismate into 4-hydroxyphenylpyruvate. Biochim Biophys Acta 160:188–195.

Davis WD, Davidson BE (1982): The nucleotide sequence of *aroG*, the gene for 3-deoxy-*D*-arabinoheptulosonate-7-phosphate synthetase (phe) in *Escherichia coli* K12. Nucleic Acids Res 10:4045–4058.

Davis BD (1953): Autocatalytic growth of a mutant due to accumulation of an unstable phenylalanine precursor. Science 118:251–252.

Denenu EO, Demain AL (1981): Derivation of aromatic amino acid mutants from a methanol-utilizing yeast, *Hansenula polymorpha*. Appl Environ Microbiol 41:1088–1096.

Durham DR, Phibbs PV (1982): Fractionation and characterization of the phosphoenolpyruvate: fructose 1-phosphotransferase system from *Pseudomonas aeruginosa*. J Bacteriol 149:534–541.

Fazel AM, Jensen RA (1979): Aromatic aminotransferases in species of coryneform bacteria. J Bacteriol 140:580–587.

Gelfand DH, Steinberg RA (1977): *Escherichia coli* mutants deficient in the aspartate and aromatic amino acid aminotransferases. J Bacteriol 130:429–440.

Hall G, Flick MB, Jensen RA (1980): Approach to recognition of regulatory mutants of cyanobacteria. J Bacteriol 143:981–988.

Hall GC, Flick MB, Gherna RL, Jensen RA (1982): Biochemical diversity for biosynthesis of aromatic amino acids among cyanobacteria. J Bacteriol 149:65–78.

Hall GC, Jensen RA (1980): Enzymological basis for growth inhibition by *L*-phenylalanine in the cyanobacterium *Synechocystis* sp. 29108. J Bacteriol 144:1034–1042.

Hall GC, Jensen RA (1981a): Regulatory isozymes of 3-deoxy-*D-arabino*-heptulosonate 7-phosphate synthase in the cyanobacterium, *Anabaena* sp. strain ATCC 29151. J Bacteriol 148:361–364.

Hall GC, Jensen RA (1981b): Isolation of cyanobacterial auxotrophs by direct selection of regulatory-mutant phenotypes. Curr Microbiol 6:189–194.

Hoch SO, Roth CW, Crawford IP, Nester EW (1971): Control of tryptophan biosynthesis by the methyltryptophan resistance gene in *Bacillus subtilis*. J Bacteriol 105:38–45.

Huang L, Montoya AL, Nester EW (1974a): Characterization of the functional activities of the subunits of 3-deoxy-*D-arabino*-heptulsonate 7-phosphate synthetase-chorismate mutase from *Bacillus* subtilis 168. J Biol Chem 249:4473–4479.

Huang L, Nakatsukasa WM, Nester EW (1974b): Regulation of aromatic amino acid biosynthesis in *Bacillus subtilis* 168. J Biol Chem 249:4467–4472.

Jensen RA (1976): Enzyme recruitment in evolution of new function. Annu Rev Microbiol 30:409–425.

Jensen RA, Byng GS (1981): The partitioning of biochemical pathways with isozyme systems. In Rattazzi MC, Scandalios JG, Whitt GS (eds): Isozymes V. New York: A.R. Liss, pp 143–175.

Jensen RA, Calhoun DH (1981): Intracellular roles of microbial aminotransferases: Overlap enzymes across different biochemical pathways. Crit Rev Microbiol 8:229–266.

Jensen RA, Calhoun DH, Stenmark SL (1973): Allosteric inhibition of DAHP synthetase by tyrosine, tryptophan and phenylpyruvate in *Pseudomonas aeruginosa*. Biochim Biophys Acta 293:256–268.

Jensen RA, Hall GC (1982): Endo-oriented control of pyramidally arranged metabolic branchpoints. Trends Biochem Sci 7:177–180.

Jensen RA, Nasser DS (1968): Comparative regulation of isoenzymic 3-deoxy-*D-arabino*-heptulosonate 7-phosphate synthetases in microorganisms. J Bacteriol 95:188–196.

Jensen RA, Nasser DS, Nester EW (1967): The comparative control of a branchpoint enzyme in microorganisms. J Bacteriol 94:1582–1593.

Jensen RA, Pierson DL (1975): Evolutionary implications of different types of microbial enzymology for *L*-tyrosine biosynthesis. Nature 254:667–671.

Jensen RA, Rebello JL (1970): Comparative allostery of microbial enzymes at metabolic branchpoints: Evolutionary implications. Dev Ind Microbiol 13:105–121.

Jensen RA, Zamir LO, StPierre M, Patel N, Pierson DL (1977): The isolation and preparation of pretyrosine accumulated as a dead-end metabolite by *Neurospora crassa*. J Bacteriol 132:896–903.

Kane JF, Jensen RA (1970a): Enzyme induction in the tryptophan biosynthetic pathway in *Bacillus subtilis*. Biochem Biophys Res Commun 38:1161–1167.

Kane JF, Jensen RA (1970b): The molecular aggregation of anthranilate synthase in *Bacillus subtilis*. Biochem Biophys Res Commun 41:328–333.

Kane JF, Stenmark SL, Calhoun DH, Jensen RA (1971): Metabolic interlock: The role of the subordinate type of enzyme in the regulation of a complex pathway. J Biol Chem 246:4308–4316.

Katagiri M, Sato R (1953): Accumulation of phenylalanine by a phenylalanineless mutant of *Escherichia coli*. Science 118:250–251.

Koch GLE, Shaw DC, Gibson F (1970): Tyrosine biosynthesis in *Aerobacter aerogenes:* Purification and properties of chorismate mutase-prephenate dehydrogenase. Biochim Biophys Acta 212:375–386.

Lingens F, Goebel W, Uesseler H (1966): Regulation der biosynthese der aromatischern aminosaeuren in *Saccharomyces cerevisiae* 1. Hemmung der enzymaktivitaeten (feedback-wirkung). Biochem Z 346:357–367.

Lingens F, Goebel W, Uesseler H (1967): Regulation der biosynthese der aromatischern aminosaeuren in *Saccharomyces cerevisiae* 2. Repression induction and aktivierung. Eur J Biochem 1:363–374.

Llewellyn DJ, Daday A, Smith GD (1980): Evidence for an artifically evolved bifunctional 3-deoxy-*D-arabino*-heptulsonate 7-phosphate synthase-chorismate mutase in *Bacillus subtilis*. J Biol Chem 255:2077–2084.

Lorence JH, Nester EW (1967): Multiple molecular forms of chorismate mutase in *Bacillus subtilis*. Biochemistry 6:1541–1552.

Nakatsukasa WM, Nester EW (1972): Regulation of aromatic amino acid biosynthesis in *Bacillus subtilis* 168. J Biol Chem 247:5972–5979.

Nester EW, Lorence JH, Nasser DS (1967): An enzyme aggregate involved in the biosynthesis of aromatic amino acids in *Bacillus subtilis:* Its possible function in feedback regulation. Biochemistry 6:1553–1562.

Palleroni NJ, Kunisawa R, Contopoulos R, Doudoroff M (1973): Nucleic acid homologies in the genus *Pseudomonas.* Int J Syst Bacteriol 23:333–339.

Patel N, Pierson DL, Jensen RA (1977): Dual enzymatic routes to *L*-tyrosine and *L*-phenylalanine via pretyrosine in *Pseudomonas aeruginosa.* J Biol Chem 252:5839–5846.

Patel N, Stenmark-Cox S, Jensen RA (1978): Enzymological basis of reluctant auxotrophy for phenylalanine and tyrosine in *Pseudomonas aeruginosa.* J Biol Chem 253:2972–2978.

Sanchez S, Demain AL (1977): Enrichment of auxotrophic mutants in *Hansenula polymorpha.* Eur J Appl Microbiol 4:45–49.

Schmidt JC, Artz SW, Zalkin H (1970): Chorismate mutase-prephenate dehydratase: Evidence for distinct catalytic and regulatory sites. J Biol Chem 245:4019–4027.

Schmidt JC, Zalkin H (1969): Chorismate mutase-prephenate dehydratase, partial purification and properties of the enzyme from *Salmonella typhimurium.* Biochemistry 8:174–181.

Schoner R, Herrmann KM (1976): 3-Deoxy-*D-arabino*-heptulosonate 7-phosphate synthetase. J Biol Chem 251:5440–5447.

Simmonds S (1950): The metabolism of phenylalanine and tyrosine in mutant strains of *Escherichia coli.* J Biol Chem 185:755–762.

Smith LC, Ravel JM, Lax SR, Shive W (1962): The control of 3-deoxy-*D-arabino*-heptulosonate 7-phosphate synthetase by phenylalanine and tyrosine. J Biol Chem 237:3566–3570.

Stackebrandt E, Woese CR (1982): The evolution of prokaryotes. In Carlile MJ, Collins JF, Moseley BEB (eds): "Molecular and Cellular Aspects of Microbial Evolution." 32nd Symp Soc Gen Microbiol. Cambridge: Cambridge Univ Press, pp 1–31.

Staub M, Denes G (1969a): Purification and properties of the 3-deoxy-*D-arabino*-heptulosonate 7-phosphate synthetase (phenylalanine sensitive) of *Escherichia coli* K12. Biochim Biophys Acta 178:588–598.

Staub M, Denes G (1969b): Purification and properties of the 3-deoxy-*D-arabino*-heptulosonate 7-phosphate synthetase (tyrosine sensitive) of *Escherichia coli* K12. Biochim Biophys Acta 178:599–608.

Stenmark SL, Pierson DL, Glover GI, Jensen RA (1974): Blue-green bacteria synthesize *L*-tyrosine by the pretyrosine pathway. Nature 247:290–292.

Wallace BJ, Pittard J (1967): Genetic and biochemical analysis of the isoenzymes concerned in the first reaction of aromatic biosynthesis in *Escherichia coli.* J Bacteriol 93:237–244.

Weigent DA, Nester EW (1976): Purification and properties of two aromatic aminotransferases in *Bacillus subtilis.* J Biol Chem 251:6974–6978.

Weiss U, Edwards JM (1980): *The biosynthesis of aromatic compounds.* New York: John Wiley and Sons.

Welch GR, Gaertner FH (1975): Influence of an aggregated multisystem on transient time: Kinetic evidence for compartmentation by an aromatic-amino acid-synthesizing complex of *Neurospora crassa.* Proc Natl Acad Sci USA 72:4218–4222.

Whitaker RJ, Byng GS, Gherna RL, Jensen RA (1981a): Comparative allostery of 3-deoxy-*D-arabino*-heptulosonate 7-phosphate synthetase as an indicator of taxonomic relatedness in pseudomonad genera. J Bacteriol 145:752–759.

Whitaker RJ, Byng GS, Gherna RL, Jensen RA (1981b): Diverse enzymological patterns of phenylalanine biosynthesis in pseudomonad bacteria are conserved in parallel with DNA-homology groupings. J Bacteriol 147:526–534.

Whitaker RJ, Fiske MJ, Jensen RA (1982a): *Pseudomonas aeruginosa* possesses two novel regulatory isozymes of 3-deoxy-*D-arabino*-heptulosonate 7-phosphate synthase. J Biol Chem 257:12789–12794.

Whitaker RJ, Gaines CG, Jensen RA (1982b): A multispecific quintet of aromatic aminotransferases that overlap different biochemical pathways in *Pseudomonas aeruginosa.* J Biol Chem 257:13550–13556.

Zurawski G, Gunsales RP, Brown KD, Yanofsky C (1981): Structure and regulation of *aroH,* the structural gene for the tryptophan-repressible 3-deoxy-*D-arabino*-heptulosonic 7-phosphate synthetase of *Escherichia coli.* J Mol Biol 145:47–73.

Isozymes: Current Topics in Biological and Medical Research
Volume 8: Cellular Localization, Metabolism, and Physiology 141–153

Purification and Characterization of Uridylylated and Unuridylylated Forms of Regulatory Protein P_{II} Involved in the Glutamine Synthetase Regulation in Escherichia coli

Sue Goo Rhee and P. Boon Chock

Laboratory of Biochemistry, National Heart, Lung, and Blood Institute, National Institutes of Health, Bethesda, Maryland 20205

I. INTRODUCTION

Glutamine synthetase (GS) plays a central role in the assimilation of ammonia in enteric bacteria [for review, see Stadtman and Ginsburg, 1974]. Cellular glutamine synthetase is regulated in response to the quality and abundance of the nitrogen source in the growth medium both at the level of enzymatic activity (by covalent modification) and at the biosynthetic level (by repression and derepression) [Magasanik and Rothstein, 1980].

Regulation of glutamine synthetase activity in Escherichia coli involves the cyclic adenylylation and deadenylylation of a unique tyrosyl group in each subunit [Stadtman and Ginsburg, 1974]. The adenylylation reaction is catalyzed by an adenylyltransferase (AT) and involves transfer of adenylyl groups from ATP to the enzyme with the concomitant formation of PP_i (Fig. 1). Because glutamine synthetase is composed of 12 identical subunits, and adenylylated subunits are catalytically inactive, the catalytic potential of the enzyme is inversely proportional to the average number ($\bar{n}$) of covalently bound adenylyl groups per enzyme molecule [Kingdon et al, 1967]. Removal of the adenylyl group from glutamine synthetase (deadenylylation) is achieved by phosphorolysis of the adenylyl-o-tryosol bond to yield ADP and unmod-

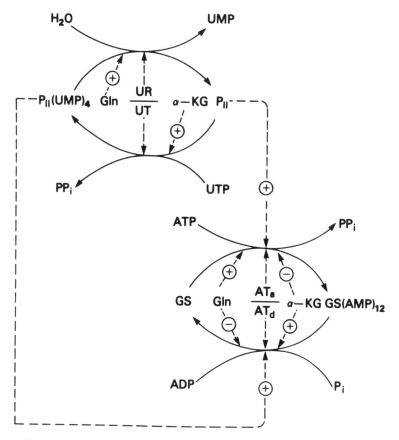

Fig. 1. The bicyclic cascade of glutamine synthetase regulation. Interrelationship between the uridylylation and deuridylylation of the P_{II} and the adenylylation and deadenylylation of glutamine synthetase (GS), and the reciprocal controls of these interconversions by glutamine (Gln) and α-ketoglutarate (α-KG) are shown. + indicates stimulation, − indicates inhibition. See text for abbreviations.

ified glutamine synthetase [Anderson and Stadtman, 1970]. This reaction is catalyzed by the same protein (AT) which catalyzed the adenylylation reaction [Anderson et al, 1970]. Because the adenylylation and deadenylylation reactions are catalyzed at separate, noninteracting catalytic sites (AT_a for adenylylation reaction and AT_d for deadenylylation reaction) on a single polypeptide chain [Rhee et al, 1978], it is evident that in the absence of appropriate regulation the two reactions will be tightly coupled, resulting simply in senseless phosphorolysis of ATP to ADP and PP_i. Indiscriminate coupling of the adenylylation and deadenylylation reaction is prevented by the action of a regulatory protein, P_{II} [Shapiro, 1969], which also exists in an unmodified form, P_{IIA}, and a modified (uridylylated) form, P_{IID} [Brown et al, 1971; Mangum et al., 1973; Adler et al, 1975] (Fig. 1). The capacity of AT to catalyze the adenylylation of GS is dependent on the concentration of P_{IIA}, whereas the capacity to catalyze the deadenylylation reaction is determined by the concentration of P_{IID} [Brown et al, 1971]. The steady-state distribution between P_{IIA} and P_{IID} is determined by the relative contributions of uridylyltransferase (UT) and a uridylyl-removing enzyme (UR). These activities are contained in a single polypeptide [Garcia et al, 1980].

The final state of adenylylation of GS is dependent on over 40 different metabolites that affect the catalytic activities of one or more of the regulatory enzymes AT_a, AT_d, UT, and UR [Stadtman and Chock, 1978]. By far, the most important of these metabolites are α-ketoglutarate and glutamine, which exhibit opposite and reciprocal effects on the adenylylation-deadenylylation and on the uridylylation-deuridylylation pairs of reactions [Stadtman and Ginsburg, 1974; Stadtman and Chock, 1978; Rhee et al, 1978].

Because GS and P_{II} are multimeric proteins composed of several identical subunits, the post translational modifications by nucleotidylylation lead to multimolecular enzyme forms. In the case of GS, various studies have been pursued on hybrid molecules (ie, enzymes composed of both adenylylated and unadenylylated subunits) which were produced in vivo or prepared in vitro by dissociation and reassociation of mixtures of fully adenylylated and fully unadenylylated forms [Stadtman et al, 1975]. Heterologous subunit interactions between adenylylated and unadenylylated subunits within these hybrid molecules affected certain catalytic parameters [Stadtman et al, 1975]. Furthermore, new methods for separating GS based on the number of adenosine monophosphate (AMP) groups attached have been developed recently by using affinity chromatography on affi-blue sepharose or chromatography on anti-AMP antibody-immunoadsorbant [Stadtman et al, 1980]. These novel techniques will facilitate the understanding of the nature of subunit interaction in GS and the significance of its dodecameric structure.

The importance of uridylylation-deuridylylation of P_{II} in the regulation of GS was further elevated when it was shown that P_{IIA} is a corepressor of GS synthesis; the presence of unuridylylated P_{II} resulted in a repression of GS synthesis which can be relieved by the conversion of P_{IIA} to P_{IID} [Magasanik and Rothstein, 1980; Foor et al, 1980].

Although the P_{II} molecule is simpler (composed of four identical subunits vs 12 subunits) and smaller (mol wt 44,000 vs 600,000) than GS, detailed studies on this regulatory protein have been hampered by difficulties in the preparation of sufficient quantities of homogeneous protein. In this paper, we describe a simplified purification method, report properties of P_{II}, and make comparisons to GS where appropriate.

II. PURIFICATION OF P_{II} AND PREPARATION OF FULLY URIDYLYLATED AND FULLY UNURIDYLYLATED P_{II}

The presence of relative low P_{II} concentrations in E coli has made it difficult to prepare sufficient quantities of P_{II}. The problem is overcome by the use of molecular cloning techniques to increase P_{II} production. A strain bearing the multicopy plasmid vector carrying the *glnB* gene (structural gene for P_{II}) was constructed by cloning a *PVUI*-generated fragment of the recombinant plasmid *PGS1*. This new strain overproduced P_{II} by 70-fold [to be published elsewhere]. It was known that the plasmid *PGS1* contained *glyA* gene [Stauffer et al., 1981] and that *glnB* gene is located closely to *glyA* gene. The use of this P_{II}-overproducing strain allowed us to prepare larger quantities of P_{II}. Table I summarizes a typical purification procedure. The purity of P_{II} at different stages of purification analyzed on sodium dodecyl sulfate acrylamide gel (13%, ratio of acrylamide to bisacrylamide was 25:1) is shown (Fig. 2). A particularly useful procedure in the P_{II} purification scheme was precipitation of most contaminating proteins in the presence of 26% β-mercaptoethanol. This step was contrived based on the fact that P_{II} protein contains neither cysteine nor cystine [Adler et al, 1975]. Because P_{II} obtained in this particular preparation was a mixture of 90% P_{IIA} and 10% P_{IID}, this mixture was treated with snake venom phosphodiesterase until less than 1% P_{IID} activity was detected. Subsequently, the P_{IIA} was separated from the reaction components by chromatography over concanavalin A (con A) sepharose. Fully uridylylated P_{II} labeled with ^3H and ^{32}P was prepared by uridylylating P_{IIA} in the presence of 5-^3H-UTP, α-^{32}P-UTP, α-ketoglutarate, and UT·UR enzyme. The uridylylation reaction mixture was incubated until no further increase in the P_{IID} activity was observed. The $^3H,^{32}P$-uridylylated P_{II} was repurified by repeating purification steps 3 and 4 described in Table I.

III. SUBUNIT ARRANGEMENT

Preliminary x-ray crystallographic studies on P_{IIA} protein indicate that four subunits in P_{IIA} assume a tetrahedral structure as depicted in Figure 3 [Suh and Rhee, unpublished results]. Because glutamine synthetase is composed of 12 identical subunits which are arranged in two superimposed hexagonal rings [Valentine et al, 1968], and because all 12 of the subunits can be adenylylated, it can exist, in principle, in 382 molecular forms which differ from each other with respect to the number (zero to 12) and distribution of adenylylated subunits within the dodecamer molecule. However, in the case

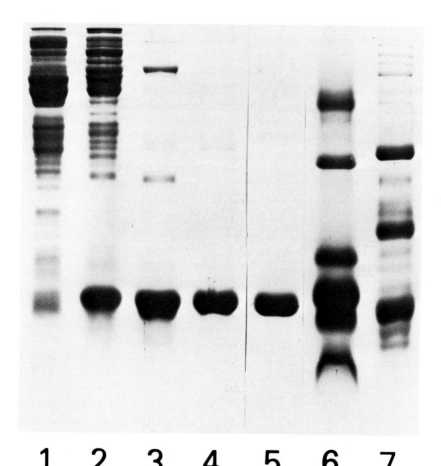

Fig. 2. SDS gel electrophoresis of P$_{II}$ at different stages of purification. Lane 1: streptomycin supernatant; lane 2: first DEAE column fraction; lane 3: supernatant from 26% β-mercapto-ethanol step; lane 4: second DEAE column fraction; lane 5: agarose column fraction; lane 6: standard proteins; ovalbumin (mol wt 43,000), α-chymotrypsinogen (25,700), β-lactoglobulin (18,400), lysozyme (14,300), cytochrome C (12,300), and bovine trypsin inhibitor (6,200); lane 7: partially purified P$_{II}$ from E coli W.

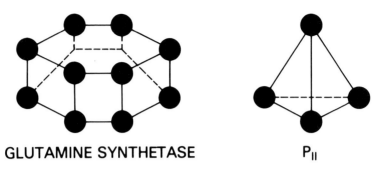

GLUTAMINE SYNTHETASE P_{II}

Fig. 3.   Subunit arrangement of P_{II} and glutamine synthetase.__

where the four subunits are arranged in a tetrahedral structure, one expects the existence of five different hybrid molecules which differ from each other with respect to the number (zero to four) of the uridine monophosphate (UMP) group attached. Existence of these five hybrid molecules has not yet been established; nevertheless, electrophoretic patterns of P_{II} suggest that different hybrid molecules do exist. Separation of fully uridylylated and fully unuridylylated P_{II} can be accomplished readily on polyacrylamide gel and a partially uridylylated P_{II} has been shown to exhibit four to five bands [Adler et al, 1975].

IV. uv SPECTRUM OF P_{II}

uv spectra of P_{IIA}, P_{IID}, and their difference spectrum are shown (Fig. 4). The difference spectrum is essentially the same as that of UMP. Using the second derivative spectrum of P_{IIA} in 6 M guanidine [Levine and Federici, 1982], protein concentration and aromatic amino acid contents could be quantitated. The ratio of phenylalanine to tyrosine to tryptophan was 4.8:2.0:0.06. This result is in excellent agreement with the result of amino acid analysis, which shows that P_{II} contains five phenylalanine and two tyrosine, but no tryptophan [Adler et al, 1975]. Assuming that the extinction coefficient of the UMP moiety is not changed when bound to P_{II}, an empirical formula for calculating the state of uridylylation (average number of UMP attached to P_{II}) and protein concentration independent of the state of uridylylation could be derived. Since the UMP moiety absorbs through the entire region of unmodified P_{II} spectrum, from 250 to 300 nm, absorption at any given wavelength is a function of both protein concentration and the state of uridylylation. Therefore, calculation of the concentration of P_{IIA} and P_{IID} requires solving two simultaneous equations:

$$A_{260} \text{ (OD/cm)} = 1.995 \, (A + D) + 9.90D + 2.92 \, A_{340}$$
$$A_{290} \text{ (OD/cm)} = 0.7011 \, (A + D) + 0.277D + 2.17 \, A_{340}$$

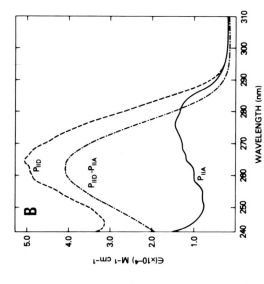

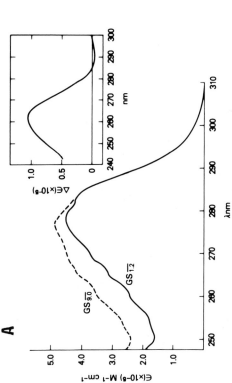

Fig. 4. A. Ultraviolet absorption spectra of GS$_{1.2}$ ( ), GS$_{9.0}$ (———), and difference spectrum between two forms (insert). B. Ultraviolet absorption spectra of P$_{IIA}$ ( ), P$_{IID}$, which contains an average number of 3.9 UMP group per tetramer (———), and difference spectrum between two forms (—·—·—·—). The spectra were recorded at room temperature in 20 mM Hepes buffer, pH 7.6. Extinction coefficients are expressed per mole of tetrameric form.

where A and D represent the subunit concentration (mM) of P_{IIA} and P_{IID}, respectively. The first, second, and third terms in the above equations represent the absorption due to the protein concentration, the uridylylated tyrosine, and light scattering correction, respectively.

In the case of glutamine synthetase, protein concentration could be obtained independently from a single protein spectrum because AMP exhibits a very low extinction coefficient at 290 nm so that the absorbance at 290 nm can be attributted solely to protein absorpion. In addition, the state of adenylylation could be calculated from the ratio of A_{260} to A_{290}.

V. AMINO ACID SEQUENCE OF A TRYPTIC UNDECAPEPTIDE CONTAINING COVALENTLY BOUND UMP

The heat denatured P_{II} $[^3H,^{32}P\text{-}UMP]_4$ (16 mg) was dissolved in 0.5 M TRIS buffer, pH 8.2, and incubated at 37°C for 13 hours in the presence of 0.5 mg of trypsin. The proteolyzed mixture was lyophilized and dissolved in 8 M guanidine containing 2% trifluoroacetic acid before injected into the high-pressure liquid chromatography (HPLC) column. A peak containing 91% of total radioactivity injected was collected (Fig. 5) and lyophilized. The peptide was found to consist of 11 amino acids and to contain an uridylylated tyrosine (Fig. 6).

Previously, a decapeptide containing an adenylyl group was isolated from adenylylated glutamine synthetase. Subsequently, it was shown that the adenylyl group is bound in phosphodiester linkage to the phenolic hydroxyl group of tyrosine (Fig. 7) by comparing the absorption spectra of adenylylated and unadenylylated peptides at alkaline pH [Shapiro and Stadtman, 1968]. The 5′-adenylyl-O-tyrosine linkage was confirmed by the study of a 21-member tryptic peptide-containing AMP moiety [Heinrikson and Kingdon, 1971]. The 5′-uridylyl-O-tyrosine linkage in P_{IID} was also suggested based

TABLE I. Purification Summary

Step	Total protein	Yield	Specific activity
1. Streptomycin	77 gm	100%	1
2. DEAE-cellulose chromatography	2.8	47	13
3. Sup from 26% β-mercaptoethanol (ppt)	0.754	29	30
4. DEAE-cellulose chromatography	0.547	26	36
5. Agarose (0.5 M) chromatography	0.459	21	36

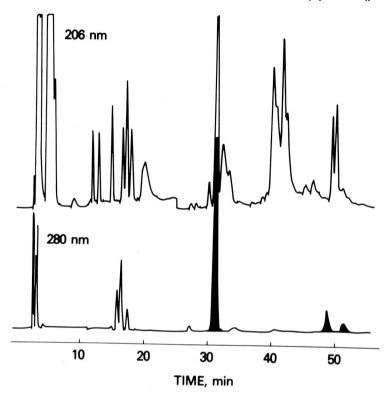

Fig. 5. High-pressure liquid chromatography (HPLC) chromatogram of tryptic peptides of P$_{II}$ [^{32}P,^{3}H-UMP] monitored at 206 nm (top) and 280 (bottom). The trypsin-digested peptides were separated on a reverse phase column (μ Bondapak C18, 3.9 mm × 30 cm, by Waters Associates) by eluting with a linear gradient generated from 0.05% trifluoroacetic acid containing 0% acetonitrile and 60% acetonitrile, respectively. Radioactivity was distributed into three peaks (represented by shaded area in bottom chromatograph): one major peak and two minot peaks containing 91% and 9% of radioactivity, respectively.

on two observations [Adler et al, 1975]: (1) tryptic digestion of ^{125}I-iodinated P$_{IIA}$ yields two radioactive peptides, while only one radioactive peptide from ^{125}I P$_{IID}$ is observed; and (2) the difference spectrum between P$_{IIA}$ and P$_{IID}$ at pH 13 is the spectrum of phenolate ion.

VI. PROPERTIES OF PHOSPHOTYROSYL P$_{II}$

Protein phosphorylation is involved in the regulation of different cellular functions of prokaryotes as it is in eukaryotes [Wang and Koshland, 1981],

Glutamine Synthetase:

$$\underset{\displaystyle |}{\overset{\displaystyle AMP}{}}$$

Ile–His–Pro–Gly–Glu–Ala–Met–Lys–Asp–Asn–Leu–Tyr–
Asp–Leu–Pro–Pro–Glu–Gly–Glu–Ala–Lys

P$_{II}$:

$$\underset{\displaystyle |}{\overset{\displaystyle UMP}{}}$$

Gly–Ala–Glu–Tyr–Met–Val–Asp–Phe–Leu–Pro–Lys

Fig. 6. Sequence of tryptic peptides containing covalently bound nucleotide.

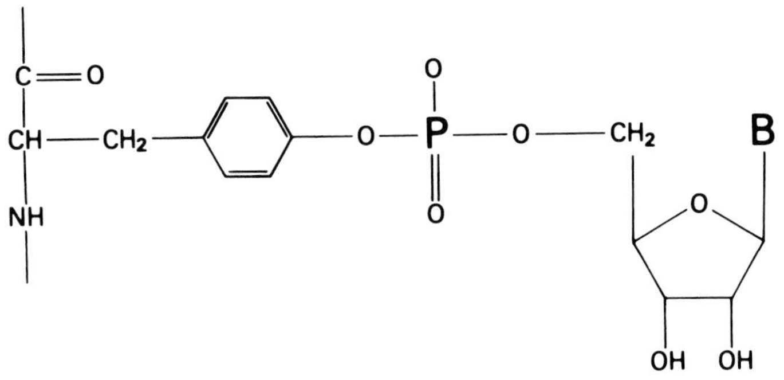

Fig. 7. Nucleotydyl-O-tyrosyl bond. B, adenine or uracil

while regulatory control by nucleotidylation seems to exist only in bacteria. In eukaryotes, phosphorylation of three amino acids, serine, threonine, and tyrosine, is observed, but only two amino acids, serine and threonine, are known to be phosphorylated in prokaryotes. In this connection, it is interesting to study the phosphotyrosyl P$_{II}$, which can be prepared by treating ^{3}H,^{32}P-uridylylated P$_{II}$ with micrococcal nuclease. As depicted in Figure 8, P$_{IID}$ activity decreases in parallel with the tritium-labeled protein in trichloroacetic acid (TCA) precipitates, and P$_{IIA}$ activity increases in parallel with the appearance of ^{3}H-uridine in TCA supernatants. The P$_{IIA}$ activity associated with the nuclease reaction mixture after incubating for 360 minutes was only 2% of the P$_{IIA}$ activity expected for unmodified P$_{II}$ at equivalent concentration. During the entire time course of incubation, ^{32}P radioactivity associated with the TCA precipitates remained constant and P$_{II}$ protein remained intact as evidenced by SDS polyacrylamide gel electrophoresis. These results indicate that indeed phosphotyrosyl P$_{II}$ was generated and the phosphotyrosyl P$_{II}$ does not activate the deadenylylation reaction catalyzed by adenylyltransferase.

Although the P$_{IIA}$ activity associated with phosphotyrosyl P$_{II}$ was low, it is proper to regard this activity as an intrinsic property of phosphotyrosyl P$_{II}$ because no significant amounts of ^{32}P radioactivity release (< 5 cpm) was observed during the incubation period. When a similar experiment to generate phosphotyrosyl glutamine synthetase from adenylated GS was performed, micrococcal nuclease did not hydrolyze 5′-adenine-phosphotyrosyl bond unless GS was unfolded completely [Martensen, 1982]. Nevertheless, snake

P$_{II}$–[^{3}H, ^{32}P–UMP]$_4$ + MICROCOCCAL NUCLEASE

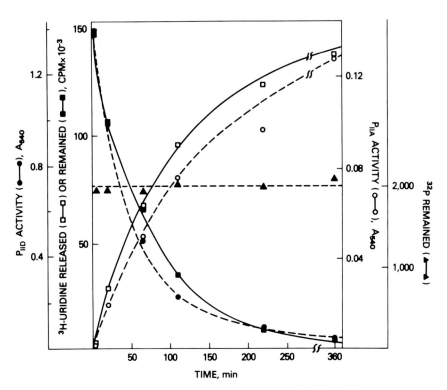

Fig. 8.   Properties of phosphotyrosyl P$_{II}$ formed by treating P$_{II}$-[^{3}H, ^{32}P-UMP]$_4$ (1.3 mg) with micrococcal nuclease (2.5 mg) in 50 mM borate buffer, pH 9.0, containing 10 mM CaCl$_2$ at 37°C. The nuclease reaction was stopped at different time intervals by adding excess EGTA. The stopped reaction mixtures were dialyzed against 10 mM Hepes buffer, pH 7.6, containing 2 mM EGTA before P$_{IIA}$ and P$_{IID}$ activities were measured by colorimetric assay [Rhee et al, 1978a,b]. The appearance of ^{3}H-uridine in 10% TCA supernatants, decrease of ^{3}H-uridylylated protein in 10% TCA precipitates, and ^{32}P radioactivity remaining in phosphotyrosyl protein were also measured with these dialyzed samples.

venom phosphodiesterase which hydrolytically removes 5'-nucleotides from the 3'-hydroxy termini of 3'-hydroxy-terminated oligonucleotides catalyzed both deadenylylation of adenylylated GS and deuridylylation of uridylylated P_{II} equally well.

The fact that phosphorylation of tyrosyl residue does not convert P_{IIA} to a P_{IID}-like molecule is distinct from an observation made with GS. Nonenzymic chemical modification (nitration or acetylation) of tyrosyl residue(s) produced alterations in catalytic parameters that are similar to alterations caused by adenylylation, even though the tyrosyl residue(s) which was chemically modified was not the one that was involved in the adenylylation [Cimino et al, 1970]. Conversion of P_{IID} to the phospho tyrosyl P_{II} will further improve separability of P_{II} hybrid molecules containing different numbers of UMP based on their differences in electrocharges.

In summary, it is now possible to obtain a large quantity of P_{II} due to the development of a P_{II}-overproducing strain and a simplified purification procedure. The subunits of this tetrameric molecule were shown to assume a tetrahedral configuration. A tryptic undecapeptide peptide containing the uridylylated tyrosine was isolated and characterized. Study of the uv spectral properties of the uridylylated and deuridylylated P_{II} allowed one to derive an empirical formula for quantitating both the protein concentration and the extent of uridylylation per P_{II} tetramer. In addition, a phosphotyrosyl P_{II} was produced by treating uridylylated P_{II} with micrococcal nuclease. This phosphotyrosyl P_{II} does not exhibit the P_{IID} activity.

VII. REFERENCES

Adler SP, Purich D, Stadtman ER (1975): Cascade control of *E. coli* glutamine synthetase. J Biol Chem 250:6264–6272.

Anderson WB, Stadtman ER (1970): Glutamine synthetase deadenylylation: A phosphorolytic reaction yielding ADP as nucleotide product. Biochem Biophys Res Commun 41:704–709.

Anderson WB, Hennig SB, Ginsburg A, Stadtman ER (1970): Association of ATP: Glutamine synthetase adenylyltransferase activity with the P_I component of the glutamine synthetase deadenylylation system. Proc Natl Acad Sci USA 67:1417–1424.

Brown MS, Segal A, Stadtman ER (1971): Modulation of glutamine synthetase adenylylation and deadenylylation is mediated by metabolic transformation of the P_{II}-regulatory protein. Proc Natl Acad Sci USA 68:2949–2953.

Cimino F, Anderson WB, Stadtman ER (1970): Ability of nonenzymic nitration or acetylation of *E. coli* glutamine synthetase to produce effects analogous to enzymic adenylylation. Proc Natl Acad Sci USA 66:564–571.

Foor F, Reuveny Z, Magasanik B (1980): Regulation of the synthesis of glutamine synthetase by the P$_{II}$ protein in *Klebsiella aerogenes*. Proc Natl Acad Sci USA 77:2636–2640.

Garcia E, Federici M, Rhee SG, Berberich MA (1980): Glutamine synthetase cascade: Enrichment of uridylyltransferase in *E. coli* carrying hybrid ColE1 plasmids. Arch Biochem Biophys 203:181–189.

Heinrikson RL, Kingdon HS (1971): Primary structure of *E. coli* glutamine synthetase: The complete amino acid sequence of tryptic heneicosapeptide containing covalently bound adenylic acid. J Biol Chem 246:1099–1106.

Kingdon HS, Shapiro BM, Stadtman ER (1967): Regulation of glutamine synthetase, VIII. ATP: Glutamine synthetase adenylyltransferase, an enzyme that catalyzes alterations in the regulatory properties of glutamine synthetase. Proc Natl Acad Sci USA 58:1703–1710.

Levine RL, Federici MM (1982): Quantitation of aromatic residues in proteins: Model compounds for second derivative spectroscopy. Biochemistry 21:2600–2606.

Magasanik B, Rothstein DM (1980): The role of glutamine synthetase in the regulation of bacterial nitrogen metabolism. In Mora J, Palacios R (eds): "Glutamine, Metabolism, Enzymology and Regulation." London: Academic Press, pp 61–68.

Mangum JH, Magni G, Stadtman ER (1973): Regulation of glutamine synthetase adenylylation and deadenylylation of enzymic uridylylation and deuridylylation of the P$_{II}$ regulatory protein. Arch Biochem Biophys 158:514–525.

Martensen TM (1982): Phosphotyrosine in proteins: Stability and quantitation. J Biol Chem 257:9648–9652.

Rhee SG, Park R, Chock PB, Stadtman ER (1978): Allosteric regulation of monocyclic interconvertible enzyme cascade systems: Use of *E. coli* glutamine synthetase as an experimental model. Proc Natl Acad Sci USA 75:3138–3142.

Shapiro B, Stadtman ER (1968): 5'-adenylyl-O-tyrosine: The novel phosphodiester residue of adenylylated glutamine synthetase from *E. coli*. J Biol Chem 243:3769–3771.

Shapiro BM (1969): The glutamine synthetase deadenylylation system from *E. coli*. Resolution into two components, specific nucleotide stimulation, and cofactor requirements. Biochemistry 8:659–670.

Stadtman ER and Ginsburg A (1974): The glutamine synthetase of *E coli:* structure and control. In Boyer PD (ed): "The Enzymes Vol 10." Academic Press, New York pp 755–807.

Stadtman ER, Ciardi JE, Smyrniotis PZ, Segal A, Ginsburg A, Adler SP (1975): Role of adenylylated glutamine synthetase enzymes and uridylylated regulatory protein enzymes in the regulation of glutamine synthetase activity in *E. coli*. In Markert CL (ed): "Isozymes, Vol 2." New York: Academic Press, pp 715–732.

Stadtman ER, Chock PB (1978): Inconvertible enzyme cascades in metabolic regulation. In Horecker BL, Stadtman ER (eds): "Current Topics in Cellular Regulation, Vol 13." New York: Academic Press, pp 53–95.

Stadtman ER, Hohman RJ, Davis JN, Wittenberger M, Chock PB, Rhee SG (1980): Subunit interaction of adenylylated glutamine synthetase. In Chapeville F, Haenni AL (eds): "Molecular Biology, Biochemistry, and Biophysics, Vol 32." Berlin: Springer-Verlag, pp 144–155.

Stauffer GV, Plamann MD, Stauffer LT (1981): Construction and expression of hybrid plasmids containing the *E. coli* glyA gene. Gene 14:63–72.

Valentine RC, Shapiro BM, Stadtman ER (1968): Electron microscopy of the enzyme from *E. coli*. Biochemistry 7:2143–2152.

Wang JYJ, Koshland DE, Jr (1981): The identification of distinct protein kinases and phosphatases in the prokaryote *S. typhimurium*. J Biol Chem 256:4640–4648.

Isozymes: Current Topics in Biological and Medical Research
Volume 8: Cellular Localization, Metabolism, and Physiology 155–174

The Alcohol Dehydrogenase Gene Complex on Chromosome 3 of the Mouse

Roger S. Holmes, John A. Duley, and James N. Burnell

School of Science, Griffith University, Nathan 4111, Queensland, Australia

I. INTRODUCTION

A. Alcohol Abuse

Alcohol is the major drug of use and abuse throughout the western world and the consequences of alcohol abuse are readily observed in our communities. Although it is generally recognized that alcohol is socially acceptable, there are always the problems of addiction and alcohol-related disease, particularly for some members of the community. Genetic factors apparently play important roles in the development of alcoholism [Oakeshott and Gibson, 1981]. Consequently, studies on the genetic regulation of the enzymes of alcohol metabolism and of other enzymes associated with the formation and degradation of addictive compounds derived from alcohol are particularly relevant to defining these genetic factors at the molecular level.

B. Alcohol Metabolism

The first step in the biological oxidation of ethanol in mammals occurs predominantly in liver and primarily via the cytoplasmic enzyme alcohol dehydrogenase (ADH; EC. 1.1.1.1) (see reviews in Havre et al [1977], Rognstad and Grunnet [1979], Cederbaum [1980], and Khanna and Israel [1980]) (Fig. 1):

$$CH_3CH_2OH + NAD^+ \rightarrow CH_3CHO + NADH + H^+ \qquad (1)$$

The enzyme has a broad substrate substrate specificity and catalyses the reversible interconversion of a wide variety of alcohols and their corresponding aldehydes and ketones, including steroids and ω-hydroxy fatty acids,

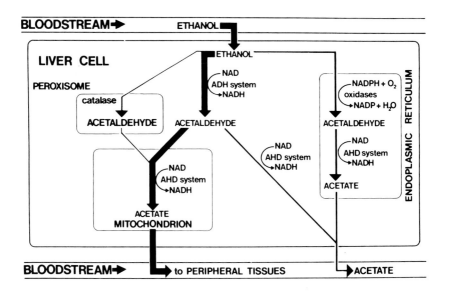

Fig. 1. Metabolism of ethanol in the hepatocyte. ADH-alcohol dehydrogenase. AHD-aldehyde dehydrogenase.

which together with ethanol may represent the "physiological" substrates for ADH [Pietruszko, 1979]. The key role of this enzyme in ethanol metabolism is exemplified by the reported 80%–90% reduction of ethanol oxidation in perfused livers and in liver cell cultures when ethanol concentrations of >0.2% and a potent ADH inhibitor, pyrazole, were used [Theiden, 1971; Lieber and DeCarli, 1972]. Metabolic analyses of a strain of deer mouse exhibiting a "null" phenotype for liver ADH by Burnett and Felder [1980] have confirmed this conclusion. The minor pathway of ethanol oxidation is predominantly catalysed by the microsomal ethanol oxidizing system (MEOS), which increases in relative activity at ethanol concentrations >0.2% [Lieber, 1977]. Liver peroxisomal catalase also catalyses ethanol oxidation in vivo but is apparently not a major contributor to metabolic flux of ingested ethanol (see discussion in Rognstad and Grunnet [1979]).

The second stage of ethanol metabolism in mammalian liver is catalysed predominantly by liver aldehyde dehydrogenase (AHD; EC. 1.2.1.3):

$$CH_3CHO + NAD^+ \xrightarrow{H_2O} CH_3COOH + NADH + H^+ \qquad (2)$$

The enzyme is differentially localized in mitochondrial, cytoplasmic, and microsomal fractions of liver extracts and exists as a variety of isozymic forms (reviewed in Timms and Holmes [1981]). Metabolic studies have indicated that the major contributor to acetaldehyde oxidation in vivo is catalysed by mitochondrial AHD [Parilla et al, 1974], although the cytoplasmic enzyme may also be involved [Petersen et al, 1977; Smolen et al, 1980].

C. Mammalian Liver ADH

Mammalian liver ADH isozymes have been extensively investigated in recent years with respect to their primary sequences, tertiary structures, and catalytic properties (see Branden et al [1975]). The three major isozymes of horse liver ADH are formed by the dimeric combination of two genetically distinct subunits, designated E (ethanol active) and S (sterol and ethanol active), forming two genetic isozymes, E_2 and S_2, and a hybrid isozyme ES. Polymorphic variation of the S subunit [Pietruszko, 1974] contributes further multiplicity in hybrid animals. Smith and co-workers [1971, 1972] have reported genetic and developmental evidence for three distinct subunits for human liver ADH, α, β, and γ, which randomly dimerize to form six ADH isozymes α_2, $\alpha\beta$, β_2, $\beta\gamma$, $\alpha\gamma$, and γ_2. In addition, Li and co-workers [Li and Magnes, 1975; Li et al, 1977] have obtained evidence for another isozyme, called π ADH, in "fresh" human liver extracts.

In contrast, studies on rodent liver ADH (using ethanol as substrate) have shown that this enzyme is apparently encoded by a single locus. Rat liver

ADH, for example, has been purified and has a single amino acid sequence [Branden et al, 1975]. Genetic analyses of mouse [Holmes et al, 1981a] and deer mouse [Burnett and Felder, 1978] liver ADH also provided evidence for a single structural locus for this enzyme.

D. Outline of Paper

The mouse (Mus musculus) is extensively used as a model organism in genetic research and in studies on biochemical and genetic aspects of alcohol metabolism. Moreover, dramatic differences in alcohol drinking behavior have been reported among inbred strains of this organism and extensive studies have been undertaken to examine the molecular basis of this phenomenon (reviewed by Gibson and Oakeshott [1981]). This communication examines genetic and biochemical aspects of ADH isozymes in the laboratory mouse and provides evidence for an ADH gene complex on chromosome 3 of this organism, comprising two structural genes and two temporal genes for ADH and a structural gene for a related enzyme, aldehyde reductase.

II. MOUSE ADH ISOZYMES

A. Tissue Distribution

The electrophoretic patterns for ADH activity extracted from various tissues of 101/H inbred mice show three major zones of activity (Fig. 2). These were further resolved and distinguished by their substrate specifities and tissue distribution. Genetic (see Genetics of ADH Isozymes in the Mouse section) and biochemical (Purification and Molecular Properties section) analyses supported the proposal for three distinct ADH isozymes, designated A_2, B_2,[1] and C_2. ADH-A_2 was characterized by its high activity in liver extracts (being the only ADH in liver using ethanol as substrate) and wide tissue distribution; ADH-B_2 is inactive with ethanol as substrate and exhibited highest activity in liver and kidney extracts; ADH-C_2 was not observed in liver extracts, being predominantly localized in stomach, male secondary sex tissues, and female reproductive tissue extracts.

B. Purification and Molecular Properties

Mouse liver (A_2) and stomach (C_2) ADH isozymes have been purified using affinity chromatographic techniques [Holmes et al, 1981a]. In addition, Kessler and Ferrell [1974] have isolated an ADH from mouse liver, which resembles ADH-B_2 in terms of its catalytic properties. Table I compares the Michaelis constants for these purified isozymes using ethanol, trans-2-hexen-1-ol, and acetaldehyde as substrates. For the oxidative direction, ADH-A_2 exhibited Km values for ethanol that were approximately three orders of magnitude lower compared with ADH-C_2, whereas the B_2 isozyme was

[1]Provisional designation; no evidence currently available regarding subunit composition.

TISSUE DISTRIBUTION OF ALCOHOL DEHYDROGENASE
ISOZYMES IN THE MOUSE

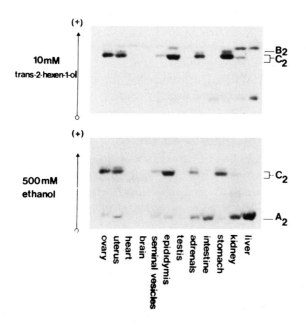

Fig. 2. Cellulose acetate zymograms of mouse tissue alcohol dehydrogenase isozymes (ADH-A_2; B_2; C_2) from adult 101/H inbred mice. Substrates used were 500 mM ethanol (lower) and 10 mM trans-2-hexen-1-ol (upper). See Duley and Holmes [1982] for details.

TABLE I. Comparative Michaelis Constants of Mouse ADH Isozymes

Substrate	ADH-A_2[a]	ADH-B_2[b]	ADH-C_2[a]
Ethanol	290 μM	inactive	133 mM
Trans-2-hexen-1-ol	2 μM	ND[c]	0.1 mM
Acetaldehyde	89 μM	2 μM	200 μM

[a]Holmes et al, 1981.
[b]Kessler and Ferrell, 1974.
[c]Active with this substrate; Km undetermined.

inactive with this substrate. In the reductive direction, both ADH-A_2 and B_2 had a low Km for acetaldehyde compared with the value for ADH-C_2 for this substrate.

It is apparent from these kinetic studies and from previous investigations into the role of liver ADH in ethanol metabolism [Havre et al, 1977], that liver ADH-A_2 is predominantly responsible for ethanol oxidation in vivo. The physiological roles of the other ADH isozymes are not known. Kessler and Ferrell [1974] have proposed that ADH-B_2 acts as a long-chain aldehyde reductase as a result of the observed activity of this enzyme with a variety of fatty aldehydes. However, these workers did not report on either the purity or the molecular weight of ADH-B_2; consequently, the wide substrate specificity observed may be due to contaminating enzymes.

III. GENETICS OF ADH ISOZYMES IN THE MOUSE

Figure 3 shows the electrophoretic patterns observed for allelic isozymes of ADH-A_2 and ADH-C_2 extracted from liver and stomach extracts, respectively, of LII Mice (a Harwell linkage testing stock segregating in the dominant gene Va, varitint-waddler), a Danish strain of mice exhibiting allelic variants for both the $Adh-1$ locus (encoding A_2 isozyme) and the $Adh-3$ locus (encoding C_2 isozyme) and F_1 hybrid mice between these two strains. Both ADH-A_2 and ADH-C_2 exhibited three-banded isozyme patterns in hybrid animals, consistent with codominant expression of the alleles and with dimeric subunit structures for these enzymes: ADH-A_2^1, ADH-A^1A^2, and ADH-A_2^2, with A^1 and A^2 being encoded by separate alleles at a single locus, designated $Adh-1^a$ (LII strain) and $Adh-1^b$ (Danish strain), respectively; and ADH-C_2^1, ADH-C^1C^2 and ADH-C_2^2, with C^1 and C^2 encoded by separate alleles at a single locus, designated $Adh-3^a$ (LII strain) and $Adh-3^b$ (Danish strain), respectively [see Holmes, 1979; Holmes et al, 1981a,b].

Analyses of the recombination frequencies for $Adh-1$, $Adh-3$, and Va loci among 126 backcross progeny of Danish strain $\times$ F_1 (Danish $\times$ LII) hybrid cross demonstrated no recominants between the two Adh loci, whereas both exhibited a recombination frequency of 4.0 $\pm$ 1.7% with Va [Holmes et al, 1981a] a known genetic marker for chromosome 3 of the mouse [Eicher and Lane, 1980]. More recent studies have examined the segregation of $Adh-1$ and $Adh-3$ among 117 F_1 (Danish $\times$ CBA/H) $\times$ CBA/H progeny and have reported no recombinants between these two loci [Holmes et al, 1982a]. Thus, combined data are consistent with the Adh loci being localized within 0.3 centimorgans on chromosome 3 of the mouse.

The distribution of allelic variants for ADH-A_2 ($Adh-1$ locus) and ADH-C_2 ($Adh-3$ locus) among 65 inbred and partially inbred strains of mice have been examined (Table II) [Holmes et al, 1982a]. The ADH-A_2^2 variant was

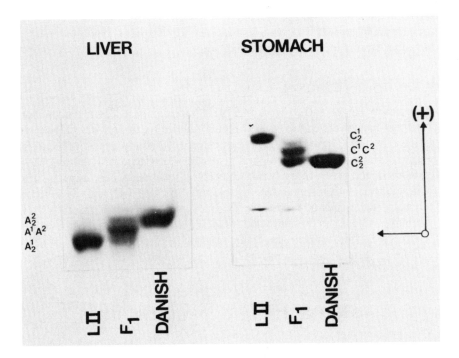

Fig. 3. Cellulose acetate zymograms of the electrophoretic variants of liver ADH-A_2 (left diagram) and stomach ADH-C_2 (right diagram) from Harwell linkage stock II (LII) mice, a Danish strain of mice and their F_1 hybrids. Proposed genotypes and phenotypes for the locus encoding the liver isozyme are $Adh\text{-}1^a1^a$, $Adh\text{-}1^bAdh\text{-}1^b$, and $Adh\text{-}1^a$ $Adh\text{-}1^b$; ADH-A_2^1, ADH-A_2^2, and (ADH-A_2^1, ADH-A^1A^2, ADH-A_2^2) for the LII, Danish and hybrid mice, respectively. Similarly, proposed genotypes and phenotypes for the locus encoding the stomach isozyme are $Adh\text{-}3^aAdh\text{-}3^a$, $Adh\text{-}3^bAdh\text{-}3^b$, and $Adh\text{-}3^aAdh\text{-}3^b$; ADH-$C_2^1$, ADH-$C_2^2$, and (ADH-$C_2^1$, DH-$C^1C^2$, ADH-$C_2^2$) for the LII, Danish and hybrid mice, respectively. Modified from Holmes et al [1981a].

TABLE II. Distribution of Allelic Variants for ADH-A_2 (Adh-1 Locus) and ADH-C_2 (Adh-3 Locus) Among Mouse Inbred Strains

Adh-1[a]	Adh-1[b]	Adh-3[a]	Adh-3[b]
64 Inbred strains	Danish strain	52 Inbred strains	8 C57BL strains Danish strain C17/Cri DDDf SF/Cam Ei

observed only in the strain derived from wild Danish mice, whereas the stomach ADH variant was observed in all C57BL strains examined and in four other strains including the Danish strain.

IV. THE *Adh-3t* TEMPORAL LOCUS

Studies by Paigen and co-workers [1975] have demonstrated that a number of genetic factors are involved in the final realization of enzyme phenotype in mouse tissues. These have been designated as structural genes, processing genes, regulator genes, and temporal genes, in accordance with the proposed functions of the genes in each case. Recent evidence has been reported for a temporal locus (designated *Adh-3t*) that regulates ADH-C_2 activity in male secondary sex tissues of the mouse [Holmes et al, 1981b].

Figure 4 illustrates the electrophoretic and activity phenotypes for ADH-C_2 extracted from stomach and epididymis tissues from C57BL/Go, BALB/c, and F_1 hybrid mice. Stomach ADH-C_2 exhibited the allelic variants and

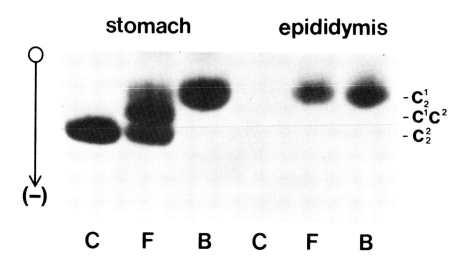

Fig. 4. Cellulose acetate zymograms illustrating the genetic variation of ADH-C_2 from C57BL/Go(c), BALB/c (B) inbred mice and their F_1 hybrids (F), extracted from stomach and epididymis tissues obtained from adult male mice. Proposed genotypes and phenotypes for the structural locus (electrophoretic variants in stomach extracts) were *Adh-3^{a}Adh-3^a*, *Adh-3^{b}Adh-3^b*, *Adh-3^{a}Adh-3^b*, and ADH-C_2^1, ADH-C_2^2, (ADH-C_2^1, ADH-C^1C^2, ADH-C_2^2) for the BALB/c, C57BL/Go, and hybrid mice, respectively. Proposed genotypes and phenotypes for the temporal locus (activity variants in epididymis extracts) were *Adh-3t^{a}Adh-3t^a*, *Adh-3t^{b}Adh-3t^b*, *Adh-3t^{a}Adh-3t^b*, and ADH-C_2^1 (high activity), null activity and ADH-C_2^1 (intermediate activity) for the BALB/c, C57BL/Go, and hybrid mice, respectively (modified from Holmes [1979]).

three-banded allellic isozyme phenotype previously discussed for this iso-zyme in section III and consistent with codominant allelic expression. How-ever, ADH-C_2^2 activity was not detectable in epididymyl extracts of C57BL/Go mice, and only ADH-C_2^1 (encoded by the Adh-3^a allele) was observed in epididymal tissue extracts of F_1 mice.

Male BALB/c mice exhibited high levels of extractable ADH-C_2^2 activity from this tissue. Genetic analyses have demonstrated that the variable activity phenotype observed for ADH-C_2 in male epididymis extracts is inherited as though controlled by a single locus (Adh-3t) with two alleles: Adh-3t^a, the normal Adh-C_2 activity phenotype; and Adh-3t^b, the null ADH-C_2 activity phenotype. Moreover, genetic analysis of ADH-C_2 activity in F_1 (C57BL/Go × C3H/He) animals and among progeny of a F_1 (C57BL/Go × C3H/c) × C57BL/Go backcross indicated that Adh-3t is closely linked and cis-acting with the structural locus (Adh-3) [Holmes, 1979].

The genetically distinct, but closely linked nature of the Adh-3 and Adh-3t genes has been confirmed by the following evidence: 1) Adh-3t is differ-entially active in various tissues; eg, lung, kidney, and stomach showed no apparent change in ADH-C_2 phenotype, whereas in seminal vesicles and epididymis the temporal locus was fully active; 2) genetic analyses examining the segregation of Adh-3 and Adh-3t among backcross progeny demonstrated one recominant among 256 animals [Holmes, 1979; Holmes et al, 1981b]; 3) with the exception of two Japanese mouse strains (ddN and KF), linkage disequilibrium has been observed among 65 inbred strains of mice between Adh-3 and Adh-3t [Holmes et al, 1982a]. Thus, the structural and temporal loci for ADH-C_2 appear to be closely but separately localized on chromosome 3 of the mouse.

Specific activity profiles of stomach and epididyml ADH-C_2 during the neonatal development of C57BL/6J, SM/J, and F_1 (SM/J × C57BL/6J) male mice supported the proposal for a temporal locus, Adh-3t [Holmes et al, 1981b] (Fig. 5). In new born mice, stomach and epididymis ADH-C_2 activ-ities were low in all animals examined. By weaning (21 days), the activity had dramatically increased in stomach extracts in all animals to near adult levels. In contrast, increases in epididymis ADH-C_2 were observed later, and only in SM/J and F_1 (SM/J × C57BL/6J) males, reaching adult levels at six weeks of age. The hybrid animals exhibited intermediate activities of ADH-C_2 compared with the C57BL/6J and SM/J parental phenotypes, which supported the concept of a cis-acting temporal locus for this enzyme.

V. THE Adh-1t TEMPORAL LOCUS

Evidence has been recently found for a locus (designated Adh-1t) with temporal gene properties, controlling the activity of ADH-A_2 in mouse kidney extracts [Holmes et al, 1982a]. Figure 6 illustrates the electrophoretic patterns

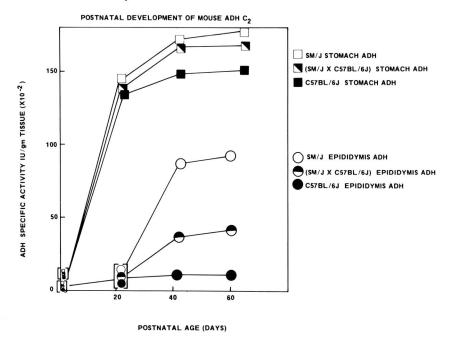

POSTNATAL DEVELOPMENT OF MOUSE ADH C$_2$

SM/J STOMACH ADH
(SM/J X C57BL/6J) STOMACH ADH
C57BL/6J STOMACH ADH

SM/J EPIDIDYMIS ADH
(SM/J X C57BL/6J) EPIDIDYMIS ADH
C57BL/6J EPIDIDYMIS ADH

Fig. 5. Postnatal development changes in ADH-C$_2$ activity in mouse stomach and epididymis extracts. □ SM/J stomach; ◨ F$_1$ (SM/J × C57BL/6J) stomach; ■ C57BL/6J stomach; ○ SM/J epididymis; ◐ F$_1$ (SM/J × C57BL/6J) epididymis; ● C57BL/6J epididymis. Each point is an average of duplicate assays from three animals (from Holmes et al [1981b]).

for ADH-A$_2$ allelic isozymes from liver, intestine, and kidney extracts from adult male and female CBA/H, Danish strain and F$_1$ hybrid mice. The enzyme exhibited a three-banded allelic isozyme pattern for hybrid mice when liver and intestine extracts were examined, consistent with the codominant gene expression and dimeric subunit structure previously discussed. In contrast, kidney ADH-A$_2$ from hybrid animals showed a skewed allelic isozyme pattern favoring the Danish allelic form. Moreover, this skewed activity phenotype was independent of the sex of the animal examined, even though adult male animals showed higher levels of ADH-A$_2$ activity in each group of animals examined. Spectrophotometric analyses of kidney ADH-A$_2$ activities from adult male and female CBA/H, Danish strain and F$_1$ hybrid mice have confirmed these observations [Holmes et al, 1982a].

Genetic analyses using F$_1$ (Danish × CBA/H) × CBA/H backcross progeny have demonstrated that the variable kidney ADH-A$_2$ activity phenotype is inherited as though controlled by a single gene (proposed designation *Adh-*

LIVER

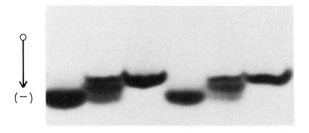

INTESTINE

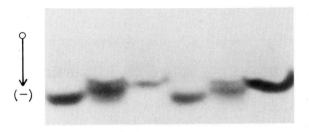

KIDNEY

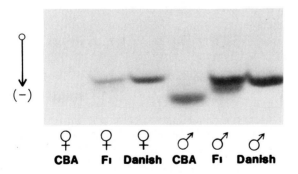

Fig. 6. Cellulose acetate zymograms of mouse liver, intestine, and kidney ADH-A$_2$ from adult male and female CBA/H, F$_1$ (Danish × CBA/H), and Danish strain mice. Note that in F$_1$ animals, liver and intestine extracts exhibited a codominant allozyme pattern, whereas in kidney, the activity is skewed toward the Danish phenotype. Also note the higher levels of kidney ADH-A$_2$ activity in male compared with female animals. Proposed genotypes and phenotypes for the proposed structural and temporal loci for ADH-A$_2$ are: CBA/H-*Adh-1*ᵃ*Adh-1*ᵃ, *Adh-1t*ᵇ*Adh-1t*ᵇ; ADH-A$_2^1$; F$_1$ (Danish × CBA/H)-*Adh-1*ᵃ*Adh-1*ᵇ; *Adh-1t*ᵇ*Adh-1t*ᵃ; ADH-A$_2^1$, ADH-A^{1}A^2, ADH-A$_2^2$; Danish strain-*Adh-1*ᵇ*Adh-1*ᵇ; *Adh-1t*ᵃ*Adh-1t*ᵃ; ADH-A$_2^2$, respectively (from Holmes et al [1982a]).

lt) with two alleles: *Adh-1t*[a], the phenotype with higher kidney ADH-A$_2$ activity (Danish strain); and *Adh-1t*[b], the phenotype exhibiting lower levels (approximately one half) of kidney ADH-A$_2$ activity. Moreover, these studies showed that the proposed temporal locus was closely linked to the structural locus upon which it is exerting its affect (no recombinants were observed between *Adh-1* and *Adh-1t* among 78 backcross animals) and that it behaves in a cis-dominant manner. Finally, it is apparent that *Adh-1t* activity is exerted independently of hormonal affects on kidney ADH-A$_2$ [Ohno et al, 1970].

VI. MOUSE ALDEHYDE REDUCTASES

A. Nomenclature

Aldehyde reductase (AHR) is a generic term used to describe the activities of a number of enzymes catalysing the reduction of various aliphatic, aromatic, and biogenic aldehydes, aldoses, and ketones in the presence of reduced nicotinamide adenine dinucleotide phosphate (NADPH). The alcohol dehydrogenases also catalyse the reduction of aldehydes, but usually prefer NADH as coenzyme and exhibit broad substrate specificites [Branden et al, 1975; Pietruszko, 1979]. There are reductases of narrower substrate specificity, however, which preferentially utilize NADPH as coenzyme, and it is this latter group that are commonly referred to as aldehyde reductases [Wermuth et al, 1977; Turner and Whittle, 1981].

The major form of AHR in most mammalian tissues is hexonate dehydrogenase [O'Brien and Schofield, 1980] or the "high-Km" AHR [Rivett et al, 1981]. This enzyme is identified by its low molecular weight (40,000), monomeric subunit structure, its sensitivity to barbiturate and valproate inhibition, and its utilization of glucuronate as a substrate. A second form of AHR is aldose reductase [O'Brien and Schofield, 1980], or the "low-Km" enzyme [Whittle and Turner, 1981]. This reductase is also of low molecular weight (32,000), monomeric subunit structure and apparently functions primarily in the polyol pathway but may also play a role in the reductive catabolism of nonadrenaline [Turner and Whittle, 1981]. Evidence has been also presented for reductases specific for succinic semialdehyde [Rumigny et al, 1980; Rivett et al, 1981] and ketosteroids or aromatic ketones [Pietruszko and Chen, 1976; Sawada and Hara, 1979, Sawada et al, 1979a,b]. Multiple forms of these aldehyde reductases (AHRs) have been reported for liver and brain tissues from a variety of mammalian sources [Ris and von Wartburg, 1973; Wermuth et al, 1977; Tulsiani and Touster, 1977; Kaufman et al, 1979; Branlant and Biellmann, 1980; Whittle and Turner, 1981]. A third form of aldehyde reductase has been recently observed in mouse liver (proposed designation AHR-A_2) [Duley and Holmes, 1982], the properties of which will be summarized.

B. Electrophoretic Analysis of Mouse AHRs

Figure 7 illustrates a zymogram of NADPH-dependent AHR activity from mouse tissue extracts using p-nitrobenzaldehyde as substrate. The designation of the three major zones of activity as hexonate dehydrogenase (designated HDH-A), AHR-A_2 (an aldehyde reductase of dimeric subunit structure [see Duley and Holmes, 1982] and ADH-C_2 is based on substrate and inhibitor specificities in the case of the first two enzymes and by the use of specific stains and previously established variants for ADH-C_2 [Holmes, 1979]. ADH-A_2 activity was not observed because 2 mM pyrazole was used in the stain to specifically inhibit this enzyme. Aldose reductase activity was also not observed under the conditions used in this experiment.

AHR-A_2 activity was observed in liver extracts with some activity also in small intestine. In contrast, hexonate dehydrogenase was more widely distributed and exhibited highest activity in kidney extracts, whereas ADH-C_2 was localized predominantly in stomach and reproductive tissue extracts.

C. Molecular Properties and Genetics of Aldehyde Reductase A_2

Aldehyde reductase A_2 has been purified from 101/H mouse liver, and its molecular properties have been investigated. The enzyme resembled the ADHs in terms of native molecular weight (80,000) and subunit composition (dimeric) but exhibited distinctive kinetic properties [Duley and Holmes, 1982]. AHR-A_2 catalysed only the reductive reaction and utilized both NADH and NADPH as coenzymes [J.N. Burnell, T.-L. Seeley, R.S. Holmes, unpublished results]. Further studies are required to establish the physiological substrate(s) for this enzyme.

From an examination of 60 inbred strains of mice, three allelic variants for AHR-A_2 were observed [Duley and Holmes, 1982]. Genetic analyses demonstrated that these variants are inherited as codominant alleles at a single locus (designated *Ahr-1*). A null activity variant (allelic designation *Ahr-1[b]*) was observed in all C57BL strains examined and in eight other strains; an electrophoretic variant (allele designated *Ahr-1[c]*) was observed in the castaneus strain of mice (Table III).

The results of examining the progeny of a F_1 (C57BL/6J × LII) × C57BL/6J backcross for segregation of the loci *Adh-3, Va* (loci previously discussed in section III) and *Ahr-1* revealed that this aldehyde reductase locus is closely linked to the alcohol dehydrogenase gene near the chromosome 3 marker in the mouse, *Va* (varitint-waddler). No recombinants were observed between *Adh-3* and *Ahr-1* among 100 backcross progeny [Duley and Holmes, 1982].

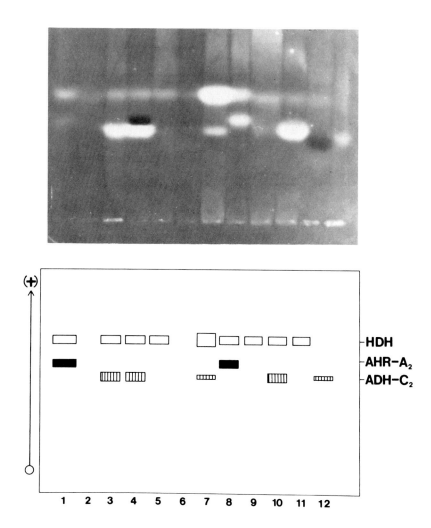

Fig. 7. Cellulose acetate zymogram and diagrammatic illustration of the tissue distribution of aldehyde reductases from adult male CBA/H inbred mice. Reductase activities are hexonate dehydrogenase (HDH □), aldehyde reductase A_2 (AHR-A_2 ■); and ADH-C_2 (▥), which show up as clear zones on a dark background. The substrate overlay contained 5 mM p-nitrobenzaldehyde and 0.7 mM NADPH, buffered at pH 7.0, with 2 mM pyrazole to inhibit ADH-A_2 activity. Lighter regions of diaphorase activity are also apparent, as well as two darker zones of tissue pigment (samples 4 and 11). Tissue extracts: 1) small intestine, 2) skeletal muscle, 3) epididymis, 4) stomach, 5) testis, 6) spleen, 7) kidney, 8) liver, 9) brain, 10) lung, 11) heart, and 12) adrenals (from Duley and Holmes [1982]).

TABLE III. Distribution of Allelic Variants for *Ahr-1*[1] Among Mouse Inbred Strains

	Ahr-1[a]	*Ahr-1*[b]	*Ahr-1*[c]
Proposed genotypes			
Proposed phenotypes	AHR-A$_2^1$	Null	AHR-A$_2^3$ [2]
Inbred Strain Distribution	50 strains, eg, BALB/c C3H/He	13 strains, eg, C57BL strains	castaneus

[1]Proposed structural locus for minor liver isozyme of aldehyde reductase A$_2$ (AHR-A$_2$).
[2]Electrophoretically distinct.

VII. THE *Adh* GENE COMPLEX ON CHROMOSOME 3 OF THE MOUSE

This communication has reviewed recent genetic and biochemical analyses from our laboratory that have provided evidence for an alcohol dehydrogenase gene complex on chromosome 3 of the mouse. Table IV lists the known genetic components that constitute this complex together with their proposed functions, while Figure 8 illustrates the localization of the *Adh* gene complex with respect to other loci on chromosome 3.

These reuslts have considerable genetic significance since it has been established for a number of multilocus enzymes and proteins that recent gene duplication during evolution has resulted in the tandem positioning of the resultant loci on the genome [Ohno, 1970]. Genetic cloning and nucleotide sequencing studies for the α and β globin gene complexes on chromosomes 16 and 11, respectively, in man have confirmed the role of tandem gene duplication in the generation of multiple loci during evolution [Proudfoot and Maniatis, 1980; Efstratiadis et al, 1980].

Amino acid sequence studies on horse ADH isozymes also support the proposal that recent gene duplications of the primordial mammalian *Adh* locus have given rise to multiple loci. For example, the extent of sequence divergence between the E and S subunits is restricted to only six amino acid substitutions [see Branden et al, 1975].

It is proposed that recent gene duplication events have given rise to the two *Adh* loci and the *Ahr-1* locus on chromosome 3 in the mouse. Their close linkage, as well as the similarities in native molecular weight, subunit composition, and catalytic functions of the enzymes encoded by these loci lend support to this hypothesis.

The comparative kinetic properties of the mouse ADH-A$_2$ and C$_2$ isozymes and AHR-A$_2$, as well as the differential gene regulation of these enzymes resulting in their specific tissue distributions demonstrate, however, that considerable divergence in functional aspects of these enzymes has occurred. Mouse ADH-A$_2$ has retained the characteristic kinetic properties of mammalian liver ADHs, with submillimolar Km values for ethanol and a broad specificity for alcohol substrates, as well as being strongly inhibited by

TABLE IV. Genetic Components of the Alcohol Dehydrogenase Gene Complex on Chromosome 3 of the Mouse

Structural genes	
1. *Adh-1*	Encoding the major liver isozyme of alcohol dehydrogenase (ADH-A$_2$)
2. *Adh-3*	Encoding the major stomach isozyme of alcohol dehydrogenase (ADH-C$_2$)
3. *Ahr-1*	Encoding the minor liver isozyme of aldehyde reductase (AHR-A$_2$)
Proposed temporal genes	
1. *Adh-3t*	Cis-acting temporal locus regulating ADH-C$_2$ activity in male secondary sex tissues
2. *Adh-1t*	Cis-acting temporal locus regulating ADH-A$_2$ activity in kidney

pyrazole. Mouse ADH-C$_2$, however, has Michaelis constants for short-chain aliphatic alcohol substrates that are three orders of magnitude higher than ADH-A$_2$ and is insensitive to pyrazole as an inhibitor [Holmes et al, 1981a]. This latter compound binds with the liver ADH-NAD$^+$ binary complex to form a ternary inhibited enzyme complex [see Branden et al, 1975]. Even more striking are the divergent catalytic properties of AHR-A$_2$, encoded by a locus in the *Adh* gene complex. This enzyme does not apparently function as an alcohol dehydrogenase and behaves as an aldehyde reductase, exhibiting activity with both NADH and NADPH as coenzymes.

It seems likely then that dramatic changes have occurred in the active site regions of mouse ADH isozymes A$_2$ and C$_2$, and the apparently genetically related enzyme, AHR-A$_2$, following gene duplications and subsequent evolutionary divergence.

In addition to the three structural loci recognized in this *Adh* gene complex, two additional genetic elements have been observed that behave in a manner similar to that of temporal genes for β-glucuronidase, described by Paigen and co-workers [1975]. In each case, the proposed temporal locus behaved in a highly tissue-specific and isozyme-specific manner and controlled the activity phenotype for ADH-A$_2$ or ADH-C$_2$ in a cis-dominant fashion.

VIII. CONCLUSIONS

Two structural loci encoding distinct isozymes of mouse alcohol dehydrogenase (ADH), ADH-A$_2$ (liver isozyme) and ADH-C$_2$ (stomach isozyme), and a structural gene encoding the minor liver isozyme of aldehyde reductase (AHR-A$_2$) are closely linked on chromosome 3 near *Va*. It is proposed that these loci have arisen from recent gene duplication events during mammalian evolution. Considerable divergence in temporal gene activity (regulating differential tissue distribution) and catalytic characteristics for these enzymes has occurred. Evidence for two closely linked cis-acting temporal genes

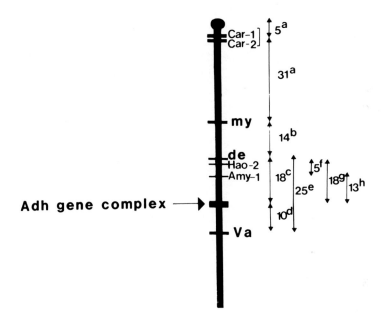

Fig. 8. Positioning of the *Adh* gene complex on chromosome 3 of the mouse. ● designates centromere; the numbers designate reported recombination frequencies between loci. Genetic loci included *Car-1/Car-2*, carbonic anhydrase; *my*-blebs; *de*-droopy ear; Hao-2-hydroxyacid oxidase; *Amy-1*, amylase; *Va*, varitint-waddler. Data obtained from a) Davisson et al, 1976; b) Davisson and Roderick, 1979; c) Holmes et al, 1981b; d) Holmes, 1979; e) Lane and Eicher, 1979; f) Holmes, 1978; g) Holmes, 1977; h) BonHomme et al, 1979. It should be noted that the data do not allow the positioning of some of these genes to be made certainty, eg, *de/Hao-2* (modified from Holmes et al [1981b]).

(designated *Adh-1t* and *Adh-3t*), regulating the activities of kidney ADH-A$_2$ and epididymis ADH-C$_2$, respectively, has also been obtained for this *Adh* gene complex.

IX. ACKNOWLEDGMENTS

This research was supported by grants from the Australian Research Grants Scheme and the Australian Associated Brewers. We are grateful to the following for supplying inbred strains of mice used in this study: Dr. J. Hilgers, Netherlands Cancer Institute, Amsterdam; Ms. H. Randelia, Cancer Research Institute, Bombay; Dr. S. Imai, Nara Medical College, Japan; Dr. M.F. Lyon, MRC Radiobiology Unit, Harwell, England; Dr. M. Holmes, Walter and Eliza Hall Institute, Melbourne; Dr. E. Eicher, Jackson Laboratory, Maine; and Dr. V. Chapman, Roswell Park Memorial Institute, Buffalo, New York.

X. REFERENCES

Bonhomme F, Benmehdi F, Britton-Davidian J, Martin S (1979): Analyse genetique de croisements interspecifiques Mus musculus L × Mus spretus lataste: Liaison de *Adh-1* avec *Amy-1* sur le chromosome 3 et de *Est-14* avec *Mod-1* sur le chromosome 9. CR Acad Sci Paris 289:545–548.

Brändén C-I, Jörnvall H, Eklund H, Furugren B (1975): Alcohol dehydrogenases. In Boyer PD (ed): "The Enzymes." New York: Academic Press, Vol 2, pp 103–190.

Branlant G, Biellmann JF (1980): Purification and some properties of aldehyde reductases from pig liver. Eur J Biochem 105:611–619.

Burnett KG, Felder MR (1978): Genetic regulation of liver alochol dehydrogenase in Peromyscus. Biochem Genet 16:443–453.

Burnett KG, Felder MR (1980): Ethanol metabolism in Peromyscus genetically deficient in alcohol dehydrogenase. Biochem Pharmacol 29:125–130.

Cederbaum AI (1980): Regulation of pathways of alcohol metabolism by the liver. Mt Sinai J Med 47:317–328.

Davisson MT, Eicher EM, Green MC (1976): Genes on chromosome 3 of the mouse. J Hered 67:155–156.

Davisson MT, Roderick TH (1979): Personal communication. Mouse News Letter 16:19.

Duley JA, Holmes RS (1982): Biochemical genetics of aldehyde reductase in the mouse. *Ahr-1:* A new locus linked to the alcohol dehydrogenase gene complex on chromosome 3. Biochem Genet (in press).

Efstratiadis A, Posakony JW, Maniatis T, Lawn RM, O'Connell C, Spritz RA, De Riel JK, Forget BG, Weissman SM, Slightom JL, Blechl AE, Smithies O, Baralle FE, Shoulders CC, Proudfoot NJ (1980): The structure and evolution of the human β-globin gene family. Cell 21:653–668.

Eicher EM, Lane PW (1980): Assignment of LGXVI to chromosome 3 in the mouse. J Hered 71:315–318.

Gibson JB, Oakeshott JG (1981): Genetics of biochemical and behavioural aspects of alcohol metabolism. Aust NZ J Med 11:128–131.

Havre P, Abrams MA, Corrall RJM, Yu LC, Szczepanik PA, Feldman HB, Klein P, Kong MS, Margolis JM, Landan BR (1977): Quantitation of pathways of ethanol metabolism. Arch Biochem Biophys 182:14–23.

Holmes RS (1977): The genetics of α-hydroxyacid oxidase and alcohol dehydrogenase in the mouse: Evidence for multiple loci and linkage between *Hao-2* and *Adh-3*. Genetics 87:709–716.

Holmes RS (1978): Genetics of hydroxyacid oxidase isozymes in the mouse: Localization of *Hao-2* on LG XVI. Heredity 41:403–406.

Holmes RS (1979): Genetics and ontogeny of alochol dehydrogenase isozymes in the mouse: Evidence for a cis-acting regulator gene *(Adt-1)* controlling C_2 isozyme expression in reproductive tissues and close linkage of *Adh-3* and *Adt-1* on chromosome 3. Biochem Genet 17:461–472.

Holmes RS, Albanese R, Whitehead FD, Duley JA (1981a): Mouse alcohol dehydrogenase isozymes: Products of closely localized duplicating genes exhibiting divergent kinetic properties. J Exp Zool 217:151–157.

Holmes RS, Andrews SJ, Beechey CV (1981b): Genetic regulation of alcohol dehydrogenase C_2 in the mouse: Developmental consequences of the temporal locus *(Adh-3t)* and positioning of *Adh-3* on chromosome 3. Dev Genet 2:89–98.

Holmes RS, Duley JA, Imai S (1982a): Alcohol dehydrogenase isozymes in the mouse: Genetic regulation, allelic variation among inbred strains and sex differences of liver and kidney A_2 isozyme activity. Anim Blood Groups Biochem Genet (in press).

Holmes RS, Duley JA, Hilgers J (1982b): Sorbitol dehydrogenase genetics in the mouse: A "null" mutant in a European C57BL strain. Anim Blood Groups Biochem Genet (in press).

Kaufman EE, Nelson T, Goochee C, Sokoloff L (1979): Purification and characterization of an NADP-linked alcohol oxido-reductase which catalyses the interconversion of hydroxybutyrate and succinic semialdehyde. J Neurochem 32:699–712.

Kessler RJ, Ferrell WJ (1974): The purification and properties of an alcohol dehydrogenase from mouse liver. Int J Biochem 5:365–374.

Khanna JM, Israel Y (1980): Ethanol metabolism. Int Rev Physiol 21:275–315.

Lane PW, Eicher EM (1979): Gene order in linkage group XVI of the house mouse. J Hered 70: 239–244.

Li T-K, Magnes LJ (1975) Identification of a distinctive form of alcohol dehydrogenase in human livers with high activity. Biochem Biophys Res Commun 63:202–208.

Li T-K, Bosron WF, Dafeldecker WP, Lange LG, Vallee BL (1977): Isolation of π-alcohol dehydrogenase of human liver: Is it a determinant of alcoholism? Proc Natl Acad Sci USA 74:4378–4381.

Lieber CS, DeCarli LM (1972): The role of the hepatic microsomal ethanol oxidizing system (MEOS) for ethanol metabolism in vivo. J Pharmacol Exp Ther 181:279–287.

Lieber CS (1977): Metabolism of ethanol. In Lieber CS (ed): "Metabolic Aspects of Alcoholism." Baltimore: University Park Press, pp 1–29.

Oakeshott JG, Gibson JB (1981): The genetics of human alcoholism: A review. Aust NZ J Med 11:123–128.

O'Brien MM, Schofield PJ (1980): Polyol pathways of human brain. Biochem J 187:21–30.

Ohno S (1970): "Evolution by Gene Duplication." New York: Springer Verlag.

Ohno S, Stenius C, Christian L, Harris C, Ivey C (1970): More about the testosterone induction of kidney alcohol dehydrogenase activity in the mouse. Biochem Genet 4:565–577.

Paigen K, Swank AT, Tomino S, Ganschow RE (1975): The molecular genetics of mammalian β-glucuronidase. J Cell Physiol 85:379–392.

Parilla RK, Ohkawa K, Landers KO, Zimmerman UP, Kobay-Ashi J, Williamson JR (1974): Functional compartmentation of acetaldehyde oxidation in rat liver. J Biol Chem 249:4926–4933.

Petersen DR, Collins AC, Deitrich RA (1977): Role of liver cytosolic aldehyde dehydrogenase isozymes in control of blood acetaldehyde concentrations. J Pharmacol Exp Ther 201:471–481.

Pietruszko R (1974): Polymorphism of horse liver alcohol dehydrogenase. Biochem Biophys Res Commun 60:687–694.

Pietruszko R (1979): Nonethanol substrates of alcohol dehydrogenase. In Majchrowicz N (ed): "Biochemistry and Pharmacology of Ethanol." New York: Plenum Press, Vol 1, pp 87–106.

Pietruszko R, Chen F-F (1976): Aldehyde reductase from rat liver is a 3-α-hydroxysteroid dehydrogenase. Biochem Pharmacol 25:2721–2725.

Proudfoot NJ, Maniatis T (1980): The structure of a human α-globin pseudogene and its relationship to α-globin gene duplication. Cell 21:537–544.

Ris MM, von Wartburg JP (1973): Heterogeneity of NADPH-dependent aldehyde reductase from human and rat brain. Eur J Biochem 37:69–77.

Rivett AJ, Smith IL, Tipton KF (1981): The enzymes catalyzing succinic semialdehyde reduction in rat brain. Biochem Pharmacol 30:741–747.

Rognstad R, Grunnet N (1979): Enzymatic pathways of ethanol metabolism. In Majchrowicz N (ed): "Biochemistry and Pharmacology of Ethanol." New York: Plenum Press, Vol 1, pp 65–85.

Rumigny JF, Maitre M, Cash C, Mandel P (1980): Specific and non-specific succinic semialdehyde reductases from rat brain: Isolation and properties. FEBS Lett 117:111–119.

Sawada H, Hara A (1979): The presence of two NADPH-linked aromatic aldehyde-ketone reductases different from aldehyde reductase in rabbit liver. Biochem Pharmacol 28:1089–1094.

Sawada H, Hara A, Hayashilsara M, Alakayama T (1979a): Guinea pig liver aromatic aldehyde-ketone reductases identical with 17β-hydroxysteroid dehydrogenase isozymes. J Biochem 86:883–892.

Sawada H, Hara A, Kato F, Nakayama T (1979b): Purification and properties of reductases for aromatic aldehydes and ketones from guinea pig liver. J Biochem 86:871–879.

Smith M, Hopkinson DA, Harris H (1971): Developmental changes and polymorphism in human alcohol dehydrogenase. Ann Hum Genet 34:257–271.

Smith M, Hopkinson DA, Harris H (1972): Alcohol dehydrogenase isozymes in adult human stomach and liver: Evidence for activity of the ADH_3 locus. Ann Hum Genet 35:243–253.

Smolen A, Atkinson N, Petersen DR (1980): The role of liver cytosolic aldehyde dehydrogenase in ethanol metabolism in DBA and C57BL mice. In Thurman RG (ed): "Alcohol and Aldehyde Metabolizing Systems IV." New York and London: Plenum Press, pp 627–634.

Thieden HID (1971): The effect of ethanol concentration on ethanol oxidation in rat liver slices. Acta Chem Scand 25:3421–3426.

Timms GP, Holmes RS (1981): Genetics and ontogeny of aldehyde dehydrogenase isozymes in the mouse: Evidence for a locus controlling the inducibility of the liver microsomal isozyme. Biochem Genet 19:1223–1236.

Tulsiani DRP, Touster O (1977): Resolutions and partial characterization of two aldehyde reductases of mammalian liver. J Biol Chem 252:2545–2550.

Turner AJ, Whittle SR (1981): Functions of aldehyde reductases. Biochem Soc Trans 9:279–281.

Wermuth B, Münch JDB, von Warburg JP (1977): Purification and properties of NADPH-dependent aldehyde reductase from human liver. J Biol Chem 252:3821–3828.

Whittle SR, Turner AJ (1981): Differential sensitivity of aldehyde reductase isozymes to sodium valproate. Biochim Biophys Acta 657:94–105.

Isozymes: Current Topics in Biological and Medical Research
Volume 8: Cellular Localization, Metabolism, and Physiology 175–193

The Role of Alcohol Dehydrogenase and Aldehyde Dehydrogenase Isozymes in Alcohol Metabolism, Alcohol Sensitivity, and Alcoholism

H. Werner Goedde, Dharam P. Agarwal, and Shoji Harada

Institute of Human Genetics, University of Hamburg, 2000 Hamburg 54, Butenfeld 32, Federal Republic of Germany

This paper is dedicated to Professor Dr. G.W. Löhr on his 60th birthday.

I. INTRODUCTION

As part of a study to characterize alcohol metabolizing enzymes in humans, we investigated autopsy and biopsy tissue specimens, cultured fibroblasts, erythrocytes, and hair roots. The present paper describes the heterogeneity of isozymes catabolizing alcohol and acetaldehyde in different organ and tissue extracts detected by starch gel electrophoresis, isoelectric focusing, substrate specificity, and inhibitor sensitivity. Possible implications of isozyme variations in alcohol intoxication and alcoholism are discussed.

II. ISOZYMES OF ALCOHOL DEHYDROGENASE
A. Isozyme Composition and Polymorphism

Human liver alcohol dehydrogenase (alcohol: NAD$^+$ oxidoreductase, ADH; EC 1.1.1.1), is one of the main enzymes involved in alcohol metabolism. ADH exhibits multiple molecular forms; the common isozymes being formed by random association of α, β, γ polypeptide subunits controlled by three separate structural gene loci, ADH_1, ADH_2, and ADH_3, respectively. [Smith et al, 1973]. The isozymes exist as homodimers ($\alpha\alpha$, $\beta\beta$, $\gamma\gamma$) or heterodimers ($\alpha\beta$, $\alpha\gamma$, $\beta\gamma$) depending upon combinations of identical or nonidentical monomers (Fig. 1). The isozymes determined by ADH_2 and ADH_3 locus are

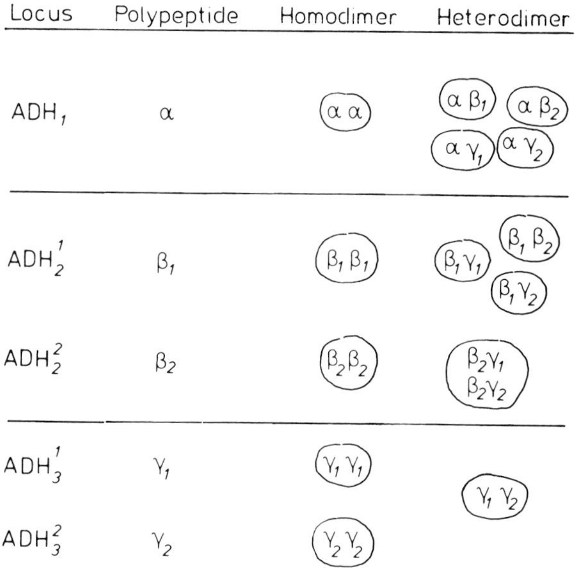

Fig. 1. Various polypeptide combinations of homodimers and heterodimers of ADH isozymes encoded by three gene loci.

polymorphic giving rise to additional homodimers ($\beta_2\beta_2$, $\gamma_2\gamma_2$) and heterodimers ($\alpha\beta_2$, $\alpha\gamma_2$, $\beta_1\beta_2$, $\beta_1\gamma_2$, $\beta_2\gamma_1$, $\beta_2\gamma_2$, $\gamma_1\gamma_2$). Different ADH isozymes are separable as distinct enzyme activity bands on starch gel electrophoresis [Harada et al, 1978a]. A typical pattern of human liver ADH isozymes is shown in Figure 2. An atypical form of ADH (variation at the ADH_2 locus), first described by von Wartburg et al [1965] with a catalytic activity several times higher than that of the normal enzyme, has been found in about 10%–20% of Caucasians and in about 85% of Orientals (Table I).

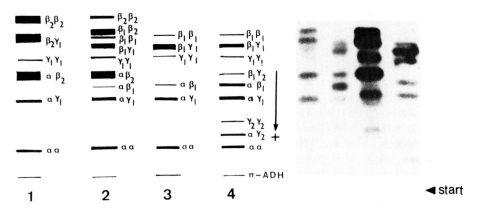

Fig. 2. Liver ADH isozyme patterns obtained by prolonged high-voltage starch gel electrophoresis. 1, $ADH_2$2, $ADH_3$1; 2, $ADH_2$2-1, $ADH_3$1; 3, $ADH_2$1, $ADH_3$1; 4, $ADH_2$1, $ADH_3$2-1 (from Harada et al [1980b] with permission).

TABLE I. Frequency of Human Liver Atypical Alcohol Dehydrogenase in Different Populations

Subject group	% Atypical	Reference
Swiss	20	von Wartburg and Schürch [1968]
English	5	Edwards and Evans [1967]
English	10	Smith et al [1971]
German	8,7	Käferstein et al [1976]
German	9	Harada et al [1978]
German	14	Schulz et al [1976]
Japanese	88	Fukui and Wakasugi [1972]
Japanese	98	Ogata and Mizohata [1973]
Japanese	85	Stamatoyannopoulos et al [1975]
Chinese	85	Teng et al [1979]
Indians	0	Teng et al [1979]
Vietnamese	86	Goedde et al [1980]

This molecular form of ADH differs from the normal enzyme in pH optimum, substrate specificity, and sensitivity toward metal binding reagents and is inhibited by thiourea [von Wartburg and Schürch, 1968]. Additional forms of ADH (π-ADH, X-ADH and ADH $_{Indianapolis}$) with more cathodic or more anodic mobilities have been reported recently [Li et al, 1977; Bosron et al, 1980; Pares and Vallee, 1981]. These isozymes differ in their pH optima, substrate specificity, and kinetic characteristics. The ADH$_{Indianapolis}$ variant seems to be confined to Black American populations [Agarwal et al, 1981a].

B. Physiologic Significance of ADH Isozymes

The atypical ADH which has relatively higher activity at physiologic pH may oxidize ethanol to acetaldehyde more rapidly and could be responsible for the initial intoxication reactions to alcohol in Japanese and other Orientals [Stamatoyannopoulos et al, 1975]. However, no significant difference in the rate of alcohol degradation was observed between normal and atypical ADH phenotype carriers [Edwards and Evans, 1967; Schulz et al, 1976]. Recently, the pyrazole insensitive π-ADH with a very high Km for ethanol has been discussed as a possible determinant of alcoholism [Li et al, 1977].

III. ISOZYMES OF ALDEHYDE DEHYDROGENASE

A. Isozyme Composition of Different Organs

NAD-dependent aldehyde dehydrogenase (ALDH, EC 1.2.1.3), the second major enzyme of alcohol metabolism, is responsible for the oxidation of acetaldehyde and other aldehydes in human liver and mammalian tissues [Weiner, 1979]. Horse liver ALDH was shown to be a tetramer with a molecular weight of about 250,000. Different forms of ALDH and their biochemical characteristics as well as different isoelectric points have been described in horse and rat liver by Weiner et al [1974]. Two isozymes of ALDH from human liver have been purified by Greenfield and Pietruszko [1977]. The so-called enzyme 1, with a molecular weight of about 245,000 has a low Km (8 μM) for NAD and a high Km (100 μM) for acetaldehyde. The enzyme 2, with a molecular weight of about 225,000 has a high Km (70 μM) for NAD and low Km value (2–3 μM) for acetaldehyde at pH 9.5. The enzymes 1 and 2 probably consist of unequal subunits with a molecular weight of 54,800 and 54,200, respectively. Further studies on ALDH isozymes using starch gel electrophoresis showed that human liver ALDH consists of at least four main isozymes with different electrophoretic mobility. [Harada et al, 1978b].

By gel slab isoelectric focusing, Goedde et al [1979a] could also demonstrate four different ALDH isozymes in kidney, liver, lung, muscle, heart, stomach, brain, and spleen (Fig. 3). The two rapidly migrating isozymes, ALDH I and ALDH II (enzyme 2 and 1), respectively, according to Greenfield and Pietruszko [1977]), were found mainly in liver and kidney. In other tissues, these isozymes showed variable staining intensities. In stomach and lung, an additional slowly migrating isozyme band (ALDH III) was observed. This isozyme was also detected as a weak band in spleen, liver, and kidney. ALDH IV isozyme was found mainly in liver and kidney, while a very weak activity band was also found in heart, intestine, and skin extracts. The ALDH isozymes were also demonstrated in skin biopsies and cultured skin fibroblasts as well as in hair roots by Goedde et al [1979a, 1980] and in erythrocytes by Goedde and Agarwal [1981] and Agarwal et al [1982a]. While fibroblasts, hair roots, and scalp skin showed mainly ALDH I and II, erythrocytes showed only the ALDH II band.

ALDH I, II, and IV from liver homogenates and ALDH III from stomach homogenates were partially purified by column isoelectric focusing [Harada et al, 1980a]. The isoelectric focusing pattern of the separated isozymes is shown in Figure 4. The Km values for the four isozymes with propionaldehyde and NAD are given in Table II.

B. Isozyme Variation

Stamatoyannopoulos et al [1975] found no variation in the ALDH isozymes in 40 livers from Japanese individuals analyzed postmortem by electrophoresis. Only two anodal bands were detected in all the specimens studied. We

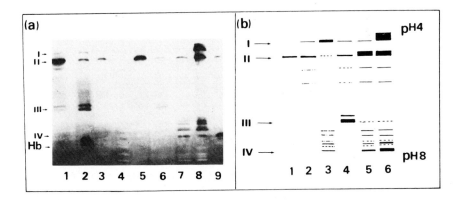

Fig. 3. Isoelectric focusing of ALDH isozymes. (a) 1, Stomach; 2, lung; 3, muscle; 4, heart; 5, intestine; 6, skin; 7, kidney; 8, liver; 9, erythrocytes. (b) Diagrammatic scheme of isozyme pattern in different tissues: 1, erythrocytes; 2, intestine, muscle, spleen, brain; 3, heart; 4, lung, stomach, skin; 5, kidney; 6, liver. Main isozyme sets are indicated by I, II, III, and IV (from Goedde et al [1979a] with permission).

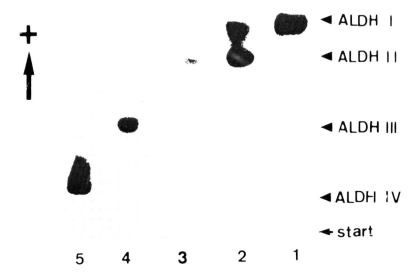

Fig. 4. Partially purified ALDH isozymes obtained by preparative isoelectric focusing. In lane 1, ALDH; in lane 2, a mixed sample of purified ALDH I and II; in lane 3, ALDH II; in lane 4, ALDH III; and in lane 5, ALDH IV (from Harada et al [1980a] with permission).

TABLE II. Km Values for Propionaldehyde and NAD at pH 9.5 (Lineweaver-Burk Plots) of Four ALDH Isozymes

Isozymes	Km values (μM)	
	Aldehyde	NAD
ALDH I	3.5	65
ALDH II	94	24
ALDH III	930	28
ALDH IV	1,400	49

also investigated livers postmortem from Japanese and German subjects using starch gel electrophoresis and isoelectric focusing. In about 90 liver specimens from German individuals, at least four isozymes were observed; in contrast, ALDH I isozyme was missing in about half of the liver specimens from 50 Japanese individuals. A comparison of ALDH isozyme pattern of German and Japanese livers is shown in Figure 5. Three of the Japanese specimens show the "unusual" or "deficient" ALDH type (isozyme I missing). One Japanese and one German sample show the "usual type" with all the four isozyme bands present [Goedde et al, 1979b]. Similar findings have

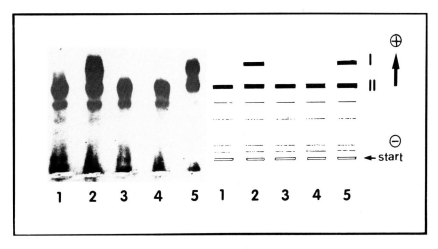

Fig. 5. Liver ALDH isozyme patterns obtained by starch gel electrophoresis of liver homogenatis from Japanese (1–4) and European (5) individuals. 1, 3, and 4 correspond to the unusual type; 2 and 5 correspond to the usual type (from Goedde et al [1979b] with permission).

been reported by Teng [1981] in livers from Chinese subjects examined postmortem.

Our studies revealed that the unusual ALDH type with a deficiency of isozyme I has a lower mean specific activity and a higher Km for acetaldehyde than the usual ALDH. The pH optima for the usual and unusual liver ALDH were found to be 9.7 and 9.0, respectively. While the activity of the usual ALDH was inhibited about 20%–30% with disulfiram, the activity of the unusual ALDH was inhibited up to 90% [Harada et al, 1980b].

C. Detection and Properties of ALDH Isozymes in Other Tissues

The detection of ALDH isozymes in human biopsies and cultured fibroblasts enabled us to study the interindividual variation of ALDH isozymes in humans [Goedde et al, 1979a]. However, the use of fibroblasts for such studies was limited by the difficulty of getting sufficient number of biopsy samples and cultured fibroblasts. Using sensitive methods, we could also detect ALDH isozymes in hair root lysates [Goedde et al, 1980; Agarwal et al, 1981b]. A comparison of usual and unusual ALDH types in liver, fibroblasts, and hair roots is shown in Figure 6. The close similarity of patterns for ALDH isozymes I and II in the three tissues is evident. Isolated isozymes from liver, hair roots, and scalp skin when mixed together gave similar mobility. Thermostability studies showed similar properties (Fig. 7). Various

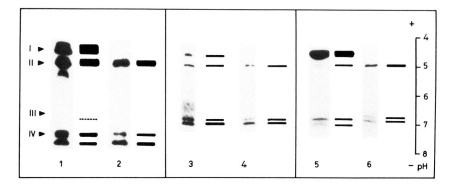

Fig. 6. Isoelectric focusing pattern of normal (1, 3, 5) and deficient (2,4,6) ALDH isozymes: liver (1,2), fibroblasts (3,4), hair roots (5, 6). I–IV denote the main isozymes (from Goedde et al [1980] with permission).

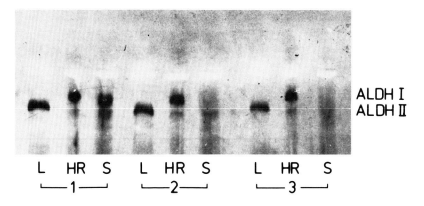

Fig. 7. Thermostability of ALDH I and II isozymes from liver (L), hair roots (HR) and scalp (S); preincubation at 50°C for 20 minutes (1), 80 minutes (2) and 120 minutes (3).

characteristics of these isozymes from different sources are compared in Table III.

D. ALDH Isozyme Deficiency in Different Populations

The frequency of the unusual ALDH in different populations was determined in hair root samples by electrofocusing techniques [Goedde et al, 1980]. As shown in Table IV, in Europeans, Egyptians, Sudanese, and Liberians, no ALDH I deficiency was observed. However, in Japanese, Vietnamese, Chinese, Indonesians, Koreans, Ecuador Indians, and Thais,

TABLE III. Kinetic Properties of Isolated ALDH-Isozymes I and II From Human Liver and Scalp

	ALDH I	ALDH II	ALDH I	ALDH II
	(Liver)		(Scalp)	
Km for acetaldehyde	3 μM	32 μM	4 μM	48 μM
Km for NAD⁺	70 μM	8 μM	200 μM	20 μM
pH-optimum	9.0	9.0	9.0	9.0
Isoelectric point (pI)	4.95	5.30	4.95	5.30
Inhibition by disulfiram (20 μM)	44%	68%	46%	47%
Thermostability 50°C, 120 Minutes	Unstable	Stable	Unstable	Stable

TABLE IV. Frequency of ALDH Isozyme I-Deficiency in Different Populations

Population	No.	ALDH I-deficiency in % of population sample
Europeans	224	0
Egyptians, Sudanese	160	0
Liberians	169	0
Chinese	196	35
Japanese	79	48
Indonesians, Koreans	35	40
Vietnamese	82	57
Thais (Northern Thailand)	110	8
Highland Indians (Equador)	33	39

the deficiency of ALDH I was observed in different frequencies [Goedde et al, 1982]. Studies in Japanese, Chinese, and Vietnamese families demonstrated that the deficiency of ALDH isozyme I is genetically transmitted [Goedde et al, 1980; Goedde and Agarwal, 1981; Agarwal et al, 1981b].

E. ALDH Isozyme Deficiency and Alcohol Sensitivity

In Oriental and American Indian populations, a marked sensitivity to ethanol accompanied by a higher steady-state concentration of acetaldehyde has been observed [Ewing et al, 1974; Mizoi et al, 1979; Zeiner et al, 1979]. The characteristic symptoms of alcohol sensitivity include dysphoria, facial flushing, elevation of skin temperature, abdominal discomfort, muscle weakness, dizziness, and increased heart rate [Wolff 1972, 1973]. Table V shows the incidence of flushing reactions in various populations.

TABLE V. Alcohol Sensitivity (Facial Flushing) in Different Populations and Ethnic Groups

Subject group	Frequency of sensitivity (%)	Reference
Caucasians		
Europeans	4	Wolff [1972]
Europeans	10	Zeiner et al [1977]
North Americans	12	Ewing et al [1974]
American Indians		
North American Indians	50	Wolff [1973]
North American Mongoloids	80	Wolff [1973]
American Indians with European ancestory	90	Wolff [1973]
Orientals		
Japanese	58	Mizoi et al [1979]
Japanese	85	Morikawa et al [1968]
Japanese, Korean Chinese, Taiwanese	83	Wolff [1972]
Chinese	57	Zeiner et al [1979]
Hapa Haole (Hawaii)	60	Wilson et al [1978]
Vietnamese	60	Goedde et al [1980]

Until recently, it was believed that the so-called atypical ADH with higher catalytic activity at physiological pH found in very high frequency in Orientals, could oxidize ethanol to acetaldehyde faster than the normal ADH and may thus produce adverse reactions to alcohol [Stamatoyannopoulos, 1975; von Wartburg, 1980].

In view of the ALDH isozyme variation in the Japanese, we postulated that the frequently observed alcohol sensitivity in these individuals could be due to the inability to metabolize acetaldehyde quickly and effectively in the absence of ALDH I, which has higher affinity for acetaldehyde [Goedde et al, 1979b]. These individuals consequently would be exposed to elevated blood acetaldehyde concentrations, leading to the release of catecholamines followed by flushing symptoms. Our subsequent studies in the Japanese confirmed that the deficiency of ALDH I isozyme and not the presence of an atypical ADH may be the determining factor in alcohol sensitivity [Goedde et al, 1980; Agarwal et al, 1981b].

A correlation between facial flushing and raised blood acetaldehyde level in conjunction with ALDH I deficiency was observed in 44 healthy Japanese individuals. Based on the presence or the absence of the ALDH isozyme I in hair root lysates [Goedde et al, 1980], these individuals were grouped either as usual or deficient type, respectively. Blood alcohol and acetaldehyde levels were estimated by gas chromatography in these individuals after alcohol loading [Harada et al, 1981]. All the subjects with the deficient type of aldehyde dehydrogenase experienced flushing and other cardiovascular symptoms after alcohol intake. Mean values for peak blood acetaldehyde were significantly higher in the deficient group (34.4 μmole/liter) than in the normal group (2.1 μmole/liter). However, mean blood ethanol levels were almost the same (10.3 and 10.93 mmole/liter) in the two groups. These data support the contention [Goedde et al, 1979b] that ALDH rather than ADH is mainly responsible for the raised blood acetaldehyde levels associated with the flushing symptoms in Orientals.

Since the frequency of flushing subjects in Japan has been found to be only about 50% (32% highly flushing and 18% slightly flushing [Mizoi et al, 1979], a higher rate of ethanol metabolism due to an atypical ADH (frequency in Japan about 85%) cannot explain the higher blood acetaldehyde level in flushing subjects only. Individuals deficient in ALDH I isozyme may be at higher risk to acetaldehyde-related organ damage and also to complications in utero resulting from maternal and alcohol abuse.

F. Relationship Between Alcohol Sensitivity and Disulfiram-Ethanol Reaction

Disulfiram is widely used as an alcohol aversive agent because it inhibits the oxidation of acetaldehyde leading to toxic reactions. The symptoms of disulfiram-ethanol reactions are very similar to the symptoms of alcohol sensitivity associated with deficiency of ALDH I isozyme. However, in vitro, disulfiram inhibits mainly the high Km isozyme [Greenfield and Pietruszko, 1977]. To explain this discrepancy, we studied the inhibitory properties of the degradation products of disulfiram [Harada et al, 1982]. Diethylamine was found to be inhibitory mainly to the isozyme I of ALDH with a low Km for acetaldehyde (Table VI). It is likely that in vivo, too, diethylamine inhibits the ALDH I isozyme leading to the accumulation of acetaldehyde. Thus, a common mechanism may underlie the disulfiram-ethanol reaction and alcohol sensitivity in Orientals deficient in the ALDH isozyme I.

IV. THE ROLE OF ADH AND ALDH ISOZYMES IN ALCOHOL-RELATED PROBLEMS

A. Isozyme Variation and Incidence of Alcoholism in Japan

When 175 Japanese alcoholics were compared with 133 nonalcoholic patients and 105 healthy Japanese controls, only about 2% of the alcoholics

TABLE VI. Inhibitory Effect of Disulfiram and Its Metabolites on ALDH Activity In Vitro (Substrate: Propionaldehyde)

Inhibitor (final concentration)	Inhibition at pH 7.0 (% of control ± SE)	
	ALDH I	ALDH II
Disulfiram (20 μM)	0 ± 5	100 ± 3
Diethyldithiocarbamate (1 mM)	0 ± 5	17 ± 7
Carbon disulfide (10 mM)	0 ± 3	0 ± 3
Diethylamine (10 mM)	91 ± 10	11 ± 4

were found to be deficient in ALDH isozyme I whereas in the other two groups, more than 40% had the deficient type of ALDH (Table VII). Our preliminary data suggest a possible protective effect of ALDH isozyme I deficiency against alcoholism in the Japanese. The individuals with ALDH I isozyme deficiency may have a physiological aversion against alcohol drinking. Indeed, the incidence of alcoholism in Japan is considerably lower than in other Western countries. However, such an association needs more support from data on acetaldehyde levels, ADH phenotypes, flushing reactions, as well as the prevalence of alcoholism in Japanese and other Oriental populations.

B. Subcellar Distribution of ALDH Isozymes in Alcoholic Liver

Owing to the heterogeneity of ALDH isozymes and their differential distribution in liver cell components, it is still unclear which of the two major isozymes is mainly affected in alcohol-related hepatic damage in humans leading to impairment of oxidative metabolism of acetaldehyde. In a preliminary study [Agarwal et al, 1982b], we isolated mitochondrial and cytosolic ALDH isozymes from cirrhotic and noncirrhotic fatty livers by preparative isoelectric focusing. The mitochondrial fraction was rich in ALDH I isozyme and the cytosolic fraction in isozyme II. Based on specific enzyme activity, ALDH I was invariably lower in alcoholic livers than in controls (Fig. 8). More studies are needed, however, to elucidate the role of ALDH isozymes in the hepatic metabolism of acetaldehyde in normal and alcoholic individuals.

C. Erythrocyte ALDH: A Possible Biochemical Marker of Alcoholism

Several recent studies indicate that human erythrocytes possess significant ALDH activity [Maring et al, 1982; Inoue et al, 1982]. The erythrocyte ALDH appears to be very similar to the disulfiram-sensitive, cytosolic isozyme of human liver. After electrophoresis or isoelectric focusing, red cell ALDH shows a single activity band with mobility and pI value identical to

TABLE VII. Distribution of ALDH Phenotypes in Japanese Subjects

| | ALDH phenotypes | | | | |
| | Deficient | | Normal | | |
Subjects	No.	(%)	No.	(%)	Total
Healthy	43	(41.0)	62	(59.0)	105
Alcoholic	4	(2.3)	171	(97.6)	175
Drug dependent	23	(48.9)	24	(51.1)	47
Schizophrenic	36	(41.9)	50	(58.1)	86

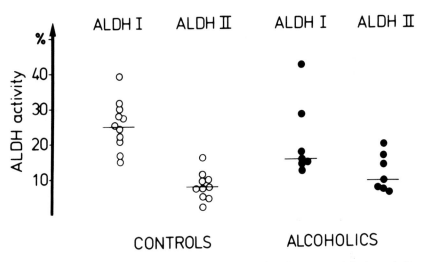

Fig. 8. Activity of isolated ALDH isozyme as percent of total enzyme activity in crude liver homogenate from controls and alcoholic individuals.

human liver ALDH II isozyme (Fig. 9). No qualitative variation in erythrocyte ALDH has been detected so far in any Caucasian or Oriental population. The isozyme band was found to be much weaker in chronic alcoholics than in healthy subjects.

Significantly decreased ALDH isozyme activities were observed in chronic alcoholics when compared with healthy controls, nonalcoholic psychiatric patients, and subjects with nonalcoholic hepatic complications [Agarwal et al, 1982a]. As shown in Figure 10, the percentage of alcoholics whose red cell ALDH activity was less than 1 mU/ml blood was much higher than the control groups. Thus, the measurement of ALDH in erythrocytes may offer yet another sensitive biochemical marker of alcoholism.

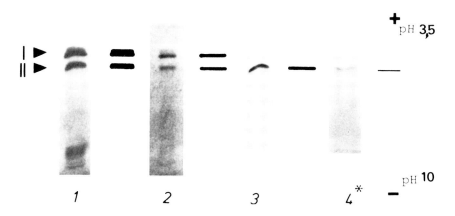

Fig. 9. Isoelectric focusing comparison of isozyme bands of ALDH in liver (1), hair roots (2), and erythrocytes from a normal (3) and an alcoholic individual (4) (from Goedde and Agarwal [1981] with permission).

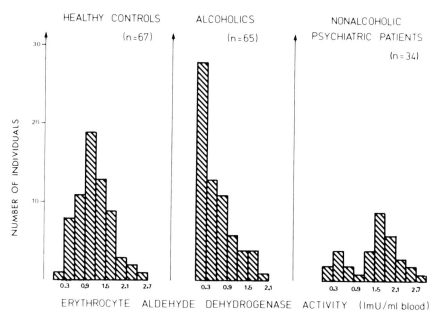

Fig. 10. Frequency distribution of erythrocyte ALDH activity in healthy controls, alcoholics, and nonalcoholic psychiatric patients.

D. ADH Activity in Serum From Alcoholic and Healthy Individuals

The highest ADH activity has been observed in liver. The appearance of this enzyme in serum may reflect liver damage after alcohol misuse, and determination of plasma ADH in patients with alcohol-related disorders may be of diagnostic and prognostic value. We studied the activity of plasma ADH in chronic alcoholics and nonalcoholic psychiatric patients compared with healthy blood donors using a sensitive spectrophotometric technique according to Skursky et al [1979]. To assess the extent of hepatic complications, glutamic-pyruvic transaminase (GPT) and serum γ-glutamyltranspeptidase (γ-GT) values were included in this comparative study. In alcoholic patients, plasma ADH activity was significantly higher compared with healthy blood donors. However, nonalcoholic psychiatric patients had the same elevated activity as alcoholics. This elevation of ADH activity in the two groups, however, was observed only when GPT and γ-GT values were also elevated. Therefore, plasma ADH enzyme level alone may not be useful as a marker of alcoholism but could be of value when measured in combination with other biochemical markers. Further investigations are needed to clarify whether the increased plasma ADH activity is the result of liver impairment in alcoholics and if so whether it could compensate the oxidative metabolism of alcohol in alcoholics with liver injury.

E. ALDH Isozymes and Metabolism of Biogenic Amines

It is not known whether biological "hypersensitivity" prevents euphoric effects of alcohol at a later stage of intoxication. It is to be expected, however, that individuals with increased acetaldehyde levels would experience numerous toxic effects attributable to acetaldehyde. An important question is whether elevated acetaldehyde levels could explain a propensity to alcoholism by the production of higher levels of catecholamine condensation products, which may then mediate an actual addiction. Aldehydes produced from biogenic amines and acetaldehyde from ethanol may react to form alkaloids, such as tetrahydropapaverolines (THP) and tetrahydroisoquinolines (TIQ) [Davis and Walsh, 1970; Cohen, 1976; Collins et al, 1973; Deitrich and Erwin, 1975; Tabakoff et al, 1973].

Davis and Walsh [1970] suggested that THP, which is formed by the reaction of dopamine and 3,4-dihydroxyphenylacetaldehyde (DOPAL), may play an important role in the chronic and addictive effects to ethanol. DOPAL is produced in various mammalian tissues via oxidative deamination of dopamine, serotonin, and norepinephrine. Since brain is the primary target site for intoxication and addiction effects of alcohol, it may be important to understand the enzymology of DOPAL degradation in human brain. In a preliminary study, we analyzed different brain regions in autopsy samples for NAD-dependent ALDH. On subcellular fractionation, ALDH activity with DOPAL as substrate was found to be localized in extracts from corpus striatum. The bulk of the activity was found in mitochondrial, microsomal, and cytosolic fractions but not in the nuclear fraction; two main isozyme bands were detected that corresponded with the activity bands obtained with propionaldehyde or acetaldehyde as substrates and also had similar isoelectric points.

V. SUMMARY AND CONCLUSIONS

Isozymes of alcohol dehydrogenase (ADH) and aldehyde dehydrogenase (ALDH) were studied in human organs and tissues using sensitive analytical techniques. Both ADH and ALDH showed an extensive polymorphism among different racial groups. In liver extracts and other tissues of Japanese an isozyme of ALDH (ALDH I) with a low Km for acetaldehyde was found to be deficient. The ALDH isozyme deficiency might account for the marked initial sensitivity to alcohol in Orientals owing to their impaired acetaldehyde oxidizing capacity. Significantly low erythrocyte ALDH activity was noted more frequently in chronic alcoholics than in healthy controls. After sub-cellular fractionation of livers from alcoholics a preferential damage of mitochondrial ALDH isozyme was observed.

The metabolism of acetaldehyde has received considerable attention in the past few years, owing to the toxic effects of this substance. Rapid progress has been made in the understanding of the multiple molecular forms of ADH and ALDH in human tissues. Our recent studies have demonstrated that the isozymes of ALDH may play an important role in the pathogenesis of alcohol-related organ damage and in the biological sensitivity to alcohol in certain ethnic groups. A possible protection of ALDH I deficiency against alcoholism in Japanese has been discussed. More recent reports [Imprain et al, 1982; Jones, 1982] indicate that, in addition to the enzymatically active ALDH II, tissues from Orientals deficient in ALDH I isozyme contain enzymatically inactive, immunologically cross-reactive material homologous with ALDH I. Thus, the absence of ALDH I isozyme is not due to a regulatory mutation, a gene deletion, or a nonsense mutation, but probably results from a structural mutation. These studies further emphasize that variation in isozymes of ADH and ALDH may be responsible for the predisposition and susceptibility to alcohol-related behavioral complications.

VI. ACKNOWLEDGMENTS

We are grateful to Mrs. Dr. Doris Meier-Tackmann, Mrs. Susann Wolken, Mr. Jürgen Dehtling, Mr. Luis Tobar-Rojas for research contributions. The skillful assistance of Mrs. Elly Losenhausen and Mrs. Ute Gössler is thankfully acknowledged. We are also indebted to Prof. Dr. Du Ruofu and Priv.

Doz. Dr. Ulrich Bienzle, Mrs. Dr. Laila Hussein, Priv. Doz. Dr. Axel Kröger, Mrs. Heide-G. Benkmann, Prof. Dr. U. Mohr, and Mr. V. Thitapura for help in collection of blood and hair root samples. The work presented here was supported by grants from Stiftung Volkswagenwerk, Hannover, and Deutsche Forschungsgemeinschaft, Bonn.

VII. REFERENCES

Agarwal DP, Meier-Tackmann D, Harada S, Goedde HW (1981a): A search for the Indianapolis-variant of human alcohol dehydrogenase in liver autopsy samples from North Germany. Hum Genet 59:170–171.

Agarwal DP, Harada S, Goedde HW (1981b): Racial differences in biological sensitivity to ethanol: The role of alcohol dehydrogenase and aldehyde dehydrogenase isozymes. Alcoholism: Clin Exp Res 5:12–16.

Agarwal DP, Tobar-Rojas L, Meier-Tackmann D, Harada S, Schrappe O, Kaschkat G, Goedde HW (1982a): Erythrocyte aldehyde dehydrogenase: A biochemical marker of alcoholism? International Titisee—Symposium on Alcohol Metabolism in Humans and its Enzymes, January 21–24. Alcoholism Clin and Exp Res 6:437, 1982.

Agarwal DP, Dethling J, Wolken S, Harada S, Goedde HW (1982b): Subcellular distribution and properties of ALDH isozymes in autopsy livers from normals and alcoholics. International Titisee—Symposium on Alcohol Metabolism in Humans and its Enzymes, January 21–24. Alcoholism Clin and Exp Res 6:432, 1982.

Bosron WF, Li TK, Vallee BL (1980): New molecular forms of human liver alcohol dehydrogenase: isolation and characterization of $ADH_{Indianapolis}$. Proc Natl Acad Sci USA 77:5784–5788.

Cohen G (1976): Alkaloid products in the metabolism of alcohol and biogenic amines. Biochem Pharmacol 25:1123–1128.

Collins A, Cashaw JL, Davis VE (1973): Dopamine-derived tetrahydroisoquinoline alkaloids: Inhibitors of neuroamine metabolism. Biochem Pharmacol 22:2337–2348.

Davis EV, Walsh MJ (1970): Alcohol, amines, and alkaloids: A possible basis for alcohol addiction. Science 167:1005–1007.

Deitrich RA, Erwin VG (1975): Involvement of biogenic amine metabolism in ethanol addiction. Fed Proc 34:1962–1968.

Ewing JA, Rouse BA, Pellizzari ED (1974): Alcohol sensitivity and ethnic background. Am J Psychol 131:206–210.

Edwards JA, Evans DAP (1967): Ethanol metabolism in subjects possessing typical and atypical liver alcohol dehydrogenase. Clin Pharmacol Ther 8:824–829.

Fukui M, Wakasugi C (1972): Liver alcohol dehydrogenase in a Japanese population. Jpn J Legal Med 26:46–51.

Goedde HW, Agarwal DP, Harada S (1979a): Alcohol metabolizing enzymes: Studies of isozymes in human biopsies and cultured fibroblasts. Clin Genet 16:29–33.

Goedde HW, Agarwal DP, Harada S (1980): Genetic studies on alcohol metabolizing enzymes: Detection of isozymes in human hair roots. Enzyme 25:281–86.

Goedde HW, Agarwal DP (1981): Alkohol metabolisierende Enzyme. Eigenschaften, genetisch bedingte Heterogenität und Bedeutung für den Alkoholstoffwechsel des Menschen. J Clin Chem Clin Biochem 19:179–189.

Goedde HW, Agarwal DP, Harada S, Meier-Tackmann D (1982): ALDH polymorphism and alcohol sensitivity: Biochemical and population genetic studies. International Titisee—Symposium on Alcohol Metabolism in Humans and Its Enzymes, January 21–24. Alcoholism Clin and Exp Res 6:434, 1982.

Goedde HW, Harada S, Agarwal DP (1979b): Racial differences in alcohol sensitivity: A new hypothesis. Hum Genet 51:331–34.

Greenfield NJ, Pietruszko R (1977): Two aldehyde dehydrogenases from human liver: Isolation via affinity chromatography and characterization of the isozymes. Biochem Biophys Acta 483:35–45.

Harada S, Agarwal DP, Goedde HW (1978a): Human liver alcohol dehydrogenase isozyme variation: Improved separation methods using prolonged high voltage starch gel electrophoresis and isoelectric focusing. Hum Genet 40:215–220.

Harada S, Agarwal DP, Goedde HW (1978b): Isozyme variations in acetaldehyde dehydrogenase (E. C. 1.2.1.3.) in human tissues. Hum Genet 44:181–185.

Harada S, Agarwal DP, Goedde HW (1980a): Electrophoretic and biochemical studies of human aldehyde dehydrogenase isozymes in various tissues. Life Sci 26:1771–1780.

Harada S, Agarwal DP, Goedde HW (1981): Aldehyde dehydrogenase deficiency as cause of facial flushing reaction to alcohol in Japanese. Lancet ii:982.

Harada S, Agarwal DP, Goedde HW (1982): Mechanism of alcohol sensitivity and disulfiram ethanol reaction. Substance and alcohol actions, Misuse 3:107–115.

Harada S, Misawa S, Agarwal DP, Goedde HW (1980b): Liver alcohol dehydrogenase and aldehyde dehydrogenase in the Japanese: Isozyme variation and its possible role in alcohol intoxication. Am J Hum Genet 32:8–15.

Impraim C, Wang A, Yoshida A (1982): Structural mutation in a major human aldehyde dehydrogenase gene results in loss of enzyme activity. Am J Hum Gen 34:837–841.

Inoue K, Ohbora Y, Fukunaga M, Yamasawa K (1982): Oxidation and uptake of acetaldehyde by intact human erythrocytes. International Titisee—Symposium on Alcohol Metabolism in Humans and Its Enzymes, January 21–24. Alcoholism, Clin and Exp Res 6:433, 1982.

Jones GL, Teng, YS, Shaw, DC (1982): Comparative enzymological, immunological and chemical properties of purified isozymes of aldehyde dehydrogenase from human liver and erythrocytes-implications for ethnic differences in alcohol metabolis. International Titisee-Symposium on Alcohol Metabolism in Humans and its Enzymes, January 21–24. Alcoholism Clin and Exp Res 6:435, 1982.

Käferstein H, Berghaus G, Detmar J (1976): "Normale" und "atypische" Alkoholdehydrogenase—Einflussfaktoren auf die Enzymaktivitäten der Leber. Blutalkohol 13:144–155.

Li TK, Bosron WF, Dafeldecker WP, Lange LG, Vallee BL (1977): Isolation of the alcoholdehydrogenase of human liver: Is it a determination of alcoholism? Proc Natl Acad Sci USA 74:4378–4381.

Maring JA, Weigand K, Brenner HD, von Wartburg JP (1982): Aldehyde oxidizing capacity of erythrocytes in normal and alcoholic individuals. International Titisee—Symposium on Alcohol Metabolism in Humans and Its Enzymes, January 21–24. Alcoholism, Clin and Exp Res 6:433, 1982.

Mizoi Y, Ijiri I, Tatsuno J, Kijima T, Fujiwasa S, Adachi J, Hishida S (1979): Relationship between facial flushing and blood acetaldehyde levels after alcohol intake. Pharmacol Biochem Behav 10:303–311.

Morikawa Y, Matsusaka J, Kuratsune M, Tsukamoto S, Mikisumi S (1968): Plethysmographic study of effects of alcohol. Nature 220:186–187.

Ogata S, Mizohata M (1973): Studies on atypical human liver alcohol dehydrogenase in Japanese. Jpn J Stud Alcohol 8:33–44.

Pares Y, Vallee BL (1981): New liver alcohol dehydrogenase forms with unique kinetic characteristics. Biochem Biophys Res Commun 98:122–130.

Schulz W, Kreuzberg S, Neymeyer HG, Schwarz U, Pachaly A (1976): Über die Häufigkeit der atypischen ADH in Leberbiopsiematerial und den Einfluss auf den Äthanolumsatz in vivo. Kriminalistik und forensische Wissenschaften 26:109–111.

Skursky L, Kovár J, Stachová M (1979): A sensitive photometric assay for alcohol dehydrogenase activity in blood serum. Anal Biochem 99:65–71.

Smith M, Hopkinson DA, Harris H (1971): Developmental changes and polymorphism in human alcohol dehydrogenase. Ann Hum Genet 34:251–278.

Smith M, Hopkinson DA, Harris H (1973): Studies on the properties of the human alcohol dehydrogenase isozymes determined by the different loci ADH_1, ADH_2, and ADH_3. Ann Hum Gen 37:49–67.

Stamatoyannopoulos G, Chen SH, Fukui F (1975): Liver alcohol dehydrogenase in Japanese: High population frequency of atypical form and its possible role in alcohol sensitivity. Am J Hum Genet 27:789–96.

Tabakoff B, Anderson R, Alivisatos GA (1973): Enzymatic reduction of biogenic aldehydes in brain. Mol Pharmacol 9:428–437.

Teng YS, Jehan S, Lie-Injo LE (1979): Human alcohol dehydrogenase ADH_2 and ADH_3 polymorphism in ethnic Chinese and Indians of West Malaysia. Hum Genet 53:87–90.

Teng YS (1981): Human liver aldehyde dehydrogenase in Chinese and Asiatic Indians: Gene deletion and its possible implication in alcohol metabolism. Biochem Genet 19:107–113.

von Wartburg JP (1980): Acetaldehyde. In Merton Sandler (ed): "Psychopharmacology of Alcohol." New York: Raven Press, pp 137–147.

von Wartburg JP, Papenberg J, Aebi H (1965): An atypical human alcohol dehydrogenase. Can J Biochem 43:889–898.

von Wartburg JP, Schürch PM (1968): Atypical human liver alcohol dehydrogenase. Ann New York Acad Sci 151:936–964.

Weiner H (1979): Aldehyde dehydrogenase: Mechanism of action and possible physiological roles. In Majrowitz CE, Noble EP (eds): "Biochemistry and Pharmacology of Ethanol." New York: Plenum Press, Vol. 1, pp 107–124.

Weiner H, King P, Hu JHJ, Bensch WR (1974): In Thurman RG, Yonetani T, Williamson JW, Chance B (eds): "Alcohol and Aldehyde Metabolizing Systems." New York: Academic Press, pp 101–113.

Wilson JR, McClearn GE, Johnson RC (1978): Ethnic variation in the use and effects of alcohol. Drug Alcohol Depend 3:147–151.

Zeiner AR, Parades A, Christensen CH (1979): The role of acetaldehyde in mediating reactivity to an acute dose of ethanol among different racial groups. Alcoholism, Clin and Exp Res 3:11–18.

Isozymes: Current Topics in Biological and Medical Research
Volume 8: Cellular Localization, Metabolism, and Physiology 195–217

Aldehyde Dehydrogenase Isozymes

Regina Pietruszko

Center of Alcohol Studies, Rutgers University, New Brunswick, New Jersey 08903

I. INTRODUCTION

Ethanol is metabolized mainly in the liver; only about 2%–10% of the ethanol consumed is eliminated via kidney and lungs [Lieber, 1977]. The liver cell contains three pathways of ethanol metabolism, each located within a different subcellular compartment: the alcohol dehydrogenase pathway in the cytosol, the microsomal ethanol metabolizing system in the endoplasmic reticulum, and the catalase in the peroxisomes. Acetaldehyde is generated by all three pathways and is oxidized to acetic acid by nicotinamide-adenine dinucleotide (NAD)-linked aldehyde dehydrogenase (E.C.1.2.1.3) which catalyzes the irreversible reaction shown in Figure 1. The substrates constitute a wide range of aldehydes including straight-chain and branched aliphatic, 2-enoic, aromatic, 2-hydroxy, and 2-halogenated aldehydes [Kraemer and Deitrich, 1968; Blair and Bodley, 1969; Bodley and Blair, 1971; Feldman and Weiner, 1972a; Eckfeldt et al, 1976] as well as aldehyde metabolites of biogenic amines [Davis et al, 1967a,b; Feldstein et al, 1967]and corticosteroids [Monder and Wang, 1973; Monder and Bradlow, 1977; Martin and Monder, 1978; Monder et al, 1982].

II. OCCURRENCE AND CLASSIFICATION

NAD-linked aldehyde dehydrogenase is widely distributed in nature [see reviews: Jakoby, 1963; Weiner, 1979; Pietruszko, 1980]. In mammals it occurs in greatest concentrations in the liver, which normally serves as the source of enzyme for purification. The enzyme exists as isozymes which are specific to different subcellular locales [Deitrich, 1966; Marjanen, 1972; Tottmar et al, 1973; Crow et al, 1974; Horton and Barrett, 1975; Koivula, 1975; Koivula and Koivusalo, 1976; Siew et al, 1976; Eckfeldt and Yonetani, 1976a; Sugimoto et al, 1976; Lebsack et al, 1981; Lindahl, 1981]. On the basis of subcellular distribution three categories of isozymes are known: cytoplasmic, mitochondrial, and microsomal. Irrespective of their subcellular localization, aldehyde dehydrogenase isozymes have been divided into two broad classes on the basis of their K_m values with short-chain aliphatic aldehydes: isozymes with micromolar K_m values for short-chain aliphatic aldehydes and isozymes with millimolar K_m values for the same compounds [Tottmar et al, 1973]. These two classes are usually referred to as "low K_m" or "high K_m" isozymes, respectively. Both classes are widely distributed and occur in all mammalian species examined (Table I). Both "low K_m" and "high K_m" isozymes can occur within the same subcellular compartment, and have been partially purified from rat liver mitochondria [Siew et al, 1976] and cytoplasm [Truesdale-Mahoney et al, 1981].

$$\text{Aldehyde} + \text{NAD} + H_2O \longrightarrow \text{Acid} + \text{NADH} + H^+$$

Fig. 1. Reaction catalyzed by aldehyde dehydrogenase.

TABLE I. Subcellular Distribution of Aldehyde Dehydrogenase in Different Species

Species	Reference	Mitochondria		Microsomes		Cytoplasm		Units used
		"High K_m"	"Low K_m"	"High K_m"	"Low K_m"	"High K_m"	"Low K_m"	
Rat	Tottmar et al [1973][a]	31.6 ± 6.6	30.3 ± 2.8	89.3 ± 11.6	1.1 ± 0.4	—	—	nmoles/min/mg protein
	Horton and Barrett [1975][b]	25.1 ± 2.7	25.5 ± 2.0	85.2 ± 9.8	1.5 ± 0.4	2.6 ± 0.5	0.4 ± 0.05	nmoles/min/mg protein
Mouse	Lebsack et al [1981][c]	683 ± 354	1,430 ± 120	651 ± 36	6.0 ± 5.0	439 ± 39	120 ± 9	nmoles/min/g liver
	Smolen et al [1981b][d]							nmoles/min/mg protein
BALB/cJ (B/c)		14.31 ± 0.83	3.19 ± 0.33	3.26 ± 0.25	—	5.84 ± 0.64	—	
DBA/2J (D2)		20.13 ± 0.68	3.51 ± 0.25	2.84 ± 0.2	—	14.19 ± 1.61	—	
C57BL/6J		21.38 ± 0.80	4.43 ± 0.21	4.62 ± 0.58	—	9.30 ± 0.66	—	
C3H/2lbg (C3)		15.5 ± 0.88	3.96 ± 0.43	2.86 ± 0.24	—	8.53 ± 1.07	—	
Baboon	Lebsack et al [1981][c]	345	1,275	84	—	169	207	nmoles/min/g liver
Man	Koivula [1975][e]	26	32	8	1	32	25	Percentage of total activity

Assays used:

[a]Tottmar et al [1973]: pyrophosphate, pH 8.8, 0.5 mM NAD, 0.1 mM pyrazole, 2 μM rotenone, 0.05 and 5.0 mM acetaldehyde.
[b]Horton and Barret [1975]: pyrophosphate, pH 8.8, 0.5 mM NAD, 1.0 mM sodium amytal, 0.025 and 5.0 mM acetaldehyde.
[c]Lebsack et al [1981]: phosphate, pH 7.4, MgCl₂ 1.15 mM, 2 μM rotenone, 0.5 mM NAD, 200 μM 4-methyl pyrazole, 0.05 and 5 mM acetaldehyde.
[d]Smolen et al [1981b]: phosphate, pH 7.4, 1 mM NAD, 1 mM pyrazole, 0.05 and 5.0 mM propionaldehyde.
[e]Koivula [1975]: pyrophosphate, pH 8.0, 1.33 mM NAD, 1.67 mM pyrazole, 0.06 and 18.0 mM acetaldehyde.

A. "High K_m" Isozymes of Aldehyde Dehydrogenase

Nakayasu et al [1978] isolated a constitutive microsomal rat liver aldehyde dehydrogenase with millimolar K_m values for acetaldehyde. Human postmortem livers also contain "high K_m" isozymes [Edson and Pietruszko, 1979; Harada et al, 1980]. The molecular properties of some of the "high K_m" isozymes from species other than man (see below) are different from the "low K_m" isozymes. The microsomal isozyme from rat liver has been reported to have a subunit mol wt of 51,000 daltons (similar to that of "low K_m" isozymes from other species) but the mol wt of the intact enzymes was found to be 360,000 daltons [Nakayasu et al, 1978].

A second group of "high K_m" aldehyde dehydrogenase isozymes are inducible by treatment with compounds such as phenobarbital or carcinogens. Inducible aldehyde dehydrogenases have been partially purified from rat and mouse liver [Deitrich et al, 1977; Smolen et al, 1981] and characterized. The molecular weight of the phenobarbital-induced cytoplasmic isozyme from rat liver was found to be 72,000 daltons and that of tetrachlorodibenzo-p-dioxin-induced isozyme, 122,000 daltons [Deitrich et al, 1977]. Aldehyde dehydrogenase from mouse liver cytoplasm, inducible threefold during pregnancy, had a molecular weight of 60,000 daltons [Smolen et al, 1981].

B. "Low K_m" Isozymes of Aldehyde Dehydrogenase

During ethanol metabolism, the steady state levels of acetaldehyde are low (ca about 100 μM in the liver; ca 10–20 μM in peripheral blood); thus, interest has been focused on the "low K_m" enzymes. Only fragmentary information is available about "high K_m" isozymes since purification procedures tend to eliminate them. Thus, properties of the isolated isozymes do not represent the total properties of aldehyde dehydrogenase present in the liver. Two "low K_m" isozymes have been isolated from the livers of sheep, horse, man and cow [Feldman and Weiner, 1972a; Eckfeldt et al, 1976; Greenfield and Pietruszko, 1977; Hart and Dickinson, 1977; Leicht et al, 1978; MacGibbon et al, 1979; Takahashi et al, 1979]. The sheep liver isozymes were purified from cytoplasm and mitochondria following subcellular fractionation [Hart and Dickinson, 1977; MacGibbon et al, 1979], while those from horse liver were identified by subcellular fractionation [Eckfeldt and Yonetani, 1976a] and by electrophoresis. Takahashi et al [1979] have identified the beef mitochondrial aldehyde dehydrogenase.

1. Molecular and catalytic properties. The mitochondrial isozyme from each species has a K_m value for acetaldehyde of ca 10^{-6} M and is relatively insensitive to disulfiram (tetraethyl thiuram disulfide—a drug used therapeutically to cause alcohol aversion). The cytoplasmic isozyme from each species has a K_m value for acetaldehyde of ca 10^{-5} M and is extremely sensitive to disulfiram, by which it is instantaneously inhibited at stoichiometric concentrations [Kitson, 1975; Eckfeldt et al, 1976; Kitson, 1978; Dickinson and Berrieman, 1979]. The two isozymes isolated from a single species differ from each other much more than the correspondingly localized isozymes from different species. Similarities rather than differences between different species are apparent from this comparison. Both isozymes are tetramers of ca 200,000 mol wt consisting of four subunits; the subunit size (ca 50,000) is somewhat larger than that of a typical dehydrogenase (ca 40,000).

All "low K_m" aldehyde dehydrogenase isozymes exhibit esterase activity with p-nitrophenyl acetate as substrate. The esterase activity is inhibited by aldehyde substrates and by chloral—a substrate analog [Feldman and Weiner, 1972b; Sidhu and Blair, 1975a; Eckfeldt and Yonetani, 1976b; MacGibbon et al, 1978; Hart and Dickinson, 1978; Takahashi et al, 1979; Takahashi and Weiner, 1981; Vallari and Pietruszko, 1982]—and stimulated by NAD and NADH. By titration with NADH two active sites per tetramer have been detected in the cytoplasmic and mitochondrial isozymes from horse liver [Takio et al, 1974; Eckfeldt and Yonetani, 1976b; Takahashi and Weiner, 1981]. The number of titratable active sites in the horse mitochondrial isozyme has, however, been reported to increase to four in the presence of Mg^{++} [Takahashi and Weiner, 1980]. Sheep cytoplasmic isozyme binds four NADH/molecule but in a two-step binding sequence [MacGibbon et al, 1977a]. All of the above experiments suggest that the active sites on aldehyde dehydrogenase molecules may not be equivalent—a situation also manifested by glyceraldehyde-3-phosphate dehydrogenase. In cases where only half of the total active sites appear to function at a given time this concept of site nonequivalence is often referred to as "half-site reactivity."

2. Catalytic mechanism. The chemical steps, reaction intermediates, and the catalytic groups utilized by aldehyde dehydrogenase in the oxidation of aldehydes remain virtually unknown but are believed to closely resemble those determined for glyceraldehyde-3-phosphate dehydrogenase [Eckfeldt and Yonetani, 1976b; Duncan and Tipton, 1971]. Weiner [1979] has proposed the general scheme shown in Figure 2. In this scheme, the carbonyl carbon of the aldehyde is attacked by the enzyme nucleophile (N), which is believed to be an active sulfhydryl, to form a thiohemiacetal. Upon removal of the hydride to NAD, a thioester results which then undergoes hydrolysis to form the acid product. It has been predicted that enzymes which follow this model will also exhibit esterase activity, since an attack by the enzyme on the ester would directly lead to the formation of the acyl intermediate. Because of the general susceptibility of aldehyde dehydrogenase to sulfhydryl reagents [Deitrich, 1967] and because aldehydes readily react with sulfhydryl groups in nonenzymic systems the sulfhydryl group is postulated to be the nucleophile (N) seen in Figure 2. The sulfhydryl group has also been demonstrated to be involved in the catalytic function of glyceraldehyde-3-phosphate dehydrogenase [Park et al, 1961; Harris and Waters, 1976].

3. Kinetic mechanism. The kinetic mechanism of the mitochondrial iso-zyme from horse liver was found to be sequential and compulsory ordered with NAD binding to the enzyme first [Feldman and Weiner, 1972b]. Based on increasing maximal velocity with the increase of polarity of the aldehyde side chain and the observation of a "burst" in stopped flow experiments upon mixing the enzyme with NAD and aldehyde, deacylation (step 8 in Fig. 1) has been postulated as the rate-limiting step in the overall reaction. For the human enzyme (now identified as human mitochondrial, see below) a random kinetic mechanism with a preferred pathway in which NAD binds first has been described by Sidhu and Blair [1975b].

The kinetic mechanism of the horse cytoplasmic F_1 isozyme has been described by Eckfeldt and Yonetani [1976b]; the isozyme follows a strictly ordered kinetic mechanism with NAD binding first, as previously found for the horse mitochondrial isozyme. However, for the cytoplasmic isozyme, coenzyme dissociation, and not deacylation, is the rate-limiting step. Cy-toplasmic isozymes from other species were found to follow a similar mech-anism [MacGibbon et al, 1977b,c; Vallari and Pietruszko, 1981].

Thus, it appears that the cytoplasmic and mitochondrial "low K_m" aldehyde dehydrogenase isozymes differ in the rate-limiting steps of the catalyzed reaction. The cytoplasmic isozymes appear to follow the reaction sequence: 1, 2, 3, 4, 5, 7, while the mitochondrial isozymes follow the sequence: 1, 2, 3, 4, 6, 8 in Figure 2.

4. Activators and inhibitors. The activity of aldehyde dehydrogenase can be modified by micromolar concentrations of divalent or trivalent metals [Venteicher et al, 1977] resulting in either activation or in inhibition, de-

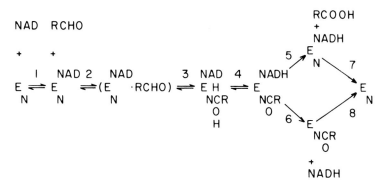

Fig. 2. Catalytic mechanism of aldehyde dehydrogenase. E, enzyme active site; N, enzyme nucleophile such as OH or SH.

pending on the concentration of the metal. The mitochondrial isozyme from horse liver is reported to be activated by Mg^{++} [Takahashi and Weiner, 1980; Takahashi et al, 1980] via a mechanism involving dissociation of the isozyme into a dimer. Aldehyde dehydrogenase from rabbit liver [Maxwell and Topper, 1961; Maxwell, 1962; Duncan, 1977] is either inhibited or activated by steroids, depending on the steroid used. The inhibitors of aldehyde dehydrogenase can be divided into three broad groups:

(1) Inhibitors used in kinetic experiments, such as acetophenone, chloral or NAD analogs, inhibit via a reversible binding to the active site [Deitrich and Hellerman, 1963; Kraemer and Deitrich, 1968; Blair and Bodley, 1969; Feldman and Weiner, 1972a; Sidhu and Blair, 1975b].

(2) Inhibitors which are employed in in vivo experiments and inhibit via a metabolite. These inhibitors do not inhibit aldehyde dehydrogenase in vitro and include cyanamide [Deitrich et al, 1976], whose inhibitory metabolite is not yet known, coprine (N-5(1-hydrocyclopropyl) glutamine, a mushroom toxin) [Hatfield and Schaumberg, 1975], whose likely metabolite, cyclopropanone, has been shown to be an inhibitor of the yeast aldehyde dehydrogenase [Wiseman and Abeles, 1979], and pargylline [Lebsack et al, 1977; DeMaster and Nagasawa, 1978; Nakanishi et al, 1980], of which propiolaldehyde has been shown to be an inhibitory metabolite [Shirota et al, 1979].

(3) Sulfhydryl reagents which inhibit aldehyde dehydrogenase include p-chloromercuribenzoate, Ellman's reagent iodoacetamide, and disulfiram. Cytoplasmic isozymes show unusual sensitivity to disulfiram [Crow et al, 1974; Kitson, 1975, 1978; Eckfeldt et al, 1976; Sugimoto et al, 1976; Greenfield and Pietruszko, 1977].

III. HUMAN ALDEHYDE DEHYDROGENASES

A. Electrophoretic Pattern and Identity

When human liver homogenates are electrophoresed on starch gel (Fig. 3) four bands of aldehyde dehydrogenase activity are visualized after staining for activity. These bands are marked I, II, III, and IV according to electrophoretic mobility. We have purified band I and band II isozymes from human liver to homogeneity [Greenfield and Pietruszko, 1977; Hempel et al, 1982a] and named them isozymes E_2 and E_1, respectively (please note that although these designations do not coincide with their relative electrophoretic mobilities they do follow the nomenclature previously established for horse liver by Eckfeldt et al [1976] based on the functional similarity of the isozymes). We have also partially purified several isozymes migrating as band III. Bands III and IV were also partially purified by Harada et al [1980]. The properties of all four bands are summarized in Table II. Thus, bands I and II represented by E_2 and E_1 isozymes are both "low K_m" aldehyde dehydrogenases and bands III and IV represent "high K_m" aldehyde dehydrogenases. The molecular weights of all the isozymes are similar: ca 200,000–250,000 daltons [Edson and Pietruszko, 1979; Harada et al, 1980].

1. Comparison of E_1 and E_2 isozymes with those from other species. Subcellular fractionation assigning E_1 and E_2 isozymes to subcellular compartments has never been done on human liver. In the autopsy liver the membranes are probably lysed, since both E_1 and E_2 are isolated from what appears to be the cytoplasmic fraction. In molecular properties, however, including K_m values for substrates, susceptibility to inhibition by disulfiram (E_1 is very sensitive to disulfiram) and the fact that NADH dissociation is the rate-limiting step of kinetic mechanism [Vallari and Pietruszko, 1981], the E_1 isozyme resembles closely the cytoplasmic isozymes from horse [Eckfeldt and Yonetani, 1976b] and sheep [MacGibbon et al, 1979] liver. The molecular and catalytic properties of the E_2 isozyme, including K_m values for substrates, relative insensitivity to inhibition by disulfiram, and the kinetic mechanism [Vallari and Pietruszko, manuscript in preparation], resembles mitochondrial aldehyde dehydrogenase from horse [Feldman and Weiner, 1972a,b] and sheep [Hart and Dickinson, 1977, 1978] liver.

2. Structural comparison of E_1 and E_2 isozymes and their assignment to different subcellular compartments. Antibodies to homogeneous E_1 and

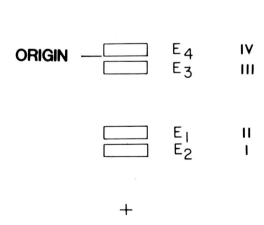

Fig. 3. Schematic representation of the electrophoretic separation of human aldehyde dehydrogenase isozymes on starch gel (conditions as in Greenfield and Pietruszko [1977]). Roman numerals denote the nomenclature of isozyme bands as used by Harada et al [1980].

TABLE II. Some Catalytic and Molecular Properties of Human Aldehyde Dehydrogenases

Nomenclature		K_m (acetaldehyde) μM (pH)		K_m (NAD) μM (pH)		Molecular weight (daltons, method used)
Harada et al [1980]	Greenfield and Pietruszko [1977]					
I	E_2	3.5 (9.5)[a] 2.4 (9.5)[b] 0.3 (9.6)[c] 5.0 (9.6)[e]	3.0 (7.0)[b] 7.5 (7.2)[e]	65 (9.5)[a] 200 (9.6)[d] 620 (9.6)[e]	70 (7.0)[b] 590 (7.2)[e]	235,000 (gradient gel)[a] 225,000 (gradient gel)[b] 200,000 (gel filtration)[c]
II	E_1	94.0 (9.5)[a] 120.0 (9.5)[b]	30 (7.0)[b] 57 (7.2)[f]	24 (9.5)[a] 8 (9.5)[b]	40 (7.0)[b] 7 (7.2)[f]	240,000 (gradient gel)[a] 245,000 (gradient gel)[b]
III	E_3	930 (9.5)[a] 7,100 (9.0)[g]	3,300 (7.0)[g]	28 (9.5)[a] 55 (9.0)[g]	84 (7.0)[g]	252,000 (gradient gel)[a] 230,000 (gradient gel)[g]
IV	E_4	1,400 (9.5)[a]		49 (9.5)[a]		257,000 (gradient gel)[a]

[a]Harada et al [1980].
[b]Greenfield and Pietruszko [1977].
[c]Bodley and Blair [1971].
[d]Blair and Bodley [1969].
[e]Kraemer and Deitrich [1968].
[f]Vallari and Pietruszko [1981].
[g]Edson and Pietruszko [1979].

E_2 isozymes were developed in the rabbit by the Grand Island Biological Company and by us. An antibody of high titer was impossible to produce but the one obtained was able to be used in immunodiffusion experiments. Anti-E_1 antibody cross-reacted with the E_2 isozyme and the anti-E_2 antibody cross-reacted with E_1 isozyme, showing that the E_1 and E_2 isozymes were structurally related. Subunit electrophoresis in SDS gels did not indicate major differences beteen E_1 and E_2 subunits; however, when subunit electrophoresis was done in 8 M urea, electrophoretic differences between E_1 and E_2 subunits were readily demonstrable [Hempel et al, 1982a], showing that the E_1 and E_2 isozymes did not share subunits. Structural similarity between these isozymes as depicted by the interaction with the antibody must, therefore, result from sequence similarity within regions of the different polypeptide chains composing E_1 and E_2 molecules. Attempts to further resolve the subunits of either isozyme by electrophoresis were not successful, suggesting that both isozymes may be homotetramers. The possibility of nonidentical subunits composing these isozymes cannot, however, be excluded. Both isozymes were separately subjected to fragmentation with CNBr (which cleaves the peptide chains at Met residues) and the molecular weights of the fragments were determined. The fragments of the following molecular weight were obtained from the E_1 isozyme: 5,600; 7,200; 7,500; 9,000; 11,200; 16,000. Fragments from the E_2 isozyme had the following molecular weights: 6,900; 7,300; 8,000; 8,900; 10,000; 12,000. Only two CNBr fragments of the two isozymes were of similar size. The 9,000 fragment of the E_1 was similar to the 8,900 fragment of the E_2 and the 7,200 fragment was similar to the 7,300 fragment of the E_2. The other fragments of the two isozymes had different molecular weights indicating that Met is distributed

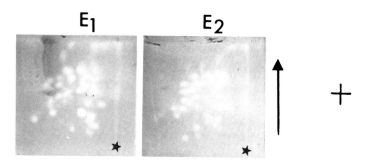

Fig. 4. Peptide maps from tryptic digests of human liver aldehyde dehydrogenases E_1 and E_2. Ascending chromatography (direction indicated by arrow) was performed first followed by electrophoresis for 45 minutes at 450 V at 12°C [Hempel et al, 1982a]. Peptides were detected with fluorescamine. Star, application points.

at different relative positions in the primary structure of the E_1 and E_2 subunits. Tryptic peptide maps of E_1 and E_2 isozymes were obtained from several different preparations of E_1 and E_2 isozymes following ^{14}C-carboxymethylation, and the mobilities of the different peptides were compared. Although approximately 38 tryptic peptides were produced from both isozymes only 13 from each isozyme migrated to the same locations with 25 migrating to distinct locations. The total sulfhydryl content of the E_1 and E_2 isozymes appears to be the same (36 sulfhydryl groups/molecule) but by autoradiography eight cysteine-containing peptides were detected in the E_1 isozyme and only six in the E_2 isozyme. Only one of the cysteine-containing peptides of the two different isozymes comigrated. Typical tryptic peptide maps of the E_1 and E_2 isozymes are shown in Figure 4. The substantial differences observed suggest that E_1 and E_2 isozymes are coded for by distinct gene loci. The CNBr fragment maps (Fig. 5) show differences between the E_1 and E_2 isozymes that are even more apparent. Similarity in the size of the subunits

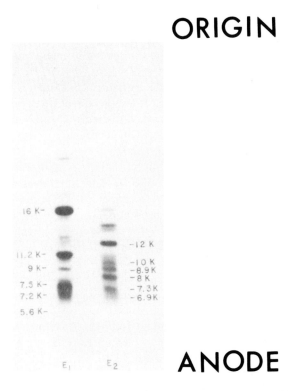

Fig. 5. Maps of fragments obtained by cyanogen bromide digestion of E_1 and E_2 isozymes. Polyacrylamide gels (16% w/v) contained sodium dodecyl sulfate [Hempel et al, 1982a]. Peptides are identified by molecular weight; the unlabeled peptides are probably partial cleavage products.

together with the fact that hybrids between E_1 and E_2 isozymes have never been observed suggest that E_1 and E_2 isozymes are separated from each other within the cell. This, together with their general resemblance to the cytoplasmic and mitochondrial isozymes from horse and sheep liver (see above), makes it possible to assign E_1 and E_2 to the cytoplasmic and the mitochondrial compartments of the human liver, respectively.

B. Mechanism of Inhibition of Aldehyde Dehydrogenase by Disulfiram

In the treatment of alcoholism, disulfiram (Antabuse) is widely used to produce alcohol aversion. Its administration prior to drinking alcoholic beverages results in unpleasant symptoms such as blurred vision, nausea, and flushing of the face and neck [Hald and Jacobson, 1948]. Involvement of aldehyde dehydrogenase in the mechanism of disulfiram therapy was strongly indicated by elevated levels of blood acetaldehyde following alcohol consumption [Reed et al, 1976; Ewing et al, 1979]. However, when aldehyde dehydrogenase was first purified from human liver [Kraemer and Deitrich, 1968; Blair and Bodley, 1969] it was found to be only slightly inhibited by disulfiram. Upon realization that aldehyde dehydrogenase occurs in isozymes with distinct subcellular distributions a second isozyme was isolated (E_1, the cytoplasmic isozyme [Greenfield and Pietruszko, 1977]) which was shown to be highly sensitive to disulfiram. Although disulfiram was known to be a general sulfhydryl reagent [Neims et al, 1966] many enzymes with essential sulfhydryl groups were not inhibited by the reagent, suggesting that aldehyde dehydrogenase inhibition must occur by a mechanism that may differ from the one described for the general reaction.

The exact mechanism of disulfiram inhibition of human aldehyde dehydrogenase was elucidated only recently [Vallari and Pietruszko, 1982]. When disulfiram was reacted with the E_1 isozyme at a 2:1 or less than a 2:1 molar ratio the activity was abolished proportionally to the amount of disulfiram added and radioactivity was recovered in the dialyzate as diethyl dithiocarbamate in an amount equal to the ^{14}C-disulfiram used initially in the incubation. Thus, the enzyme became inhibited without retaining any label from disulfiram. When the inhibited-unlabeled enzyme was treated with 2-mercaptoethanol the activity was totally regained suggesting that disulfiram caused disulfide bridge formation between vicinal sulfhydryl groups of the enzyme. Analysis for total sulfhydryl content following inactivation of E_1 isozyme with disulfiram at a 2:1 molar ratio of disulfiram to enzyme showed the total sulfhydryl content to decrease from 34 to 30 per 216,000 mol wt. The mechanism of inhibition of aldehyde dehydrogenase by disulfiram is shown in Figure 6. The proposed mechanism appeared at first to be inconsistent with previous reports [Deitrich and Erwin, 1970] which demonstrated that inhibition by disulfiram in vivo is irreversible and requires de novo protein synthesis for aldehyde dehydrogenase activity to be regained. We have found, however, that glutathione (a physiological reducing agent) cannot be substituted for mercaptoethanol to reverse disulfiram inhibition. Some structural features of the isozyme (repelling by charge is one possibility) prevent reduction of the disulfide by glutathione, but not by 2-mercaptoethanol.

C. Chemical Modification of Aldehyde Dehydrogenase

Hart and Dickinson [1977], employing sheep liver mitochondrial aldehyde dehydrogenase, first noted that iodoacetamide inhibited the sheep liver mitochondrial isozyme in a manner similar to disulfiram. Iodoacetamide produces stable covalent derivatives of protein sulfhydryl groups and is readily available in ^{14}C form. The relationship between catalytic activities of the E_1 and E_2 isozymes and the mole fraction of iodo^{14}C-acetamide incorporated is shown in Figure 7. As with disulfiram only partial activity loss occurred. Two molecules of iodo^{14}C-acetamide were incorporated into the E_1 isozyme with a concomitant activity loss of approximately 90%, whereas only one molecule was incorporated into the E_2 isozyme, which underwent a concomitant activity loss of about 80%. The inactivation of both isozymes with iodoacetamide was facilitated by NAD, whereas propionaldehyde and chloral (a substrate analog) protected against inactivation [Hempel and Pietruszko, 1981]. After treatment with iodo^{14}C-acetamide the E_1 and E_2 molecules were labeled and then subjected to cyanogen bromide fragment and tryptic peptide mapping. Both cyanogen bromide and tryptic maps demonstrated that the label was specifically incorporated into a single tryptic peptide and a single cyanogen bromide fragment in either isozyme [Hempel and Pietruszko, 1981].

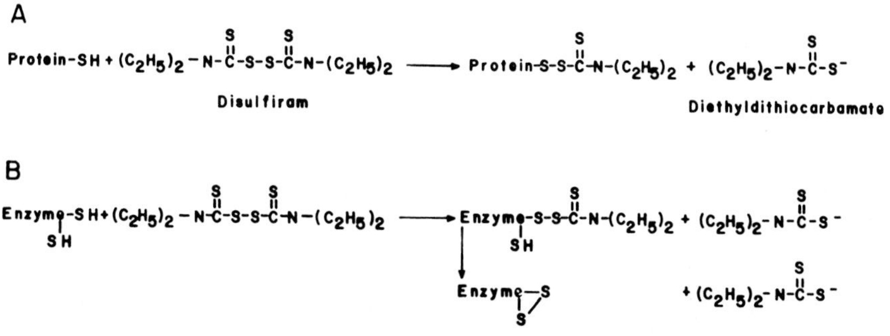

Fig. 6. A. Reaction proposed by Neims et al [1966] as the general mechanism by which protein sulfhydryl groups are covalently modified by disulfiram. B. Proposed mechanism of inhibition of aldehyde dehydrogenase by disulfiram. (Copyright 7 May 1982 by the American Association for the Advancement of Science.)

The tryptic peptide, specifically labeled by iodo[14]C-acetamide, has been isolated from the E_1 isozyme [Hempel, 1981]. Sequence analysis [Hempel et al, 1982b] reveals a peptide consisting of 35 amino acids with carboxy terminal Arg and amino terminal Ser. The peptide contains three Cys in the sequence at positions 3, 29, and 30. Cys 30 is the residue that selectively incorporates iodo[14]C-acetamide.

Although cytoplasmic aldehyde dehydrogenase is much more sensitive to disulfiram inhibition than the mitochondrial isozyme, the catalytic activity

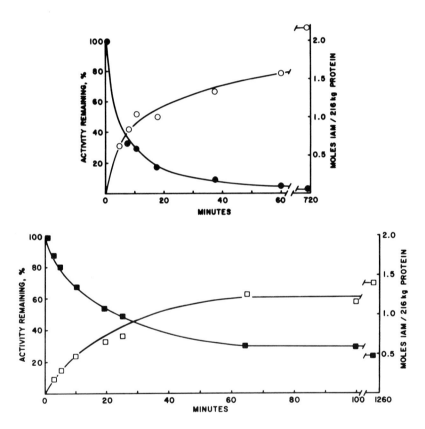

Fig. 7.   Relationship between loss of catalytic activity and incorporation of label from iodo[14]C-acetamide as a function of time. Both isozymes were incubated with 36-fold molar excess of iodo[14]C-acetamide at 25°C. E_1 (1.34 mg/ml): solid circles, activity remaining; circles, label incorporated. E_2 (1.15 mg/ml): solid squares, activity remaining; squares, label incorporated. With E_1 isozyme incorporation of label continues until two molecules of iodo[14]C-acetamide are finally incorporated; with E_2 isozyme incorporation of label does not proceed beyond 1 molecule/molecule of enzyme and 80% of catalytic activity loss.

of either isozyme is never fully abolished by disulfiram. The cytoplasmic isozyme from horse, sheep, and human liver [Eckfeldt et al, 1976; Greenfield and Pietruszko, 1977; Kitson, 1978] exhibits only a small residual activity (5%–10% of the control activity) and the mitochondrial isozymes retain about 50% of the control activity which cannot be abolished by the addition of excess disulfiram. Iodoacetamide is similar to disulfiram in the effectiveness of its inhibition of the E_1 isozyme. However, iodoacetamide is more effective than disulfiram in inhibiting the E_2 isozyme abolishing approximately 80% of its catalytic activity. We have also found that disulfiram protects the E_1 isozyme against incorporation of iodo^{14}C-acetamide [Hempel et al, 1982b], suggesting that the sulfhydryl group of E_1 isozyme with which disulfiram reacts might be the same Cys 30 (see above) with which iodoacetamide reacts. If the assumption is made that iodoacetamide and disulfiram both react with Cys 30 of the labeled tryptic peptide (see above), then Cys 29 appears to be the other likely participant in the enzyme disulfide.

1. Stoichiometry of active sites vs incorporation of iodo^{14}C-acetamide. The active site number of the E_1 and E_2 isozymes could not be determined by titration with NADH [Hempel and Pietruszko, 1981; Vallari and Pietruszko, 1981]. By employing stopped-flow spectrophotometry and measuring the amplitude of the "burst" for the first turnover, four catalytically functional sites were found in the E_1 isozyme [Vallari and Pietruszko, 1981]. The E_2 isozyme is extremely difficult to obtain with the full catalytic activity [Sidhu and Blair, 1975b; Hempel et al, 1982a] of 2.6 μmoles/min/mg. The average catalytic activity of our good preparations was 1.5 μmoles/min/mg. When we used an E_2 isozyme with an activity of 1.65 μmoles/min/mg we obtained 2.4 active sites by stopped-flow spectrophotometry. By setting up the following proportions:

$$\frac{2.4}{1.65} = \frac{X}{2.6} = 3.8$$

we obtain a number suggesting that a fully active E_2 probably also has four active sites/molecule.

Aldehyde dehydrogenase from other species appears to function via half of its sites [Eckfeldt and Yonetani, 1976b; MacGibbon et al, 1977a; Takahashi and Weiner, 1980]. In the case of the human E_1 and E_2 isozymes the stoichiometry of incorporation of iodo^{14}C-acetamide also corresponds to half of the experimentally determinable active sites. We have no evidence, however, for half-site function, since the stopped-flow procedure (which is based on catalytic function) gives four active sites per molecule of E_1 isozyme and suggests that four catalytically active sites exist per molecule of E_2 isozyme. It appears, therefore, that the current data are insufficient to involve or exclude the aldehyde dehydrogenase active sites as the site of interaction with iodo[14]C-acetamide or disulfiram.

2. Possibility of regulatory sites. Aldehyde dehydrogenase catalyzes dehydrogenation of aldehydes as well as hydrolysis of esters (see above) and its catalytic activity can be modified by divalent and trivalent metals [Venteicher et al, 1977; Takahashi and Weiner, 1980]. Aldehyde dehydrogenase isolated from rabbit liver [Maxwell and Topper, 1961; Maxwell, 1962; Duncan and Tipton, 1971] is sensitive to steroids which can either inhibit or stimulate its activity. Furthermore, the mitochondrial isozyme from sheep liver has been shown [Hart and Dickinson, 1978] to be a subject to catalytic activity regulation by "hysteresis" [Frieden, 1979], suggesting conformational alterations during the catalytic cycle. As previously mentioned, the subunit size of aldehyde dehydrogenase is approximately 10,000 daltons more than that of other dehydrogenases. This increased subunit size could exist for a specific reason, such as the accommodation of additional catalytic or regulatory sites. Thus, the fact that the catalytic activity of either E_1 or E_2 isozyme is never completely lost upon incorporation of iodoacetamide or reaction with disulfiram might signify that the superreactive sulfhydryl group is located away from the active site. The possibility that iodoacetamide is incorporated into regulatory, rather than catalytic, sites of aldehyde dehydrogenase cannot be, therefore, disregarded.

The above experiments demonstrate that a superreactive sulfhydryl exists in the aldehyde dehydrogenase molecule. Chemical modification of this sulfhydryl results in a profound alteration of the catalytic activity of the isozymes, suggesting that it is important irrespective of whether its localization is at the active site or away from the active site. Because inactivation of both isozymes by iodoacetamide and disulfiram suggests that they bind to the same site and because vicinal sulfhydryls have been demonstrated by disulfiram inhibition as well as by the primary structure of the iodo[14]C-acetamide-reacting peptide (see above) the possibility should be considered that chemical modification via disulfide formation may be a mode of regulation of aldehyde dehydrogenase activity. Introduction of disulfide bonds between vicinal sulfhydryls is one of the well-established posttranslational modifications occurring in proteins in vivo [Wold, 1981].

IV. PHYSIOLOGICAL ROLE OF ALDEHYDE DEHYDROGENASE

Aldehydes with different R groups of varying chain lengths are widely distributed in nature. The most simple of them constitute food flavor substances [Schauenstein et al, 1977]. Others are important metabolic intermediates. Some, like glyceraldehyde-3-phosphate, are metabolized by specific aldehyde dehydrogenases. However, biogenic aldehydes, arising from biogenic amines by the action of monoamine oxidase, are metabolized via aldehyde dehydrogenase [Tipton et al, 1977]. Another class of compounds which might constitute physiological substrates of aldehyde dehydrogenases are aldehyde metabolites of corticosteroids [Monder and Bradlow, 1977].

Ethanol has been shown to interfere with biogenic aldehyde metabolism [Davis et al, 1967a,b; Feldstein et al, 1967; Lahti and Majchrowicz, 1969; Tank et al, 1976], apparently through competition for the same enzyme. Experiments with perfused rat liver [Parrilla et al, 1974] indicate that acetaldehyde metabolism is mitochondrial as do experiments with isolated rat liver mitochondria [Eriksson et al, 1974; Lindros, 1974; Hasamura et al, 1975], thus involving mitochondrial aldehyde dehydrogenase in the process. However, those Orientals which lack the mitochondrial E_2 isozyme still can metabolize ethanol, although less effectively [Agarwal et al, 1981]. The lack of the E_2 isozyme does not seem to cause significant metabolic problems, other than in ethanol metabolism, suggesting that the conversion of normal physiological aldehydes is probably also catalyzed by other isozymes of aldehyde dehydrogenase. It appears, therefore, that physiological substrates and acetaldehyde may not be competing for the mitochondrial E_2 isozyme but may compete for other isozymes of aldehyde dehydrogenase including the cytoplasmic E_1 isozyme and even the "high K_m" isozymes, although the latter are thought not to be involved in acetaldehyde metabolism. However, no information about the role of the "high" K_m isozymes in biogenic and steroid aldehyde metabolism is available. Based upon our preliminary data on the human E_3 isozyme [Edson and Pietruszko, 1979] we know that K_m values for aliphatic aldehydes decrease rapidly with the increase in chain length of the aldehyde; thus, the K_m value which is 3 mM with acetaldehyde becomes 0.016 mM with hexanaldehyde. "High K_m" aldehyde dehydrogenase isozymes might, therefore, function most effectively in the metabolism of long-chain aldehydes (such as plasmalogens) or aldehydes of more complex structures.

V. CONCLUSION

Aldehyde dehydrogenase comprises a group of enzymes with quite distinct molecular weights: Some enzymes are dimers [Deitrich et al, 1976; Smolen et al, 1981a], others tetramers [Feldman and Weiner, 1972; Eckfeldt et al, 1976; Greenfield and Pietruszko, 1977; Takahashi et al, 1979] or even hexamers [Nakayasu et al, 1978]. The subunit molecular weights also range from 30,000 to 60,000 daltons and K_m values for short-chain aliphatic aldehydes differ by three orders of magnitude. At present most of the information available is about "low K_m" tetramers since these were first isolated and characterized. The data available on aldehyde dehydrogenase isozymes from horse, ox, sheep, and man demonstrate conclusively that "low K_m" isozymes with tetrameric quaternary structure exist in these species. These data, however, do not exclude the presence of other molecular weight forms. Dimers have been recently isolated from rodents [Deitrich et al, 1977; Smolen et al, 1981a]; however, it is not clear if tetrameric isozymes also occur in rodents, and conversely, whether dimers are also present in man, sheep, ox, and horse. In rodents, "high K_m" isozymes comprise a large portion of total aldehyde dehydrogenase activity (Table I); more information about these isozymes than is presently available is necessary in order to be able to better understand their role in metabolism.

More extensive research is also required to fully understand the varied physiological roles of aldehyde dehydrogenases. The existence of isozymes with different structural and functional properties as well as with different subcellular locales suggests a very refined aldehyde metabolism in higher organisms. Aldehyde dehydrogenase comprises a large portion (more than 1%) of total protein present in human liver. Whether this is a reflection of the physiological importance of aldehyde dehydrogenation or whether the enzyme performs another function (perhaps not yet identified) will probably emerge from future studies. The great reactivity of aldehydes and their resultant toxicity may be responsible for varied subcellular localization of the isozymes, but this could also result because of some critical regulation of hormonal levels. Involvement of aldehyde dehydrogenase in the metabolism of biogenic amines and corticosteroids is well established [Davis et al, 1967a,b; Monder and Bradlow, 1977].

Alcoholism is frequently associated with disorders reflected in altered steroid levels and metal ion membrane permeability [Lieber, 1977] as well as in the decreased levels of aldehyde dehydrogenase activity and the resultant increased levels of toxic acetaldehyde. Catalytic activity of aldehyde dehydrogenase isozymes can be modified by small molecules such as steroids or even by divalent and trivalent metals, suggesting that these agents may play a role in the in vivo enzyme activity regulation. Whether the action of these molecules at the level of aldehyde dehydrogenase could explain some problems associated with alcoholism has to be established by future work. It will eventually be necessary to partition the contribution of each isozyme of aldehyde dehydrogenase to fully understand their role in normal and abnormal alcohol metabolism.

VI. ACKNOWLEDGMENTS

The financial support of NIAAA grant AA00186 and research scientist development award KO2 AA00046 is acknowledged.

VII. REFERENCES

Agarwal DP, Harada S, Goedde HW (1981): Racial differences in biological sensitivity to ethanol: The role of alcohol dehydrogenase and aldehyde dehydrogenase isozymes. Alcoholism Clin Exp Res 5:12–16.

Blair AH, Bodley FH (1969): Human liver aldehyde dehydrogenase: Partial purification and properties. Can J Biochem 47:265–272.

Bodley FH, Blair AH (1971): Substrate characteristics of human liver aldehyde dehydrogenase. Can J Biochem 49:1–5.

Crow KE, Kitson TM, MacGibbon AKH, Batt RD (1974): Intracellular localisation and properties of aldehyde dehydrogenases from sheep liver. Biochim Biophys Acta 350:121–128.

Davis VE, Brown H, Huff JA, Cashaw J (1967a): The alteration in serotonin metabolism to 5-hydroxytryptophol by ethanol ingestion in man. Lab Clin Med 69:132–140.

Davis VE, Brown H, Huff JA, Cashaw J (1967b): Ethanol-induced alterations in norepinephrine metabolism in man. Lab Clin Med 69:787–799.

Deitrich RA (1966): Tissue and subcellular distribution of mammalian aldehyde-oxidizing capacity. Biochem Pharmacol 15:1911–1922.

Deitrich RA (1967): Diphosphopyridine nucleotide-linked aldehyde dehydrogenase. III. Sulfhydryl characteristics of the enzyme. Arch Biochem Biophys 119:263–263.

Deitrich RA, Bludeau P, Stock T, Roper M (1977): Induction of different rat liver supernatant aldehyde dehydrogenases by phenobarbital and tetrachlorodibenzo-dioxin. J Biol Chem 262:6169–6176.

Deitrich RA, Erwin VG (1970): Mechanism of the inhibition of aldehyde dehydrogenase in vivo by disulfiram and diethyldithiocarbamate. Mol Pharmacol 7:301–307.

Deitrich RA, Hellerman L (1963): Diphosphopyridine nucleotide-linked aldehyde dehydrogenase. II. Inhibitors. J Biol Chem 238:1683–1689.

Deitrich RA, Tronell PA, Worth WS, Erwin GV (1976): Inhibition of aldehyde dehydrogenase in brain and liver by cyanamide. Biochem Pharmacol 25:2733–2737.

DeMaster EG, Nagasawa HT (1978): Inhibition of aldehyde dehydrogenase by propiolaldehyde, a possible metabolite of pargyline. Res Commun Chem Pathol Pharmacol 21:497–505.

Dickinson FM, Berrieman S (1979): The separation of sheep liver cytoplasmic and mitochondrial aldehyde dehydrogenases by isoelectric focussing, and observations on the purity of preparations of the cytoplasmic enzyme, and their sensitivity towards inhibition by disulfiram. Biochem J 179:709–712.

Duncan RJ (1977): The action of progesterone and diethyl stilbestrol on the dehydrogenase and esterase activities of a purified aldehyde dehydrogenase from rabbit liver. Biochem J 161:123–130.

Duncan RUS, Tipton KF (1971): The kinetics of pig brain aldehyde dehydrogenase. Eur J Biochem 22:538–543.

Eckfeldt JH, Yonetani T (1976a): Subcellular localization of the F1 and F2 isozymes of horse liver aldehyde dehydrogenase. Arch Biochem Biophys 175:717–722.

Eckfeldt JH, Yonetani T (1976b): Kinetics and mechanism of the F1 isozyme of horse liver aldehyde dehydrogenase. Arch Biochem Biophys 173:273–281.

Eckfeldt J, Mope L, Takio K, Yonetani T (1976): Horse liver aldehyde dehydrogenase: purification and characterization of two isozymes. J Biol Chem 251:236–240.

Edson CR, Pietruszko R (1979): Human high Km aldehyde dehydrogenase: Purification and properties. Fed Proc 38:765(Abstract).

Eriksson CJP, Lindros KO, Forsander OA (1974): 2,4-dinitrophenol-induced increase in ethanol and acetaldehyde oxidation in the perfused rat liver. Biochem Pharmacol 23:2193.

Ewing JA, Rouse BA, Aderhold RM (1979): Studies of the mechanism of Oriental hypersensitivity to alcohol. In Galanter M (ed): "Currents in Alcoholism, Vol 5." New York: Grune & Stratton, pp 45–52.

Feldman RI, Weiner H (1972a): Horse liver aldehyde dehydrogenase. I. Purification and characterization. J Biol Chem 247:260–266.

Feldman RI, Weiner H (1972b): Horse liver aldehyde dehydrogenase. II. Kinetics and mechanistic implications of the dehydrogenase and esterase activity. J Biol Chem 247:267–272.

Feldstein A, Hoagland H, Freeman H, Williamson O (1967): The effect of ethanol ingestion on serotonin-C14 metabolism in man. Life Sci 6:53–61.

Frieden C (1979): Slow transitions and hysteretic behavior in enzymes. Annu Rev Biochem 48:471–489.

Greenfield NJ, Pietruszko R (1977): Two aldehyde dehydrogenases from human liver; isolation via affinity chromatography and characterization of the isozymes. Biochem Biophys Acta 483:35–45.

Hald J, Jacobsen E (1948): A drug sensitising the organism to ethyl alcohol. Lancet 255:1001–1004.

Harada S, Agarwal DP, Goedde WH (1980): Electrophoretic and biochemical studies of human aldehyde dehydrogenase isozymes in various tissues. Life Sci 26:1773–1780.

Harris JI, Waters M (1976): Glyceraldehyde-3-phosphate dehydrogenase. In Boyer PD (ed): "The Enzymes, Vol 13, 3rd ed." New York: Academic Press, pp 1–49.

Hart GJ, Dickinson FM (1977) Some properties of aldehyde dehydrogenase from sheep liver mitochondria. Biochem J 163:261–267.

Hart GJ, Dickinson FM (1978): Kinetic properties of aldehyde dehydrogenase from sheep liver mitochondria. Biochem J 175:899–908.

Hasmura Y, Teschke R, Lieber CS (1975): Acetaldehyde oxidation by hepatic mitochondria: Decrease after chronic ethanol consumption. Science 189:727–730.

Hatfield GM, Schaumberg JP (1975): Isolation and structural studies of coprine, the disulfiram-like constituent of Coprinus atramentarius. Lloydia 38:489–496.

Hempel JDH (1981): Chemical modification of human liver aldehyde dehydrogenases E_1 and E_2. Ph D Dissertation, Rutgers University.

Hempel JDH, Pietruszko R (1981): Selective chemical modification of human liver aldehyde dehydrogenase E1 and E2 by iodoacetamide. J Biol Chem 256:10889–10896.

Hempel JDH, Reed DM, Pietruszko R (1982a): Human aldehyde dehydrogenase: Improved purification procedure and comparison of homogeneous isoenzymes E1 and E2. Alcoholism Clin Exp Res 6:417–425.

Hempel JDH, Pietruszko R, Fietzek P, Jörnvall H (1982b): Identification of a segment containing reactive thiol in human liver cytoplasmic aldehyde dehydrogenase (isozyme E1). Biochemistry 21:6834–6838.

Horton AA, Barrett M (1975): The subcellular localization of aldehyde dehydrogenase in rat liver. Arch Biochem Biophys 167:426–436.

Jakoby WB (1963): Aldehyde dehydrogenases. In Boyer PD, Lardy H, Myrback K (eds): "The Enzymes, Vol 7, 2nd ed." New York: Academic Press, pp 203–221.

Kitson TM (1975): Th effect of disulfiram on the aldehyde dehydrogenases of sheep liver. Biochem J 151:407–412.

Kitson TM (1978): Studies on the interaction between disulfiram and sheep cytoplasmic a dehyde dehydrogenase. Biochem J 175:83–90.

Koivula T (1975): Subcellular distribution and characterization of human liver aldehyde dehydrogenase fractions. Life Sci 16:1563–1570.

Koivula T, Koivusalo M (1975): Different forms of rat liver aldehyde dehydrogenase and their subcellular distribution. Biochim Biophys Acta 397:9–23.

Kraemer RJ, and Deitrich, RA, (1968): Isolation and characterization of human liver aldehyde dehydrogenase. J Biol Chem 243:6402–6408.

Lahti RA, Majchrowicz E (1969): Acetaldehyde—an inhibitor of the enzymatic oxidation of 5-hydroxyindolacetaldehyde. Biochem Pharmacol 18:535–538.

Lebsack ME, Gordon ER, Lieber CS (1981): Effect of chronic ethanol consumption on aldehyde dehydrogenase activity in the baboon. Biochem Pharmacol 30:2273–2277.

Lebsack ME, Petersen DR, Collins AC (1977): Preferential inhibition of the low K_m aldehyde dehydrogenase activity by pargyline. Biochem Pharmacol 28:1151–1154.

Leicht W, Heinz F, Freimuller B (1978): Purification and characterization of aldehyde dehydrogenase from bovine liver. Eur J Biochem 83:189–196.

Lieber CS (1977): "Metabolic Aspects of Alcoholism." Lieber CS (ed). MTP Press, England.

Lindahl R (1981): Subcellular distribution and properties of rabbit liver aldehyde dehydrogenases. Biochem Pharmacol 30:441–446.

Lindros KO (1974): Acetaldehyde oxidation and its role in overall metabolic effects of ethanol in the liver. In Regulation of Hepatic Metabolism, Proceedings of the Alfred Benzon Symposium, Copenhagen, Munksgaard, pp 417–432 Lundquist F and Tygstrup N (Eds).

MacGibbon AKH, Blackwell LF, Buckley PD (1977b): Pre-steady-state kinetic studies on cytoplasmic sheep liver aldehyde dehydrogenase. Biochem J 167:469–477.

MacGibbon AKH, Blackwell LF, Buckley PD (1977c): Kinetics of sheep-liver cytoplasmic aldehyde dehydrogenase. Eur J Biochem 77:93–100.

MacGibbon AKH, Blackwell LF, Buckley PD (1978): Kinetic studies of the esterase activity of cytoplasmic sheep liver aldehyde dehydrogenase. Biochem J 171:533–538.

MacGibbon AKH, Motion LR, Crow KE, Buckley PD, Blackwell LF (1979): Purification and properties of sheep-liver aldehyde dehydrogenases. Eur J Biochem 96:585–595.

Marjanen L (1972): Intracellular localization of aldehyde dehydrogenase in rat liver. Biochem J 127:633–639.

Marjanen L (1973): Comparison of aldehyde dehydrogenase from cytosol and mitochondria of rat liver. Biochim Biophys Acta 327:238–246.

Martin KO, Monder C (1978): Oxidation of steroids with the 20B-hydroxy-21-oxo side chain to 20B-hydroxy-21-oic acids by horse liver aldehyde dehydrogenases. J Steroid Biochem 9:1233–1240.

Maxwell ES (1962): A study of the mechanism by which steroid hormones influence rabbit liver aldehyde dehydrogenase. J Biol Chem 237:1699–1703.

Maxwell ES, Topper YJ (1961): Steroid-sensitive aldehyde dehydrogenase from rabbit liver. J Biol Chem 236:1032–1037.

Monder C, Bradlow HL (1977): General review; carboxylic acid metabolites of steroids. J Steroid Biochem 8:897–908.

Monder C, Purkaystha R, and Pietruszko R, (1982): Oxidation of the 17-aldol (20β hydroxy-21-aldehyde) intermediate of corticosteroid metabolism to hydroxy acids by homogeneous human liver aldehyde dehydrogenases. J Steroid Biochem 17:41–49.

Monder C, Wang PT (1973): Oxidation of 21-dehydrocorticosteroids to steroidal 20-oxo-21-oic acids by an aldehyde dehydrogenase of sheep adrenal. J Biol Chem 248:8547–8554.

Nakanishi S, Yamazaki H, Nishiguchi K, Saladin R (1980): Effects of pargyline and diethyldithiocarbamate in vivo treatment on aldehyde dehydrogenase activities of submitochondrial fractions. Arch Toxicol 46:241–248.

Nakayasu H, Mihara K, Sato R (1978): Purification and properties of membrane-bound aldehyde dehydrogenase from rat liver microsomes. Biochem Biophys Res Commun 83:697–703.

Neims AH, Coffey S, Hellerman L (1966): A sensitive radioassay for sulfhydryl groups with tetraethylthiuram disulfide. J Biol Chem 241:3036–3040.

Park JH, Meriwether BP, Clodfelder P, Cunningham LW (1961): The hydrolysis of p-nitrophenyl acetate catalysed by 3-phosphoglyceraldehyde dehydrogenase. J Biol Chem 236:136–141.

Parrilla R, Ohkawa K, Lindros KO, Zimmerman U-IP, Kobayashi K, Williamson JR (1974): Functional compartmentation of acetaldehyde oxidation in rat liver. J Biol Chem 249:4926–4933.

Pietruszko R (1980): Alcohol and aldehyde dehydrogenase isozymes from mammalian liver—their structural and functional differences. In Rattazzi MC, Scandalios JG, Whitt GS (eds):

"Isozymes, Current Topics in Biological and Medical Research, Vol 4.", New York: Alan R. Liss. pp 107–130.

Reed TE, Kalant H, Gibbins RJ, Kopur BM, Ramkin JG (1976): Alcohol and aldehyde metabolism in Caucasians, Chinese and Amerinds. Can Med Assoc J 115:851–855.

Schauenstein E, Esterbauer H, Zollner H (1977): "Aldehydes in Biological Systems." London, England: Pion Limited.

Shirota FN, DeMaster EG, Nagasawa HT (1979): Propiolaldehyde, a pargylin metabolite that irreversibly inhibits aldehyde dehydrogenase. Isolation from a hepatic microsomal system. J Med Chem 22:463–464.

Sidhu RS, Blair AH (1975a): Human liver aldehyde dehydrogenase; esterase activity. J Biol Chem 250:7894–7898.

Sidhu RS, Blair AH (1975b): Human liver aldehyde dehydrogenase; kinetics of aldehyde oxidation. J Biol Chem 250:7899–4904.

Siew C, Deitrich RA, Erwin VG (1976): Localization and characteristics of rat liver mitochondrial aldehyde dehydrogenases. Arch Biochem Biophys 176:638–649.

Smolen A, Petersen DR, Collins AC (1981a): Liver cytosolic aldehyde dehydrogenase activity in the pregnant mouse. Dev Pharmacol Ther 3:31–49.

Smolen A, Wayman AL, Smolen TN, Petersen DR, Collins AC (1981b): Subcellular distribution of hepatic aldehyde dehydrogenase activity in four inbred mouse strains. Comp Biochem Physiol 69c:199–204.

Sugimoto E, Takahashi N, Kitagawa Y, Chiba H (1976): Intracellular localization and characterization of beef liver aldehyde dehydrogenase isozymes. Agr Biol Chem 40:2063–2070.

Takahashi N, Kitabatake N, Sasaki R, Chiba H (1979): Enzymatic improvement of food flavor. I. Purification and characterization of bovine liver mitochondrial aldehyde dehydrogenase. Agr Biol Chem 43:1872–1882.

Takahashi K, Weiner H, Hu JHJ (1980): Increase in the stoichiometry of the functioning active sites of horse liver aldehyde dehydrogenase in the presence of magnesium ions. Arch Biochem Biophys 205:571–578.

Takahashi K, Weiner H (1980): Magnesium stimulation of catalytic activity of horse liver aldehyde dehydrogenase. Changes in molecular weight and catalytic sites. J Biol Chem 255:8206–8209.

Takahashi K, Weiner H (1981): Nicotinamide adenine dinucleotide activation of the esterase reaction of horse liver aldehyde dehydrogenase. Biochemistry 20:2720–2726.

Takio K, Sako Y, Yonetani T (1974): Interaction of horse liver aldehyde dehydrogenase with coenzyme. In Thurman RC, Williamson JR, Yonetani T, Chance B (eds): "Alcohol and Aldehyde Metabolizing Systems." New York: Academic Press, pp 115–123.

Tank AW, Weiner H, Thurman JA (1976): Ethanol-induced alterations of dopamine metabolism in rat liver. Ann NY Acad Sci 273:219–226.

Tipton KF, Houslay MD, Turner AJ (1977): Metabolism of aldehydes in brain. Essays Neurochem Neuropharmacol 1:103–138.

Tottmar SOC, Pettersson H, Kiessling K-H (1973): The subcellular distribution and properties of aldehyde dehydrogenases in rat liver. Biochem J 135:577–586.

Truesdale-Mahoney N, Doolittle DP, Weiner H (1981): Genetic basis for the polymorphism of rat liver cytosolic aldehyde dehydrogenase. Biochem Genet 19:1275–1282.

Vallari RC, Pietruszko R (1981): Kinetic mechanism of human cytoplasmic aldehyde dehydrogenase E_1. Arch Biochem Biophys 212:9–19.

Vallari RC, Pietruszko R (1982): Human aldehyde dehydrogenase: Mechanism of inhibition by disulfiram. Science 216:637–639.

Venteicher R, Mope L, Yonetani T (1977): Metal ion effectors of horse liver aldehyde dehydrogenases. In Thurman RC, Williamson JR, Drott HR, Chance B (eds): "Alcohol and Aldehyde Metabolizing Systems." New York: Academic Press, pp 157–166.

Weiner H (1979): Aldehyde dehydrogenase: Mechanism of action and possible physiological role. In Majchrowicz E, Noble EP (eds): "Biochemistry and Pharmacology of Ethanol." New York: Plenum Press, pp 107–124.

Weiner H, Hu JHJ, Sanny CG (1976): Rate-limiting steps for the esterase and dehydrogenase reaction catalyzed by horse liver aldehyde dehydrogenase. J Biol Chem 251:3853–3855.

Wiseman JS, Abeles RH (1979): Mechanism of inhibition of aldehyde dehydrogenase by cyclopropanone hydrate and the mushroom toxin coprine. Biochemistry 18:427–435.

Wold F (1981): *In vivo* chemical modification of proteins. Ann Rev Biochem 50:783–814.

Isozymes: Current Topics in Biological and Medical Research
Volume 8: Cellular Localization, Metabolism, and Physiology 219–244

Isozymes of Human Liver Alcohol Dehydrogenase

Bert L. Vallee and Thomas J. Bazzone

Center for Biochemical and Biophysical Sciences and Medicine, Harvard Medical School, Boston, Massachusetts 02115

I. THE ISOZYMES OF HUMAN LIVER ALCOHOL DEHYDROGENASE

A. Introduction

Alcohol dehydrogenases (E.C.1.1.1.1.) are NADH-dependent enzymes that catalyze the interconversion of ethanol and other primary alcohols with the corresponding aldehydes; certain secondary alcohols and sterols are substrates also. Alcohol dehydrogenase (ADH) activity has been detected in all organisms in which it has been sought, and the enzymes isolated from a wide variety of species, including bacteria, fungi, plants, and animals, have all been shown to be zinc metalloenzymes[1] [Branden et al, 1975]. Alcohol

---

[1]The only exception thus far is the enzyme from Drosophila melanogaster, which does not contain zinc [Schwartz and Jornvall, 1976]

dehydrogenases generally are oligomers with molecular weights ranging from as low as 50,000–60,000 in plants to 150,000 in yeast, contain one or two atoms of zinc per subunit, and bind one NADH per active site. Their substrate preferences and rates of catalytic activity differ considerably.

The enzyme from a given species can usually be resolved into several isozymes whose number can differ significantly among species. Thus, the yeast enzyme for example, can be resolved into two isozymes, that of the horse into three major ones, but that of human liver into more than fifteen, as will be detailed below. Among these ADHs, that from horse liver has been studied most intensively; the primary sequence [Jörnvall, 1970] and three-dimensional structure [Brändén et al, 1973] have been determined. Aspects of the primary sequence of the human enzyme have been examined employing the unresolved mixture of the isozyme forms then available [Jörnvall and Pietrusko, 1972], but the sequences of the individual isozymes are still unknown.

Electrophoresis of human tissue homogenates on starch gel reveals multiple bands when stained for activity with ethanol as the substrate [Smith et al, 1971, 1972]. The numbers of forms and their migration relative to one another vary with the donor, the particular tissue examined, and the age of both the subject and the specimen, suggesting developmental and genetic origins and variable postmortem stabilities of different forms. The liver contains by far more ADH activity than any other organ; moreover, while other tissues appear to contain a smaller number of isozymes, the liver has a full complement characteristic of that individual and species. Accordingly, the liver has served as the major source of material in most efforts to isolate and characterize isozymes [Li, 1977].

Human liver ADH was first isolated by von Wartburg et al [1964] and fractionated into chromatographically distinct forms by Blair and Vallee [1966]. Subsequently, after three major molecular forms of horse liver ADH were found to be the dimers of dissimilar polypeptide chains, Schenker et al [1971] and Pietruszko et al [1972] concluded that similar considerations might also pertain to at least some of the molecular forms of human liver ADH then known.

For a long time, the paucity of human material as well as the laborious, low-yield isolation methods precluded both the identification and detailed studies of human ADH forms and the molecular basis for their formation and multiplicity. The development of an affinity chromatographic method for the large-scale purification of human and other ADHs [Lange and Vallee, 1976] ultimately made available sufficient quantities of individual isozymes for detailed studies. By this means, in a simple two step procedure, 200 mg of homogenous human ADH can be prepared in one day starting with crude homogenate of 600 g of liver. This preparation, which is actually an unresolved mixture of isozymes, has a subunit molecular weight of 42,000 by SDS gel electrophoresis. Sedimentation velocity experiments on the mixture are consistent with homogeneity of size indicating but minor variations in composition of the components. Like the equine enzyme, the human ADHs contain 4 g-atom of zinc/mole (2 per subunit) and are inhibited instantaneously and reversibly by 1,10-phenanthroline [von Wartburg et al, 1964; Lange et al, 1976]. Their amino acid composition differs somewhat from that of horse ADH with 50% more tyrosyl and tryptophyl residues consistent with their higher molar absorptivity. A number of differences between the horse and human enzymes are apparent (Table I).

The substrate specificity of human ADH has long been known to differ both qualitatively and quantitatively from that of the horse enzyme. In particular, human ADH is seemingly unique in its ability to catalyze the oxidation of methanol. Many other quantitative differences in substrate specificity between horse and human ADH have been noted, particularly among their steroid substrates [Pietrusko, 1979].

The affinity chromatographic method [Lange and Vallee, 1976] has made large quantities of human ADH available and this, in turn, has resulted in the recognition of the remarkable molecular heterogeneity of this enzyme and the differentiation of its multiple forms by physical, chemical, immunological, and enzymatic critiera.

B. Separation of Human Liver ADH Isozymes

The major group of isozymes that make up the bulk of human liver ADH, migrate cathodally on starch gel electrophoresis at pH 7.7 and 8.6, and its constituents share analogous though distinguishable enzymatic properties (see

TABLE I. Physical Chemical Properties of Unresolved Horse Liver and Human Liver ADH[a]

	Horse	Human
$s_{20,w}^{\circ}$	5.11 S	4.73 S
$\overline{V}$, (ml/g)	0.750	0.743
MW	84,000	85,000
f/f_o	1.23	1.33
pI	6.8	9.3
N,S (%)	14.9%N	16.6%N
	1.7%S	1.7%S
Zn	4 g-at/mole	4 g-at/mole
$E^{0.1\%}$	0.42	0.58

[a]"Unresolved" refers to the mixture of isozymes obtained by CapGapp chromatography. Therefore, it is composed mostly of Class I (see the text).

below). All of them are similarly inhibited by, and avidly bind to the potent, specific inhibitor, 4-methylpyrazole [Li and Theorell, 1969], which led to the design and synthesis of 4-[3-(N-6aminocaproyl)aminopropyl]-pyrazole (CapGapp), the derivative immobilized on Sepharose 4B [Lange and Vallee, 1976; Lange et al, 1976]. These cathodic forms are homodimers and heterodimers of three polypeptide chains designated α, β, and γ [Smith et al, 1971, 1973]. In addition both the γ—and more recently the β chains—are known to occur in subforms, ie, as γ_1 and γ_2 and as β_1 and β_2 (see below). As far as is known, the compositional and enzymatic properties of all these isozymes are quite similar.

The existence of additional classes of human ADH isozymes with markedly different properties has been recognized as a result of their failure to bind to the CapGapp affinity resin under conditions where the cathodic forms are retained. π-ADH was recognized originally by Li and Magnes [1975] based on its electrophoretic mobility, which—while still cathodic—is much more anodic than that of the (α, β, γ) group. It was also noticed that both in vivo and in vitro π-ADH is much more labile than the cathodic forms. Hence, immediate chilling of samples obtained within 12 hours postmortem is required to process and maintain the labile π-ADH activity, which emerges within one to two column volumes from the CapGapp resin. These circumstances led to the isolation of this new form, the demonstration of its unique properties, and subsequently its partial characterization [Bosron et al, 1977, 1978, 1979a].

Yet a third class of isozymes, designated χ-ADH, was identified on the basis of its truly anodic migration on starch gels, its virtually complete failure failure to be inhibited by 4-methylpyrazole and, hence, to bind to CapGapp [Parés and Vallee, 1981]. Further, it oxidizes ethanol poorly but preferentially oxidizes pentanol and other longer chain aliphatic alcohols. Hence, it is best visualized by starch gel electrophoresis using pentanol as the substrate. Thus, while χ-ADH both oxidizes and poorly stains with ethanol, it migrates anodally at pH 7.7 and 8.6.

It is apparent that the properties of π- and χ-ADH differ strikingly from one another and from those of the (α, β, γ) forms of ADH, in spite of the fact that all of them share compositional, structural, and functional characteristics typical of the mammalian ADHs as a whole. Based on these facts and yet others to be detailed, the (α, β, γ)-, π- and χ-ADHs have now been named collectively Class I, II, and III, respectively [Strydom and Vallee, 1982]. In detailing the properties of the members of these classes, the Greek letter nomenclature of individual ADH forms, based originally on other considerations [Smith et al, 1971], has been retained. In the following, the use of that terminology is intended to pertain solely to the protein chemistry and enzymological characteristics of the constituents of these three classes.

II. COMPOSITION AND ENZYMATIC CHARACTERISTICS OF HUMAN LIVER ADH ISOZYMES

A. Human Liver Class I (α, β, γ)-ADH

The electrophoretic patterns of liver homogenates on starch gel vary from individual to individual dependent upon both antemortem and postmortem history, the latter reflecting the freshness of the specimen [Li and Magnes, 1975]. In general, all human livers studied to date contain members of this predominant isozyme class in abundance; the isozymes migrate cathodally at pH 7.7 and 8.6 and stain for activity with ethanol, albeit with some variations. All constituent forms of Class I (Fig. 1) bind specifically to Cap-Gapp-Sepharose, and their mixture is isolated in two steps (Fig. 2). Subsequently, this mixture is subfractionated into its component isozymes on CM-cellulose (Fig. 3A, 4A) [Bosron et al, 1983; Burger and Vallee, 1981; Wagner et al, 1983]. The progress of subfractionation can be followed by starch gel electrophoresis (Fig. 3B, 4B). The (α, β, γ) isozymes are representative of most populations studied, the latter occuring in two forms, γ_1 and γ_2. Depending upon the liver examined, γ_1, γ_2, or both will be en-

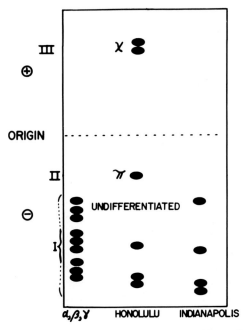

Fig. 1   Schematic representation of the relative migration positions of human ADH isozyme Classes I, II, and III on starch gel.

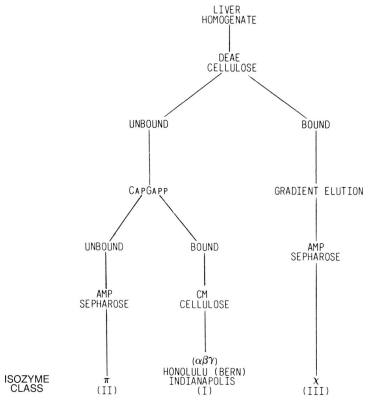

Fig.2. Isolation of the three Classes of human ADH isozymes. Classes I and II are separated from III by DEAE cellulose chromatography and purified further on AMP-Sepharose. Classes I and II are separated from each other by the CapGapp affinity resin; Class II is then purified further on AMP-Sepharose. The undifferentiated mixture of Class I isozymes is resolved on CM-cellulose.

countered. Thus, for example, in 84 of 100 liver specimens examined in a midwestern United States population, 46% contained only γ_1, 41% both γ_1 and γ_2, and 13% only γ_2 forms [Bosron et al, 1979b]. Such frequency distributions may vary with the population under examination [Smith et al, 1972; Azevedo et al, 1975; Harada et al, 1978]. The homogenates of livers from such individuals exhibit optimal ethanol oxidation at or near pH 10.5.

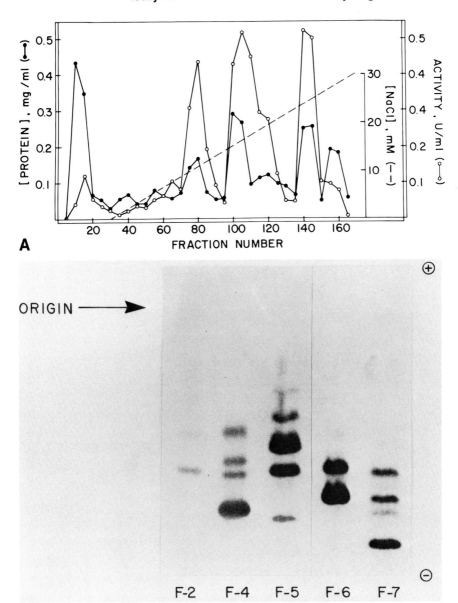

Fig. 3. A. Chromatography of Class I ADH on CM-cellulose. Elution was carried out with a gradient from 0 to 30 mM NaCl in Tris-phosphate buffer, pH 7.7 (●——●) protein, (○——○) ADH activity, (— — —) NaCl gradient. Seven groups of fractions (F) were pooled: F-1, 5–20; F-2, 50–70; F-3, 71–90; F-4, 91–110; F-5, 111–127; F-6, 135–149; F-7, 150–165. B. Starch gel electrophoresis of the pooled fractions, F, demonstrate only partial purification at this stage [Wagner et al, 1983].

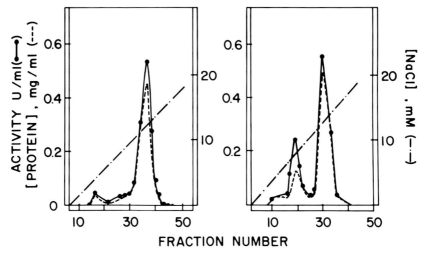

4A

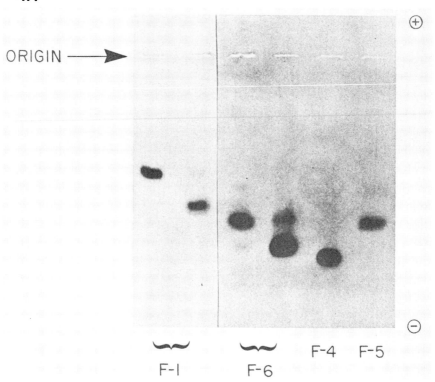

4B

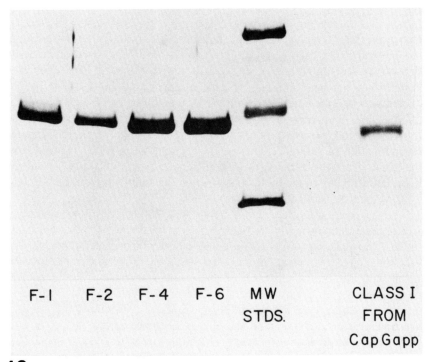

F-I   F-2   F-4   F-6   MW   CLASS I
                            STDS.   FROM
                                              CapGapp

4C

Fig. 4.   A. Rechromatography of Class I isozymes of human ADH on CM-cellulose. For rechromatography, samples were dialyzed against 5 mM sodium phosphates, pH 7.2 containing 1 mM NAD$^+$. (— — —) protein, (●———●) ADH activity, (•—•—) NaCl gradient. The sample was eluted from the resin with 75–100 ml of the same buffer followed by a linear gradient of increasing NaCl concentration (0–20 mM NaCl) in sodium phosphate, pH 7.2. Left panel: F-4 from Figure 3. Right panel: F-6 from Figure 3. B. Starch gel electrophoresis shows a single band for each peak observed. C. Electrophoresis on acrylamide in the presence of SDS shows a single band for the rechromatographed fractions at about 40,000 daltons [Wagner et al, 1983].

Bosron, Magnes, and Li[2] have performed dissociation-association experiments with the purified molecular forms of human liver ADH to determine whether or not they arise from the random recombination of the subunit chains that have been designated α, β_1, γ_1, and γ_2. Ten electrophoretically distinct molecular forms were isolated by affinity and ion-exchange chromatography from the homogenate-supernatants of livers exhibiting the "typical" pH optimum for ethanol oxidation of 10.0. Recovery of activity ranged from 40% to 80%. With four of the enzyme forms, no new enzyme activity bands were generated after treatment, indicating that they were homodimeric. In accord with the above nomenclature for the multiple human ADH enzyme forms, they were identified as $\alpha\alpha$, $\beta_1\beta_1$, $\gamma_1\gamma_1$, and $\gamma_2\gamma_2$. With the other six enzyme forms, two new enzyme activity bands appeared after dissociation-recombination. In each instance, the new activity bands were identical to two of the four homodimeric enzyme forms on starch gel electrophoresis. Hence, they are heterodimers. The electrophoretic mobility of the hetero-dimers was intermediate between those of the homodimers; they were iden-tified as $\alpha\beta_1$, $\alpha\gamma_1$, $\alpha\gamma_2$, $\beta_1\gamma_1$, $\beta_1\gamma_2$, and $\gamma_1\gamma_2$. This family of ten molecular forms, therefore, consists of isozymes formed by the apparently random recombination of subunit chains α, β_1, γ_1, and γ_2. π-ADH, isolated from the same livers by methods described previously [Li et al, 1977] did not hybridize with any of the molecular forms in this family of isozymes [Bosron WF, Magnes L, and Li T-K, unpublished[2]].

The substrate specificity, kinetic constants, and compositional and phys-icochemical data currently available for individual Class I forms are quali-tatively very similar. Thus far in Class I, three homodimers and five het-erodimers have been purified, and their specificity and kinetics examined in detail with a range of substrates spanning the specificity of the unresolved mixture known up to now (Table II) [Burger and Vallee, 1981; Wagner et al, 1983]. While there are quantitative variations both within the range of substrates for a single isozyme and among isozymes acting on a given sub-strate, there is no known instance of *qualitative* difference in specificity; compared with ethanol, however, methanol and ethylene glycol are relatively poor substrates for all human Class I isozymes examined. Among them, the $\beta_1\beta_1$ form stands out, since its k_{cat}/K_m ratios are uniformly lower than those

TABLE II. Human Class I ADH Isozymes: Substrate Specificities for Various Alcohols (0.1 M Glycine, pH 10.0, 25°)

Substrate	$k_{cat}/K_m \times 10^{-5}$, M^{-1} min^{-1}							
	$\alpha\gamma_1$	$\alpha\gamma_2$	$\alpha\beta_1$	$\gamma_2\gamma_2$	$\beta_1\gamma_2$	$\gamma_1\gamma_1$	$\beta_1\gamma_1$	$\beta_1\beta_1$
Ethanol	1.4	0.9	1.0	0.8	0.9	1.2	1.4	0.08
Methanol	0.0008	ND	0.008	0.005	0.007	0.003	0.006	0.013
Ethylene glycol	0.014	ND	0.010	0.020	0.015	0.015	0.002	0.023
Benzyl alcohol	230	300	420	84	53	180	45	0.90
Octanol	320	ND	100	ND	140	ND	58	ND
16-Hydroxy-hexadecanoic acid	120	ND	110	ND	90	78	55	8.4
Cyclohexanol	230	200	280	13	4.1	100	50	0.004

ND = Not determined.

[2]The results of Drs. T.-K. Li, L. Magnes, and W.F. Bosron here referred to were communicated to us prior to publication and are cited with their express permission.

of all the other Class I isozymes. Thus far, the comparative rates are 10-50,000-fold lower than those of the other Class I isozymes. The k_{cat}/K_m ratio for cyclohexanol is particularly low suggesting the possibility that the $\beta_1\beta_1$ isoenzyme will act slowly if at all on 3-β-steroids for which cyclohexanol is a putative model. The ratios for the heterodimers $\beta_1\gamma_2$ and $\beta_1\gamma_1$ are *not* the average of the values for the homodimers $\beta_1\beta_1$, $\gamma_1\gamma_1$, and $\gamma_2\gamma_2$; for ethanol, the ratios for the heterodimers are actually higher than for either one of the constituent homodimers, consistent with complex intersubunit cooperative effects. Nonadditive effects of the individual subunits on k_{cat} and K_m have been noted [Burger and Vallee, 1981]. In all instances, the pH optimum for alcohol oxidation is 10.0–11.0, and for all Class I forms, an ordered BiBi mechanism has been assumed on the basis of previous studies with the unresolved human enzyme [Dubied et al, 1977].

In the absence of knowledge of the primary sequence, the HPLC peptide maps of the Class I isozymes give first indications of compositional and structural resemblances [Strydom and Vallee, 1982]. The tryptic peptide maps of the individual isozymes of Class I (α, β, γ,) are closely similar, and the majority of peaks in their chromatograms are common to all forms of this group. Jointly, these peaks form the general pattern that is unique to the Class I (α, β, γ) isozymes and upon which minor differences are superimposed. The resultant maps imply that these enzymes have closely similar primary structures. These, in turn, correlate with their enzymatic properties, ie, the similarity of their kinetic constants for ethanol and marked inhibition by 4-methylpyrazole.

The HPLC map of a mixture of Class I (α, β, γ) isozymes is shown in Figure 5 for comparison with those of Classes II and III. All the isozymes of Class I are also similar immunologically. Rabbit anti-human $\beta_1\beta_1$ immune sera cross react with all of the cathodic Class I isozymes [Adinolfi et al, 1979; Alderman EM and Vallee BL, unpublished]. Moreover, rabbit and horse anti-(EE isozyme) sera cross react with the isozymes of their respective species and with all human Class I isozymes. This has been interpreted to denote structural similarity of the former and latter with that of the horse form.

B. Variant Forms Within Class I

The homogenates of livers from some individuals exhibit characteristic activity *vs* pH profiles that differ qualitatively and quantitatively from those found more commonly [von Wartburg et al, 1965; von Wartburg and Schürch, 1968]. Starch gel electrophoresis patterns of liver homogenates from some population groups contain bands that migrate cathodally to the $\beta_1\beta_1$ isozyme forms, the most cathodal ones of those encountered conventionally. A group of unusual forms, collectively designated $ADH_{Indianapolis}$[3], has been recognized based both upon dual pH optima for EtOH oxidation at pH 7 and 10 (Fig. 6) and on starch gel bands that do not correspond to any described previously [Bosron et al, 1980]. These forms were totally absent in random autopsy specimens from 53 North German and 34 Japanese individuals [Agarwal et al, 1981].

Bosron, Magnes and Li[2] [unpublished] have isolated from such livers one enzyme form that exhibits a single pH optimum at 7.0 and three with dual pH optima at 7.0 and 10.0. They propose that the $ADH_{Indianapolis}$ forms arise from a variant β subunit, $β_{Ind}$, and that the form with the single pH optimum of 7.0 is the homodimeric $β_{Ind}β_{Ind}$ isozyme. Consistent with this hypothesis, this form remains unchanged as a single activity band after dissociation-recombination experiments. On the other hand, each of the three forms with dual pH optima generated two new activity bands after this treatment, one of which was $β_{Ind}β_{Ind}$ and the other $β_1β_1$, $γ_1γ_1$, or $αα$. Hence, these forms are heterodimers; $β_1β_{Ind}$, $β_{Ind}γ_1$, and $αβ_{Ind}$, and the ADH_{Ind} enzyme forms are part of the family of Class I isozymes described above. The apparent Km values for ethanol of all four forms range from 56 to 74 mM [Bosron et al, 1980], considerably higher than those (1 to 2 mM) for the "normal" Class I forms.

Liver homogenates of yet other populations exhibit starch gel bands that also migrate more cathodally than the $β_1β_1$ one and have a pH optimum near 8.5 (Fig. 6). One such form has been found in 20% of a Swiss population sample and seems to be a heterodimer between a variant β subunit with one of the more usual $β_1β_1$ type [Berger et al, 1974]. This variant, originally named "atypical" ADH, has been designated ADH_{Bern} [Bosron et al, 1980] both to distinguish it from other similar forms and to avert the inference that its occurrence is either abnormal, infrequent, unusual, or necessarily limited to Swiss populations. In fact, this or a similar form occurs in other geographic areas and in groups of totally different racial origin. Thus, while exhaustive geographic studies have not been performed as yet, in one study, more than 80% of liver specimens from Asian donors also have enzyme bands cathodal

---

[3]The nomenclature is similar to that conventionally used for the hemoglobins. ADH forms exhibiting activity optima for ethanol oxidation at pH 7 are designated collectively as $ADH_{Indianapolis}$. Those migrating cathodally to $β_1β_1$ but exhibiting a pH optimum for ethanol oxidation at 8.5 rather than 10.0 [von Wartburg et al, 1965; von Wartburg and Schürch, 1968] are referred to collectively as ADH_{Bern} because of their initial recognition in a Swiss population. Forms similar to ADH_{Bern} are also present in 85% or more of an Asian population [Stamatoyannopoulos, 1975; Harada et al, 1980]. These forms were initially called "atypical." The chemical identities of these forms and ADH_{Bern} have not been established. Hence, the atypical ADH in liver specimens of Asian donors from Honolulu, Hawaii used in this study have been referred to a $ADH_{Honolulu}$.

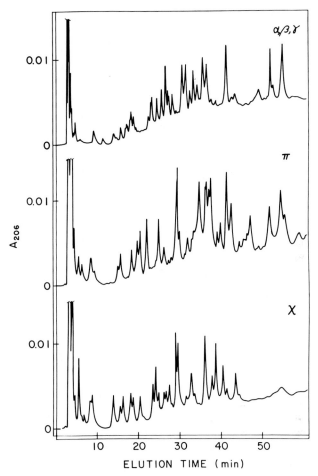

Fig. 5. Tryptic peptide HPLC profiles of the α, β, γ (Class I), π (Class II) and χ (Class III) isozymes of human ADH obtained as described by Strydom and Vallee (1982).

to $\beta_1\beta_1$, with an activity optimum near pH 8.5 [Stamatoyannopoulos et al, 1975; Harada et al, 1980]. It is not clear as yet whether the atypical isozyme forms in these livers, provisionally and collectively designated ADH$_{Honolulu}$, are identical with those now called ADH$_{Bern}$. Homogenates of livers containing ADH$_{Honolulu}$ are maximally active toward ethanol at 15 mM rather than 5 mM as observed in normal Class I livers containing neither ADH$_{Honolulu}$ nor ADH$_{Indianapolis}$.

Such an isozyme migrating cathodally to the normal $\beta_1\beta_1$ form, obtained from Asian livers, has recently been purified and characterized both struc-

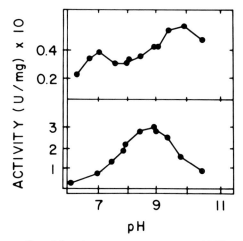

Fig. 6. pH-activity profiles of liver homogenate supernatants. ADH activity was determined with 33 mM ethanol and 2.4 mM NAD$^+$ at 25°C in 33 mM sodium phosphate, pH 6–8/33 mM sodium barbital, pH 8–9/33 mM glycine adjusted to pH 9–10.5 with NaOH. Liver specimens contain ADH$_{Indianapolis}$ (upper) and ADH$_{Honolulu}$ (lower). (After Bosron et al [1980]).

turally and enzymatically [Yoshida et al, 1981]. The atypical isozyme, which could be either ADH$_{Honolulu}$ or ADH$_{Bern}$, has an optimum for ethanol oxidation at pH 8–8.5 with a specific activity 82-fold and 26-fold higher than the normal ββ form at pH 8.5 and 10, respectively; this accounts for the rates of ethanol turnover for homogenates of livers from these individuals, that are higher overall than those for Class I. Similarly, binding constants for ethanol, acetaldehyde, NAD$^+$, and NADH are all higher for the atypical than for the typical forms. The amino acid composition of typical and atypical forms differs very little.

The atypical form is remarkably insensitive to modification by iodoacetate. In contrast, this agent rapidly and irreversibly inactivates the normal $\beta_1\beta_1$ form and, in fact, the entire mixture of unresolved Class I isozymes [Lange et al, 1975] by alkylation of an active site cysteinyl residue, similar to that alkylated in the horse liver enzyme [Li and Vallee, 1964, 1965]. Based on the analysis of tryptic peptide maps of this human variant and on the comparison of its peptide fragment sequences with those of the horse enzyme, the insensitivity of this atypical isozyme to iodoacetate has been attributed to the genetic replacement by a histidine of a cysteine corresponding to Cys-47, a metal ligand in the horse enzyme.

The relationship of this amino acid replacement to the differences in enzymatic behavior between typical and atypical forms is unknown but is reminiscent of amino acid replacements and their functional consequences in abnormal hemoglobins. The much higher specific activity of the atypical form, found in a large proportion of an Asian population, has been suggested to be related to the intolerance of this group to alcohol intake when accompanied by the "flushing" reaction; the latter in turn is thought to be related to the concentration of blood acetaldehyde [Wolff, 1972; Zeiner et al, 1979]. Alternatively, the accumulation of acetaldehyde in the blood of such individuals has been attributed to their deficiency in a form of aldehyde dehydrogenase which has a low Km and reduced capacity to metabolize acetaldehyde [Harada et al, 1980]. The available data could support either view, and further studies are needed to resolve the issue. The importance of the underlying enzymology, however, is evident; it calls for detailed structural investigations and enzymatic characterizations of all ADH isozyme forms.

C. Human Liver Class II (π)-ADH

Starch gel electrophoresis of a homogenate of some human livers obtained at autopsy within 12 hours postmortem shows an extra band that migrates less cathodally than those of Class I [Li and Magnes, 1975]. Staining in the presence of 4-methylpyrazole indicates that, unlike the Class I forms, this form is relatively insensitive to this inhibitor. Upon chromatography of a liver homogenate on the CapGapp affinity resin, this form elutes within two column volumes, consistent with its partial retardation owing to its insensitivity to the inhibitor. This pyrazole-insensitive, labile ADH was named π-ADH [Li et al, 1977]. Its purification is completed on AMP-Sepharose (Fig. 2). The K_I of the purified enzyme toward 4-methylpyrazole is 2 mM, over 1,000-fold greater than that of the Class I isozymes, thus accounting for its failure to bind to CapGapp. At 5 mM ethanol, a saturating concentration for virtually all Class I forms, the enzyme accounts for <15% of the total ADH oxidative capacity of those livers in which it is found.

The physical and chemical properties of π-ADH are similar to those of Class I and typical of the dimeric ADHs in general. Its subunit molecular weight estimated by SDS-polyacrylamide gel electrophoresis is approximately 42,000, identical to that of horse and Class I human liver ADH prepared by CapGapp-Sepharose affinity chromatography [Lange et al, 1976]. Based on ultracentrifugation, it is a dimer of 78 to 85 $\times$ 10^3 daltons with an amino acid composition similar to that of Class I. It also contains approximately four atoms of zinc per molecule of protein. Similar to the other molecular forms of the enzyme, π-ADH has a Km for NAD$^+$ of 26 μM at pH 7.5 and 40 μM at pH 10.0 [Bosron et al, 1979a], and it is not active with NADP$^+$. Its pH optimum for ethanol oxidation is above 10.0 and its substrate specificity is broad [Bosron et al, 1978, 1979a; Vallee et al, 1982; Morelock MM, Ditlow CC, Vallee BL, unpublished]. Increasing the primary alcohol chain length from two to five carbons decreases Km from 18 to 0.036

mM at pH 7.5, while k_{cat} remains relatively constant at 40–42 min^{-1} [Bosron et al, 1978]. However, π-ADH contains significantly fewer Val, Lys, and Ser but more Leu, Asp, and Tyr residues than either horse ADH or the undifferentiated mixture of Class I isozymes.

The enzymatic specificity and kinetic constants for Class II (π)-ADH obtained at pH 10 differ significantly from those for Class I (Table III). π-ADH does not oxidize methanol, ethylene glycol, and digitoxigenin at all, and oxidizes cyclohexanol even more slowly than $\beta_1\beta_1$ in Class I; its $k_{cat}/$Km for ethanol is 20- to 40-fold lower than those of Class I (excepting only the $\beta_1\beta_1$ form, which is peculiarly less active than the remainder). As a consequence, π-ADH activity becomes a significant aspect of ethanol oxidation only at high concentrations of that substrate. At intoxicating concentrations, ie, 60 mM ethanol, π-ADH can account for as much as 40% of the total ethanol oxidation rate of human liver [Li et al, 1977]. The high $k_{cat}/$Km for π-ADH with benzyl alcohol, 3-phenyl-1-propanol, octanol, and 16-hydroxyhexadecanoic acid relative to that of ethanol should also be noted. This preference for aromatic vs long chain aliphatic alcohols extends to other substrates (Table III).

The HPLC peptide map of a tryptic digest of Class II (π)-ADH [Strydom and Vallee, 1982] differs from that of either a mixture of Class I isozymes or of the individual homodimers or heterodimers (Fig. 5). Moreover, neither rabbit sera against horse or human π-ADH crossreact with the Class I human isozymes [Alderman EM and Vallee BL, unpublished]. Further, attempts to hybridize Class II (π)-ADH with the $\alpha\beta\gamma$ subunits of Class I have been unsuccessful so far [Li T-K, Magnes LJ, Bosron WF, unpublished]. Thus, the composition, structure, immunological properties, and enzymatic function of π-ADH differ significantly from those of Class I.

TABLE III. Human Class II (π)-ADH: Substrate Specificities for Various Alcohols (0.1 M Glycine, pH 10.0, 25°C)

Substrate	k_{cat} (min^{-1})	Km (mM)	$k_{cat}/$Km (M^{-1} min^{-1})
Methanol[a]			
Digitoxigenin[b]			
Ethanol	470	1.2×10^2	3×10^3
Cyclohexanol	35	2.1×10^2	1.4×10^2
Pentanol	480	9.0×10^{-2}	4.6×10^6
Benzyl alcohol	600	7.0×10^{-3}	7.4×10^7
3-Phenyl-1-propanol	520	4.0×10^{-2}	1.15×10^7

[a]No detectable activity up to 100 mM.
[b]No detectable activity up to 100 μM.

Both pyrazole and 4-methylpyrazole have been utilized in vivo and in vitro to differentiate ADH-catalyzed ethanol oxidation from that catalyzed by catalase or a microsomal ethanol oxidizing system. Both in experimental animals and in man, such studies indicate that a significant fraction of total alcohol oxidative capacity is insensitive to inhibition by pyrazole or 4-methylpyrazole [Teschke et al, 1976; Lieber, 1977; Salaspuro et al, 1978]. Since both catalase and the microsomal ethanol oxidizing system are relatively insensitive to inhibition by pyrazole compounds, it has been inferred that this residual oxidative capacity represents contributions by these enzyme systems. The identification of Class II (π)-ADH as a biochemically distinct form of human liver ADH with a K_I of 30 mM for pyrazole, and of 2 mM for 4-methylpyrazole, both as much as 1,000 times that of the Class I forms, indicates that evidence in humans for ethanol oxidizing pathways alternate to ADH cannot be based exclusively on the effects of these compounds. However, other pyrazole analogs such as 4-pentylpyrazole, 4-bromopyrazole, or 4-nitropyrazole exhibit lower K_I values ranging from 4 to 27 μM [Li and Theorell, 1969]. These compounds might be more suitable to differentiate ADH from non-ADH ethanol oxidizing capacity in man either in vitro or in vivo.

The substantially higher K_m for ethanol for π-ADH and absence of substrate inhibition up to 100 mM ethanol means that its effective contribution to ethanol metabolism varies from little or none below 3mM to 40% of the total observed at 100 mM (Fig. 7). Accordingly, this class of isozymes may relate directly to overall alcohol metabolizing capacity in man [Bosron et al, 1977]. Class II (π)-ADH has now been found also in horse [Dafeldecker WP and Vallee BL, unpublished] as well as in rhesus and squirrel monkey livers[4] [Dafeldecker et al, 1981a, 1981b].

D. Human Liver Class III (X)-ADH

Starch gel electrophoresis of crude homogenates from five adult and five infant livers and human placentas, when stained with pentanol, revealed two previously unreported ADH forms, X_1-ADH and X_2-ADH. In contrast to all other ADH isozymes reported thus far, both migrate toward the anode. Their electrophoretic mobility is consistent with a much lower pI for X_1-ADH and

---

[4]In addition to detailed studies on Macaca mulatta [Dafeldecker et al, 1981a] and Saimiri sciureus [Dafeldecker et al, 1981b], multiple isozyme forms have been detected on starch gel in all of the following primate species; Tree shrew (Tupaia glis), Potto (Peridicticus potto), owl monkey (Aotus trivirgatus), pig-tailed macaque (Macaca nemestrina), crab-eating macaque (Macaca fascicularis), Formosan Rock monkey (Macaca cyclopis), brown-headed marmoset (Saguinas fuscicollis), cotton-top marmoset (Saguinas oedipus), African green monkey (Cercopithecus aethiops), baboon (Papio papio), bonnet monkey (Macaca radiata), Patas (Erythrocebus patas), brown capucin (Cebus apella), and orangutan (Pongo pygmaeus).

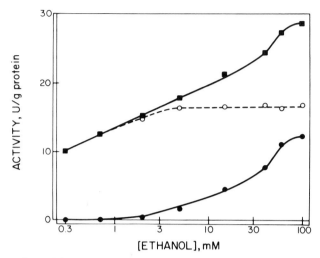

Fig. 7. Pyrazole-sensitive and -insensitive ADH activities in a liver homogenate determined with 2.4 mM NAD^+ in 0.1 M sodium phosphate, pH 7.5 without (■——■), and with (●——●) 4-methylpryazole; (○– – –○) is the difference. (From Li et al, 1977).

χ_2-ADH than for all other isozymes. Another important feature differentiates them from the other forms: pentanol is much more effective in staining them for activity than is ethanol [Parés and Vallee, 1981].

DEAE-cellulose chromatography separates χ-ADH isozymes from those of Class I and II; DEAE-cellulose binds the χ-forms of liver homogenate, while the Class I and Class II forms pass through unretarded. The χ forms are then eluted with an NaCl gradient (Fig. 2). Chromatography on agarose-hexane-AMP further separates the χ-ADHs from other proteins. The final enzyme preparation contains χ-ADHs exclusively, as evaluated by starch gel and SDS-gel electrophoresis. From 180 g of adult liver 13.8 mg (9 activity units in 0.5 M ethanol, pH 10) of the χ-ADH forms can be obtained. A 20 μM solution of the purified χ-ADH forms has a half-life of seven days when stored in 0.1 M Tris-Cl pH 8.6, 4°C.

χ-ADH shows many of the physical properties of Class I and Class II of human and horse liver ADH. Thus, by SDS-polyacrylamide gel electrophoresis, its subunit molecular weight is approximately 42,000 and, based on ultracentrifuge analysis, it is a dimer of 79–84 $\times$ 10^3 daltons, containing from 3.6 to 4.2 g-atom zinc/mole protein by atomic absorption spectrometry. It is inhibited instantaneously and reversibly by 1,10-phenanthroline and 8-hydroxyquinoline-5-sulfonic acid, and in a time-dependent manner by dipicolinic acid, demonstrating that the metal is essential for catalytic activity

[Parés and Vallee, 1981]. Like all other molecular forms of the human enzyme, X-ADH requires NAD$^+$ for oxidation and NADH for reduction; neither NADP$^+$ nor NADPH are effective.

The kinetic and immunological properties of X-ADH, however, differ significantly from those of any other mammalian ADH known so far. Short-chain (two to four carbons) primary alcohols and aldehydes do not saturate the enzyme even when tested at concentrations as high as 1 M, either at pH 10.0 or 7.5. At both pH values the activity is directly proportional to ethanol concentration up to 2 M (Fig. 8), a remarkable finding. Thus up to this concentration of ethanol, the enzyme is not saturated, though the binding constants for NAD(H) are close to those for the Class I ADH forms. At even higher ethanol concentrations substrate activation becomes apparent. In contrast, 30 mM ethanol saturates, and 100 mM begins to inhibit the cathodal forms. Primary aliphatic alcohols containing more than four carbon atoms, ω-hydroxy fatty acids among them, exhibit saturation kinetics with X-ADH, and hence, Km values can be calculated for these (Table IV). These constants, eg, 5.5 mM for hexanol and 0.4 mM for octanol at pH 10.0, are higher than the corresponding ones measured for the mixture of Class I isozymes, 12 μM and 5 μM, respectively. X-ADH, like π-ADH, does not oxidize methanol, ethylene glycol, cyclohexanol, or digitoxigenin.

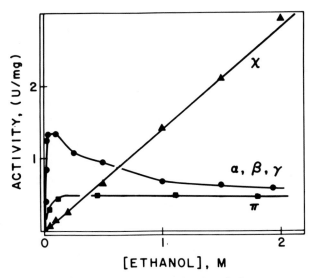

Fig. 8.   Variation of ethanol oxidizing activity as a function of substrate concentration. Activity was measured with 2.4 mM NAD$^+$ in 0.1 M glycine, pH 10.0. (▲——▲), χ (Class III) ADH; (■——■), π (Class II) ADH; (●——●), α, β, γ (Class I) ADH all obtained by the methods described in Figure 2.

TABLE IV. Human Class III (χ) ADH: Substrate Specificities for Various Alcohols (0.1 M Glycine, pH 10.0, 25°C)

Substrate	k_{cat} (min^{-1})	K_m (mM)	k_{cat}/K_m (M^{-1} min^{-1})
Methanol[a]			
Cyclohexanol[b]			
Ethanol	—	—	1.8×10^2
Hexanol	305	5.5	5.6×10^3
Octanol	312	0.4	7.8×10^5
Nonanol	34	0.4	7.8×10^5
16-Hydroxy-hexadecanoic acid	159	0.22	7.2×10^5

[a]No detectable activity up to 1.2 M.
[b]No detectable activity up to 100 mM.

The most remarkable characteristic of the X-ADHs is the fact that 12 mM 4-methylpyrazole completely fails to inhibit them, a feature critical to their isolation and potentially for their physiological function. This concentration of 4-methylpyrazole inhibits all the other ADH forms including π-ADH, which had been the one known to be least sensitive to it (K_I = 2 mM) until X-ADH was recognized[5]. Clearly, results of future studies utilizing pyrazole inhibition of liver alcohol oxidative capacity must be interpreted with these circumstances in mind.

The Class III (X)-ADH forms are the first mammalian ADHs that oxidize ethanol very poorly. If the in vitro findings apply in vivo, it is unlikely that this isozyme would play a role in the oxidation of ethanol even if this substrate were present at extraordinarily high concentrations; then save for π-ADH and the atypical variants ADH$_{Bern}$ and ADH $_{Honolulu}$, all other known ADH forms would not only be saturated but even inhibited. Further, the catalytic efficiency of Class III (X)-ADH increases as the hydrophobic chain of the alcohol is elongated. While all ADH isozymes studied previously also prefer hydrophobic alcohols, short chain primary alcohols are also excellent substrates. Class III (X)-ADH forms are much more specific in this regard, since hexanol is the shortest primary alcohol with a K_m lower than 100 mM. Thus, the substrate specificity and kinetics of the X forms are most distinctive, establishing them as Class III.

The X-ADHs are also structurally distinct from both Class I and II ADH; their HPLC peptide maps differ from those of both (Fig. 5) [Strydom and Vallee, 1982]. Moreover, rabbit anti-X antibodies do not cross react with either Class I or II isozymes [Alderman EM, Vallee BL, unpublished].

[5]The functional behavior of the Class III (X) forms is sufficiently distinctive to generate questions regarding appropriate terminology that would describe their differences, at least when assuming ethanol to be the standard substrate of this group of enzymes.

Over and above these remarkable kinetic properties, three additional, important features characterize the X-ADH forms: they have been found in all of the human livers and placentas examined so far, in the liver of premature infants, ie, in early stages of development, and their concentration is high, ie, about 0.1 mg/g of tissue. In human placenta where they seem to be the predominant forms by far, the amounts are less, however, [Parés X, Vallee BL, unpublished]. The X isozymes have also been detected in rhesus monkey [Dafeldecker et al, 1981a] and in horse liver [Dafeldecker and Vallee, 1982]. Jointly, all of these properties suggest that the X-ADH forms play an important and hitherto unrecognized role in the metabolism of alcohols and aldehydes.

III. CLASSES I, II, AND III: FUNCTIONAL INFERENCES AND IMPLICATIONS

The selective effectiveness of pyrazole inhibitors and their utility in affinity chromatography have provided a potent physicochemical approach to the isolation of human ADH isozymes. While greatly simplifying and minimizing the time for their isolation, these inhibitors have also provided a basis for differentiation of the three different classes. Isozyme separation by CapGapp, based on inhibition, correlates with their electrical charge and, hence, their electrophoretic behavior. Moreover, each of these classes differs from the others in immunological properties and substrate specificity. Within Class I, the $\beta_1\beta_1$ isozyme stands out from the remainder and, further, the variants in Class I, $ADH_{Honolulu}$ and $ADH_{Indianapolis}$, have distinctive enzymatic properties and reflect different phenotypes that may be racially determined. Agarwal et al [1981] have reported that $ADH_{Indianapolis}$ is completely absent in random samples from German and Japanese populations and has so far only been detected in livers from black Americans. The information regarding the basis for this remarkable polymorphism is incomplete though the data of Yoshida et al [1981] give first indications of functional amino acid replacements such as those in hemoglobin.

Population distribution studies have sought to correlate the frequency of occurrences of both the normal and variant forms of Class I isozymes with the racial backgrounds of the individuals and, hence, perhaps genetic determinants. However, the structural differences underlying the various subunit types are not known. In the complete absence of primary sequences, for example, the assignment of the isozymes and their subunits to specific gene loci can neither be verified nor rejected. At present, there are also no experimental data concerning substrates or other environmental factors that might induce some or all of them. Thus, current attributions of isozymes to inheritance essentially assume this mechanism in the absence of information to the contrary. While genetic factors seem clearly predominant, detection of new isozymes calls for the consideration of alternative mechanisms regarding their origin.

Enzymes with properties similar to those of human Class II and/or III have been observed in livers of many primates [Dafeldecker et al, 1981 a,b], in the horse [Dafeldecker and Vallee, 1982], in a species of mouse [Holmes et al, 1981], and in Chinese hamster [Talbot et al, 1981]. The livers of all of these species contain fewer cathodal bands than does the human. Since there is virtually no information about the in vivo function of any of the three classes in any species, their presence or absence in a given one cannot be attributed a priori to environmental or metabolic requirements or genetic factors that may underlie their persistence.

Although it is generally assumed that the function of alcohol dehydrogenases is the oxidation of ethanol, many arguments can be marshalled against this premise. Certainly, the remarkable polymorphism and the accompanying differences in substrate specificity and kinetics raise additional doubt about such a unitary hypothesis. The emerging biochemical data certainly allow for alternative assumptions. Thus, it could be postulated that the physiological function of the three classes of ADH is the oxidation or reduction of different intermediary metabolic alcohols or aldehydes that may be essential to different pathways. Such conjectures suggest that the oxidation of ethanol would not be the sole function of all of these forms, though when presented with this substrate, all will oxidize it, albeit with widely varying efficiency or, as in the case of Class III isozymes, hardly at all. The consumption of a vast excess of ethanol together with variable distribution of the ADH classes in different individuals and population groups as well as their importance to different metabolic pathways, could generate the complex manifestations and susceptibilities to both acute and chronic alcohol excess which are generally observed.

The detrimental effects of ethanol ingestion may indeed derive in part from the toxicity of its degradation product, but it could be possible also that ethanol interferes with the oxidation or reduction of critical intermediates in normal metabolic pathways. We commented on those problems some time ago, and it seems appropriate to recall our remarks even though they were made before these details on isozymes were known [Vallee, 1966]:

Alcohol dehydrogenase from the livers of different individuals can vary markedly with respect to their alcohol dehydrogenase activity. In approximately one of fifty human livers examined, the alcohol dehydrogenase activity was five to ten times higher than that normally observed, while in others it was much less. Such findings may represent first enzymatic indications of distinct individual differences in the capacity of individuals to be able to oxidize ethanol. . . . . Certain individuals seem constitutionally unable to metabolize ethanol, and some races, in particular, are thought to be intolerant to its use. Whether these observations reflect genetic variations of the intrinsic properties of different alcohol dehydrogenases is not as yet known. However, these considerations have already led to a wholly different mode of experimentation aimed at the elucidation of the problem of alcoholism on a genetic basis through attempts at isolation of variants or multiple forms of the enzyme. By isolating the enzyme from human sources, a most dependable tool seems to have been uncovered with which to study not only the oxidation of ethanol but also to investigate the pathology of alcohol metabolism in man. . . .

The exceptionally broad substrate specificity of the unresolved human and horse liver ADHs has been documented to include many metabolites, drugs, and/or poisons that are alcohols and aldehydes, among them digitoxigenin, digoxigenin, gitoxigenin, the pharmacologically active constituents of digoxin [Frey and Vallee, 1979, 1980], as well as methanol and ethylene glycol. They compete for human ADH to the point where ethyl alcohol, the least toxic of these, is the life-saving therapeutic agent of choice for intoxication with methanol or ethylene glycol [Wacker et al, 1965].

Remarkably, the specificities of the Class I isozymes on one hand and those of Class II and III on the other differ significantly with respect to these three substrates, quantitatively in regard to ethanol, qualitatively in regard to methanol and ethylene glycol (Table V). While the toxic effects of the latter two are lethal and immediate, ethanol also causes major pathology, albeit comparatively delayed. In addition to genetic factors, different environmental ones such as diet, climate, or disease might contribute to variable responses within and among different populations. The evidence for such proposals remains circumstantial, and their verification or rejection will require close and detailed examination.

The problem of varying tolerance of different individuals and its potential relationship to isozymes is similarly open. The reported capacity of some to consume quantities of ethanol considerably larger than the average [Newman, 1949; Isbell et al., 1955] could be accounted for, at least in part, by large amounts of Class II isozymes which contribute maximally to ethanol metabolism at high ethanol concentrations.

TABLE V. Substrate Specificities of Human ADH Isozyme Classes (0.1 M NaPi, pH 7.5, 25°C)

| | k_{cat}/K_m, M^{-1} min^{-1} | | |
| | Class | | |
Substrate	I	II	III
EtOH	1.1×10^5	3×10^3	100
MeOH	500	0	0
Ethylene glycol	1×10^3	0	0
Digitoxigenin	3×10^{4a}	0	0
Octanol	2×10^7	5.9×10^7	3×10^4
16-Hydroxy-hexadecanoic acid	1×10^7	5.8×10^6	1×10^6

[a]pH 7.0

Suitable genetic and/or biochemical markers are essential in serial studies whose outcome could predict physiological and pathological susceptibilities to ethanol ingestion and its consequences. Primates are appropriate experimental models for human studies. Our investigations of the isozyme patterns in rhesus and squirrel monkey livers [Dafeldecker et al, 1981a,b] and those of other authors[4] demonstrate multiple options. The identification of appropriate biochemical, immunological, and/or genetic markers in accessible human body fluids or tissues offer important experimental alternatives that are under investigation.

IV. ACKNOWLEDGMENTS

This work was supported by a grant from the Samuel Bronfman Foundation, Inc. with funds provided by Joseph E. Seagram and Sons, Inc.

V. REFERENCES

Adinolfi A, Adinolfi M, Hopkinson DA, Harris H (1979): Immunological properties of the human alcohol dehydrogenase (ADH) isozymes. J Immunogenet 5:283–296.

Agarwal DP, Meier-Tackmann D, Harada S, Goedde HW (1981): A search for the Indianapolis variant of human alcohol dehydrogenae in liver autopsy samples from North Germany and Japan. Hum Genet 59:170–171.

Azevedo ES, da Silva MCBO, Tavares-Neto J (1975): Human alcohol dehydrogenase ADH_1, ADH_2, and ADH_3 loci in a mixed population of Bahia, Brazil. Ann Hum Genet 39:321–327.

Berger D, Berger M, Wartburg J-P von (1974): Structural studies of human liver dehydrogenase isoenzymes. Eur J Biochem 50:215–225.

Blair AH, Vallee BL (1966): Some catalytic properties of human liver alcohol dehydrogenase isoenzymes. Biochemistry 5:2026–2034.

Bosron WF, Li T-K, Lange LG, Dafeldecker WP, Vallee BL (1977): Isolation and characterization of an anodic form of human liver alcohol dehydrogenase. Biochem Biophys Res Commun 74:85–91.

Bosron WF, Li T-K, Dafeldecker WP, Vallee BL (1978): Human liver alcohol dehydrogenase: Isolation and properties of a new and distinctive molecular form. In Li CJ (ed): "Versatility of Proteins." New York: Academic Press, pp 253–267.

Bosron WF, Li TK, Dafeldecker WP, Vallee BL (1979a): Human liver π-alcohol dehydrogenase: Kinetic and molecular properties. Biochemistry 18:1101–1105.

Bosron WF, Li T-K, Vallee BL (1979b): Heterogeneity and new molecular forms of human liver alcohol dehydrogenase. Biochem Biophys Res Commun 91:1594.

Bosron WF, Li T-K, Vallee BL (1980): New molecular forms of human liver alcohol dehydrogenase: Isolation and characterization of $ADH_{Indianapolis}$. Proc Natl Acad Sci USA 77:5784–5788.

Brändén C-I, Eklund H, Nordström B, Boiwe T, Söderlund G, Zeppezauer E, Ohlsson I, Åkeson Å (1973): Structure of liver alcohol dehydrogenase at 2.9-Å resolution. Proc Natl Acad Sci 70:2439–2442.

Branden I, Jörnvall H, Eklund H, Furugren B (1975): Alcohol dehydrogenases. In Boyer PD (ed): "The Enzymes, Vol 11: Oxidation-Reduction, Part A." New York: Academic Press, pp 103–190.

Burger AR, Vallee BL (1981): Substrate specificites of human liver alcohol dehydrogenase isoenzymes. Fed Proc, Fed Am Soc Exp Biol 40:1886.

Dafeldecker WP, Meadow PE, Pares, X, Vallee BL (1981a): Simian liver alcohol dehydrogenase: Isolation and characterization of isoenzymes from Macaca mulatta. Biochemistry 20:6729–6734.

Dafeldecker WP, Parex X, Vallee BL, Bosron WF, Li T-K (1981b): Simian liver alcohol dehydrogenase: Isolation and characterization of isoenzymes from Saimiri sciureus. Biochemistry 20:856–861.

Dafeldecker WP, Valle BL (1982): X Alcohol dehydrogenase isozymes of horse liver. J Prot Chem: 1:59–69.

Dubied A, Wartburg J-P von, Bohlken DP, Plapp BV (1977): Characterization and kinetics of native and chemically activated human liver alcohol dehydrogenases. J Biol Chem 252:1464–1470.

Frey WA, Vallee BL (1979): Human liver alcohol dehydrogenase: An enzyme essential to the metabolism of digitalis. Biochem Biophys Res Commun 91:1543.

Frey WA, Vallee BL (1980) Digitalis metabolism and human liver alcohol dehydrogenase. Proc Natl Acad Sci USA 77:924–927.

Harada S, Agarwal DP, Goedde HW (1978): Human liver alcohol dehydrogenase isoenzyme variations. Hum Gen 40:215–220.

Harada S, Misawa S, Agarwal DP, Goedde W (1980): Liver alcohol dehydrogenase and aldehyde dehydrogenase in the Japanese: Isozyme variation and its possible role in alcohol intoxication. Am J Hum Genet 32:8–15.

Holmes RS, Albanese R, Whitehead FD, Duley JA (1981): Mouse alcohol dehydrogenase isozymes: Products of closely localized duplicated genes exhibiting divergent kinetic properties. J Exp Zool 217:151–157.

Isbell H, Fraser HF, Wikler A, Belleville RE, Eisenman AJ (1955): An experimental study of the etiology of "rum fits" and delirium tremens. Q J Stud Alcohol 16:1–33.

Jörnvall H (1970): The primary structure of the protein chain of the ethanol-active isoenzyme. Eur J Biochem 16:25–40.

Jörnvall H, Petruszko R (1972): Structural studies of alcohol dehydrogenase from human liver. Eur J Biochem 25:283–290.

Lange LG III, Riordan JF, Vallee BL, Branden CI (1975): The role of arginyl residues in directing carboxymethylation of horse liver alcohol dehydrogenase. Biochemistry 14:3497–3502.

Lange LG, Vallee BL, (1976): Double-ternary complex affinity chromatography: Preparation of alcohol dehydrogenases. Biochemistry 15:4681–4686.

Lange LG, Sytkowski AJ, Vallee BL (1976): Human liver alcohol dehydrogenase: Purification, composition, and catalytic features. Biochemistry 15:4687–4693.

Li, T-K, Vallee BL (1964): Active center peptides of liver alcohol dehydrogenase. I. The sequence surrounding the active cysteinyl residues. Biochemistry 3:869–873.

Li T-K, Vallee BL (1965): Reactivity and function of sulfhydryl groups in horse liver alcohol dehydrogenase. Biochemistry 4:1195–1202.

Li T-K, Theorell H (1969): Human liver alcohol dehydrogenase: Inhibition by pyrazole and pyrazole analogs. Acta Chem Scand 23:892–902.

Li T-K, Magnes LJ (1975): Identification of a distinctive molecular form of alcohol dehydrogenase in human livers with high activity. Biochem Biophys Res Commun 63:202–208.

Li T-K (1977): Enzymology of human alcohol metabolism. In Meister A (ed): Adv Enzymol 45:427–483.

Li T-K, Bosron WF, Dafeldecker WP, Lange LG, Vallee BL (1977): Isolation of π-alcohol dehydrogenase of human liver: Is it a determinant of alcoholism? Proc Natl Acad Sci USA 74:4378–4381.

Lieber CS (1977): Metabolism of ethanol. In Lieber C (ed): "Metabolic Aspects of Alcoholism." Baltimore: University Park Press, pp 1–29.

Newman HW (1949): Maximal consumption of ethyl alcohol. Science 109:594–595.

Pares X, Vallee BL (1981): New human liver alcohol dehydrogenase forms with unique kinetic characteristics. Biochem Biophys Res Commun 98:122–130.

Pietruszko R, Theorell H, Zalenski C de (1972): Heterogeneity of alcohol dehydrogenase from human liver. Arch Biochem Biophys 153:279–293.

Pietruszko R (1979): Nonethanol substrates of alochol dehydrogenase. In Majchrowicz E, Noble EP (eds): "Biochemistry and Pharmacology of Ethanol, Vol. 1." New York: Plenum Press, pp 87–106.

Salaspuro M, Lindros KO, Pikkarainin PH (1978): Effect of 4-methylpyrazole on ethanol elimination rate and hepatic redox changes in alcoholics with adequate or inadequate nutrition and in nonalcoholic controls. Metabol 27:631–639.

Schenker TM, Teeple LJ, Wartburg J-P von (1971): Heterogeneity and polymorphism of human-liver alcohol dehydrogenase. Eur J Biochem 24:271–279.

Schwartz MF, Jörnvall H (1976): Structural analyses of mutant and wild-type alcohol dehydrogenases from Drosophila melanogaster. Eur J Biochem 68:159–168.

Smith M, Hopkinson DA, Harris H (1971): Developmental changes and polymorphism in human alcohol dehydrogenase. Ann Hum Gen 34:251–271.

Smith M, Hopkinson DA, Harris H (1972): Alcohol dehydrogenase isozymes in adult human stomach and liver: Evidence for activity of the ADH_3 locus. Ann Hum Gen 35:243–253.

Smith M, Hopkinson DA, Harris H (1973): Studies on the properties of the human alcohol dehydrogenase isozymes determined by the different loci ADH_1, ADH_2, ADH_3. Ann Hum Gen 37:49–67.

Stamatoyannopoulos G, Chen S-H, Fukui M (1975): Liver alcohol dehydrogenase in Japanese: High population frequency of atypical form and its possible role in alcohol sensitivity. Am J Hum Genet 27:789–796.

Strydom DJ, Vallee BL (1982): Characterization of human alcohol dehydrogenase isozymes by high-performance liquid chromatographic peptide mapping. Anal Biochem 123:422–429.

Talbot BG, Qureshi AA, Cohen R, Thirion J-P (1981): Purification and properties of two distinct groups of ADH isozymes from Chinese hamster liver. Biochem Genet 19:813–829.

Teschke R, Hasumura Y, Lieber CS (1976): Hepatic ethanol metabolism: Respective roles of alcohol dehydrogenase, the microsomal ethanol oxidizing system and catalase. Arch Biochem Biophys 175:635–643.

Vallee BL (1966): Alcohol metabolism and metalloenzymes. Therapeutic Notes 73:71–74.

Vallee BL, Frey WA, Dafeldecker WP, Bosron WF, Li T-K (1982): Substrate specificity and characteristics of π-alcohol dehydrogenase and otherhuman liver ADH isoenzymes. In Kaplan NO, Robinson A (eds): "From Cyclotrons to Cytochromes." New York: Academic Press, pp 469–483.

von Wartburg J-P, Bethune JL, Vallee BL (1964): Human liver-alcohol dehydrogenase: Kinetic and physicochemical properties. Biochemistry 3:1775–1782.

von Wartburg J-P, Papenberg J, Aebi H (1965): An atypical human alcohol dehydrogenase. Can J Biochem 43:889–898.

von Wartburg J-P, Schürch PM (1968): Atypical human liver alcohol dehydrogenase. Ann NY Acad Sci 151:936–946.

Wacker WEC, Haynes H, Druyan R, Fisher W, Coleman JE (1965): Treatment of ethylene glycol poisoning with ethyl alcohol. JAMA 194:1231–1233.

Wagner FW, Burger AR, Vallee BL (1983): Kinetic properties of human liver alcohol dehydrogenase: oxidation of alcohols by Class I isoenzymes. Biochemistry 22:1857–1863.

Wolff P (1972): Ethnic differences in alcohol sensitivity. Science 125:449–451.

Yoshida A, Impraim CC, Huang I-Y (1981): Enzymatic and structural differences between usual and atypical human liver alcohol dehydrogenases. J Biol Chem 256:12430–12436.

Zeiner AR, Paredes A, Christensen DH (1979): The role of acetaldehyde in mediating reactivity to an acute dose of ethanol among different racial groups. Alcoholism 3:11–18.

Isozymes: Current Topics in Biological and Medical Research
Volume 8: Cellular Localization, Metabolism, and Physiology 245-261

Differences in the Isozymes Involved in Alcohol Metabolism Between Caucasians and Orientals

Akira Yoshida

Department of Biochemical Genetics, City of Hope Research Institute, Duarte, California 91010

I. INTRODUCTION

The majority of Mongoloids (Chinese, Japanese, Koreans, American Indians, and Eskimos) are "alcohol sensitive," ie, they exhibit rapid facial flushing, elevation of skin temperature, and increase in pulse rate after drinking a moderate amount of alcohol, whereas only <5% of Caucasians are alcohol sensitive. This difference could be related to genetic differences in the enzymes involved in alcohol metabolism. Indeed, distinctive differences have been found in liver alcohol dehydrogenase (ADH) and aldehyde dehydrogenase (ALDH) between Caucasians and Orientals. Human liver contains several cytosolic ADH and microsomal ADH. One of the major cytosolic ADH isozymes, controlled by the ADH_2 locus, differs in these populations. Most Caucasians have the usual ADH_2^1 enzyme, whereas nearly 90% of Orientals have the atypical ADH_2^2 enzyme, which exhibits much higher enzyme activity than the usual enzyme, particularly at physiologic pH [Stamatoyannpoulos et al, 1975]. Thus, Stamatoyannopoulos et al [1975] suggested that the racial differences in alcohol sensitivity could be due to the rapid acetaldehyde formation by the superactive, atypical ADH in many Orientals. Liver aldehyde dehydrogenase components also differ in Caucasians and Orientals. Virtually all Caucasians have two major isozymes, ie, $ALDH_1$ and $ALDH_2$, whereas approximately 50% of Orientals have only the $ALDH_1$ isozyme, missing the $ALDH_2$ isozyme [Goedde et al, 1979a; Teng, 1981]. Since $ALDH_2$ has a high affinity for acetaldehyde, the absence of this isozyme could induce an elevation of acetaldehyde concentration. Goedde et al [1979a] proposed that the absence of $ALDH_2$ might be related to the high incidence of alcohol sensitivity among Orientals.

This paper describes the functional and molecular differences between the usual and atypical ADH_2 and the genetic background of the absence of $ALDH_2$ isozyme in many Orientals. The possible relationships between alcohol sensitivity and enzyme abnormalities are also discussed.

II. STRUCTURE OF USUAL AND ATYPICAL HUMAN ALCOHOL DEHYDROGENASES

Human cytosolic ADH contains several homodimers and heterodimers formed by the association of three types of subunits, α, β, and γ, which are coded for by three separate structural loci, ADH_1, ADH_2, and ADH_3, respectively (Fig. 1) [Smith et al, 1971, 1972, 1973]. The Oriental atypical enzyme contains an atypical β_2 subunit, the product of an atypical ADH_2 gene. Genetic polymorphism is found to exist also at the ADH_3 locus [Smith et al, 1972], while locus ADH_1 is probably monomorphic, poorly expressed in the adult, and more strongly expressed in the infant [Smith et al, 1971]. The usual homodimer $\beta_1\beta_1$ and the atypical homodimer $\beta_2\beta_2$ isozymes were purified to homogeneity from an usual Caucasian liver and an atypical Japanese liver (Fig. 2, 3). The usual $\beta_1\beta_1$ is more active at pH 10.5, while the atypical $\beta_2\beta_2$ exhibits maximum activity at pH 8.0. The specific activity (V_{max}/mg protein) of the atypical enzyme was several times higher at pH 10, and nearly three orders of magnitude higher at the physiologic pH, than that of the usual enzyme. Km values for ethanol, NAD, acetaldehyde, and NADH were several times higher in the atypical enzyme than in the usual enzyme (Table I). The usual enzyme was rapidly inactivated by iodoacetate, indicating the existence of an "active site cysteine" in the molecule. In contrast, the atypical enzyme was resistant to iodoacetate inactivation (Fig. 4).

For structural study, the usual and atypical enzymes were S-carboxymethylated or S-aminoethylated, and then digested by trypsin. The tryptic peptides were separated by two-dimensional paper chromatography—electro-

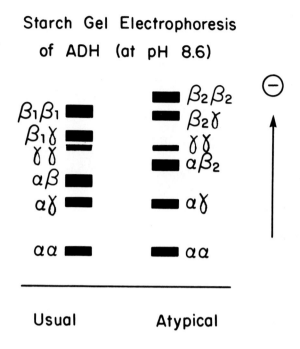

Fig. 1. Schematic starch gel electrophoresis patterns of the usual and atypical human ADH isozymes.

phoresis (Fig. 5). Determination of the amino acid composition and sequence of the peptides implicated in the structural difference revealed that the active site Cys in the usual β_1 subunit is replaced by His in the atypical β_2 subunit (Fig. 6).

The best studied ADH is the horse cytosol enzyme. The complete amino acid sequence of horse liver ADH has been reported [Jörnvall, 1970], and its three-dimensional structure was proposed based on X-ray crystallography [Eklund et al, 1976]. A "catalytic" Zn links to Cys at position 46, His at position 67, and Cys at position 174, constituting the active site of the horse enzyme [Eklund et al, 1976]. Cys at position 46 is rapidly S-carboxymethylated by iodoacetate and the enzyme becomes inactive [Jörnvall, 1970; Dahl and McKinley-McKee, 1980]. A remarkable structural homology exists between the horse and human enzyme in this part of the molecule (Fig. 6). In the usual human $\beta_1\beta_1$ enzyme, the catalytic Zn is expected to link to Cys at position 47, His at position 67, and Cys at position 174, although the exact position of this particular Cys is not yet determined. Thus, the structure of the active site of the human $\beta_1\beta_1$ enzyme should be essentially identical with

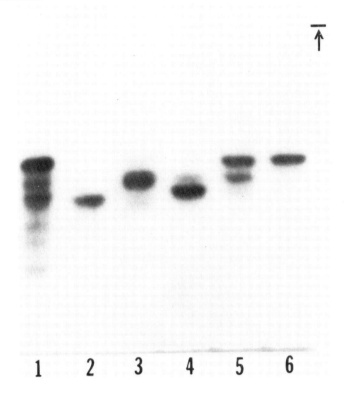

Fig. 2. (left)   Starch gel electrophoresis patterns of the usual human ADH isozymes. Elec-trophoresis was carried out at pH 8.6, and the gel was stained for enzyme activity. 1, Crude extract of liver with usual phenotype; 2, first isozyme peak eluted from CM-cellulose; 3, second isozyme peak eluted from CM-cellulose; 4, third isozyme peak eluted from CM-cellulose; 5, fourth isozyme peak eluted from CM-cellulose; 6, fifth isozyme peak eluted from CM-cellulose. The fifth isozyme peak contains only $\beta_1\beta_1$ component (details in Yoshida et al [1981]).

that of the horse enzyme. In contrast, in the atypical $\beta_2\beta_2$ enzyme, the catalytic Zn should link to His 47, His 67, and Cys 174. The resistance of the atypical enzyme to inactivation by iodoacetate is a direct consequence of the absence of a sensitive Cys in the active site of the atypical enzyme. It should be pointed out that yeast ADH has -Cys-His- linkage at the corresponding active site [Jörnvall, 1977] (Fig. 6). Yeast ADH is sensitive to iodoacetate inactivation [Yoshida, unpublished observation], indicating that Cys, but not His, is involved in constituting the active site.

Berger et al [1974] previously reported that a tryptic peptide Phe-Ala-Lys present in the usual enzyme is replaced by Phe-Pro-Lys in the atypical enzyme, presumably resulting from a single amino acid substitution from Ala

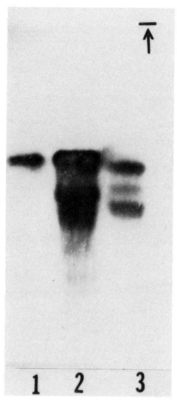

Fig. 3. (right)   Starch gel electrophoresis patterns of the usual and atypical human ADH isozymes. 1, Atypical $\beta_2\beta_2$ component isolated by CM-cellulose chromatography; 2, crude extract of liver with atypical phenotype; 3, crude extract of liver with usual phenotype (details in Yoshida et al [1981]).

to Pro. We synthesized Phe-Ala-Lys and Phe-Pro-Lys, and analyzed all of the tryptic peptides located in the same area as the synthetic tripeptides in the peptide maps. However, neither Phe-Ala-Lys nor Phe-Pro-Lys were found in β_1 and β_2. The proposed substitution Ala → Phe cannot account for the remarkable difference in sensitivity to iodoacetate found in the present study. The tripeptides, Phe-Ala-Lys or Phe-Pro-Lys, could originate from other isozyme subunits, α or δ, which might be contaminants in the enzyme preparation studied by Berger et al.

Horse ADH has a Cys-Arg linkage at position 46–47, and it has been reported that the human enzyme also has a Cys-Arg at the corresponding position [Jörnvall and Pietruszko, 1972]. However, the usual $\beta_1\beta_1$ has no such linkage; instead, Arg-Cys exists at the active site. The previous analysis

TABLE I. Kinetic Properties of Usual and Atypical Alcohol Dehydrogenase[a]

		Usual $\beta_1\beta_1$		Atypical $\beta_2\beta_2$	
		pH 8.5	pH 10.0	pH 8.5	pH 10.0
Specific activity	Ethanol → aldehyde	0.39	0.8	32	5.0
(units/mg)	Aldehyde → ethanol	1.8	0.48	1.6	12.5
K_m (mM)	Ethanol	0.37	0.78	2.1	5.0
	NAD	0.039	0.064	0.15	0.69
	Aldehyde	0.94	1.14	1.24	19.2
	NADH	0.0097	0.014	0.078	0.17

[a]The enzyme activity was assayed in 30 mM glycine/NaOH buffer at 25°C. The assay mixture for the forward reaction (ethanol → acetaldehyde) contained 1 mM NAD and various concentrations of ethanol or 10 mM ethanol and various concentrations of NAD. The assay mixture for the backward reaction (acetaldehyde → ethanol) contained 0.5 mM NADH and various concentrations of acetaldehyde, or 20 mM acetaldehyde and various concentrations of NADH.

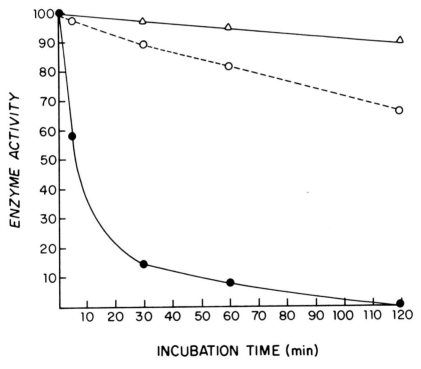

Fig. 4. Inactivation of usual $\beta_1\beta_1$ and atypical $\beta_2\beta_2$ enzymes by iodoacetate. The purified enzymes were incubated in 0.02 M Tris chloride, pH 7.5, at 25°C. The enzyme activity is expressed taking the original activity as 100. △, Usual $\beta_1\beta_1$ without iodoacetate; ●, usual $\beta_1\beta_1$ enzyme with 0.5 mM iodoacetate. ○, Atypical $\beta_2\beta_2$ enzyme with 0.5 mM iodoacetate (details in Yoshida et al [1981]).

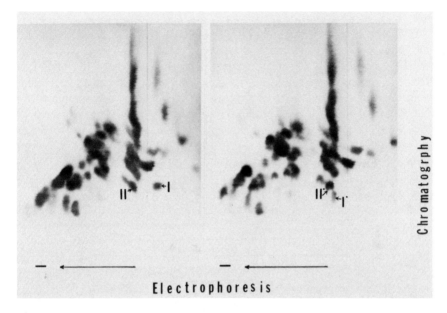

Fig. 5.   Peptide maps of tryptic digests of usual $\beta_1\beta_1$ and atypical $\beta_2\beta_2$ enzymes. The peptide marked I in $\beta_1\beta_1$ (left) is replaced by the peptide marked I' in $\beta_2\beta_2$ (right). The peptides marked II and II' are a common dipeptide, Asp-Lys, which served as a reference spot (details in Yoshida et al [1981]).

ACTIVE CENTER OF ALCOHOL DEHYDROGENASE

<u>Human</u> $\beta_1\beta_1$

```
                    50                  55                  60                  65
  -(Arg)-Cys-Thr-Asp-Asp-His-Val-Val-Ser-Gly-Asn-Cys-Val-Thr-Pro-Leu-Pro-Val-Ile-Ala-
                    70                  75                  80                  80
     Gly—His-Glu-Ala-Ala-Gly-Ile-Val-Glu-Ser-Leu-Gly-Glu-Gly-Val-Met-Thr-Val-Lys-Pro-Gly-Leu-Lys-
```

<u>Human</u> $\beta_2\beta_2$

```
  -(Arg)-His-Thr-Asp-Asp-His-Val-Val-Ser-Gly-Asn-Cys-(------------Same as Human β₁----------)
```

Horse Enzyme

```
                    50                  55                  60                  65
  -Ile-Cys—Arg-Ser-Asp-Asp-His-Val-Val-Ser-Gly-Thr-Leu-Val-Thr-Pro-Leu-Pro-Val-Ile-Ala-
                    70                  75                  80                  85
     Gly—His-Glu-Ala-Ala-Gly-Ile-Val-Glu-Ser-Ile-Gly-Glu-Gly-Val-Thr-Thr-Val-Arg-Pro-Gly-Asp-Lys-
```

Yeast Enzyme

```
      43                       50                  55                  60
  -Val-Cys-His-Thr-Asp-Leu-His-Ala-Trp-His-Gly-Asp-Trp-Pro-Leu-Pro-Thr-Lys-Leu-Pro-Leu-
                              70                  75                  80
     Val-Gly-Gly-His-Glu-Gly-Ala-Gly-Val-Val-Val-Gly-Met-Gly-Glu-Asn-Val-Lys-Gly-Trp-Lys
```

Fig. 6.   Structure of "active site" of ADH. The positions of the amino acid substitutions are underlined. The structures of usual human $\beta_1\beta_1$ and atypical human $\beta_2\beta_2$ are based on the data of Yoshida et al [1981]. The structures of the horse and yeast enzyme are based on the sequence data of Jörnvall [1970, 1977].

was made using a mixture of isozymes, and the Cys-Arg could presumably originate from α and/or γ subunits; the yield of a tryptic peptide containing this linkage was indeed very low [Jörnvall and Pietruszko, 1972]. Judging from the structure of the horse enzyme, the original form of liver ADH has Cys-Arg at the active site, and the β subunit is considered to be evolved from this form. Whatever the evolutionary mechanism, a minimum of two steps of base substitution is required to produce β_2 and β_1 or vice versa, ie, Cys $\leftrightarrow$ His. In most cases, polymorphism is considered to have originated by a single base substitution at a given locus, or by nonreciprocal crossing over. The human ADH β_1 and β_2 are exceptional in this respect, and the underlying mechanism of evolutionary divergence is worth pursuing by examining the structure of ADH isozymes and the gene structure of *ADH* loci of various mammals. The precise mechanism of ADH activity is not yet fully understood, and an explanation of the differences in kinetic properties (ie, pH optima, specific activity, Km values for the substrates and coenzyme) in terms of the structural change (ie, Cys $\rightarrow$ His at position 47) cannot be given at the present time. Future comparative kinetic and X-ray crystallographic studies of the usual and the atypical enzymes could lead us to understand in greater detail the mechanism of ADH enzymatic activity.

III. ISOZYMES OF ALDEHYDE DEHYDROGENASE

In comparison to ADH, our knowledge of ALDH is rather limited. Human and horse ALDH are tetrameric enzymes with molecular weight of about 230,000 [Greenfield and Pietruszko, 1977; Eckfeldt et al, 1976]. Human liver ALDH$_1$, an isozyme with lower anodal electrophoretic mobility at neutral to basic pH, has a low Km for NAD and a high apparent Km for acetaldehyde; ALDH$_2$, an isozyme with higher anodal electrophoretic mobility, has a high Km for NAD and a low Km for acetaldehyde [Greenfield and Pietruszko, 1977]. Comparable isozymes exist in other mammals. Although no direct evidence has been presented as yet, from the analogy of isozyme distribution in animal livers [Crow et al, 1974; Eckfeldt and Yonetani, 1976; Kitabatake et al, 1981] one can conclude that human ALDH$_1$ is of cytosolic and ALDH$_2$ is presumably of mitochondrial origin. Purification of ALDH$_1$ and ALDH$_2$ from human liver was previously reported by Greenfield and Pietruszko [1977]. Their method included 1) CM-Sephadex- and, 2) DEAE-Sephadex ion-exchange chromatography, 3) AMP-Sepharose affinity chromatography, 4) Sephadex gel filtration, and 5) DEAE-cellulose (DE-32) ion exchange chromatography. ALDH$_1$ and ALDH$_2$ were reported to be separated from each other in the last step (chromatography on DE-32). In our experience, however, the separation of ALDH$_1$ from ALDH$_2$ was not satisfactory by these authors' method; ALDH$_1$ always coeluted with ALDH$_2$, and rechromatography of this peak did not provide good separation. However, we found that chromatography on QAE-Sephadex equilibrated with 0.02 M Tris-Cl, pH 8.0, gave a satisfactory separation of the two components. Thus, we were able to isolate $ALDH_1$ and $ALDH_2$ from an usual Caucasian liver. $ALDH_1$ was also purified from an atypical Japanese liver that had no $ALDH_2$ isozyme.

Greenfield and Pietruszko [1977] reported that the molecular weight of human $ALDH_1$ was 245,000 and that of $ALDH_2$ was 225,000, ie, that $ALDH_1$ was significantly larger than $ALDH_2$. In contrast, they found that the subunit sizes, estimated by sodium dodecyl sulfate-polyacrylamide gel electrophoresis (SDS-PAGE), were almost identical for the two isozymes, ie, 54,800 and 54,200, respectively. Our data, also obtained by SDS-PAGE, show that human ALDH-1 consists of subunits with molecular weight 56,500, and ALDH-2 consists of subunits of molecular weight 52,600. No common subunit exists in the two isozymes. Thus, $ALDH_1$ is presumably a homotetramer (aaaa), and $ALDH_2$ is a different homotetramer (bbbb), although a heterotetramer model, ie, $ALDH_1$ $(aa')_2$ and/or $ALDH_2$ $(bb')_2$, cannot be ruled out.

The amino acid compositions of our preparations of human $ALDH_1$ and $ALDH_2$ are shown in Table II. For comparison, the amino acid composition of human $ALDH_1$ and $ALDH_2$ reported by Greenfield and Pietruszko [1977] and that of horse isozymes reported by Eckfeldt et al [1976] are also given in Table II. As it was noticed for the horse isozymes [Eckfeldt et al 1976], the two human isozymes have somewhat similar amino acid compositions. Substantial discrepancies, particularly in the contents of Glu, Pro, and Arg, are readily recognizable between our analytical data and those reported by Greenfield and Pietruszko [1977]. The discrepancies are far beyond usual analytical errors, and they must be attributed to the differences between our isozyme preparations and those analyzed by these authors. It should be pointed out that the amino acid compositions of the present human ALDH isozymes are very similar to that of horse isozymes (Table II). Kinetic characteristics (ie, pH activity profile, Km for NAD and for acetaldehyde) differ between $ALDH_1$ and $ALDH_2$. $ALDH_1$ had high affinity for NAD (Km = $5\mu M$) and lower affinity for acetaldehyde (Km = $22\mu M$), and $ALDH_2$ had lower affinity for NAD (Km = 16 μM) and higher affinity for acetaldehyde (Km = $3.5\mu M$) at pH 7.5. The kinetic data reported by Greenfield and Pietruszko [1977] differ from the present values, ie, Km for NAD = $40\mu M$ and Km for acetaldehyde = $30\mu M$ for $ALDH_1$; Km for NAD = $70\mu M$ and Km for acetaldehyde = $3.0\mu M$ for $ALDH_2$ at pH 7.0. Since the enzyme did not exhibit the typical Michaelis-Menten kinetics, these kinetic data should be interpreted with caution.

Rabbit antibody against $ALDH_1$ precipitated and neutralized not only $ALDH_1$ but also $ALDH_2$. Antibody against $ALDH_2$ also cross-reacted with $ALDH_1$. Thus, a structural homology exists between $ALDH_1$ and $ALDH_2$.

TABLE II. Amino Acid Composition of Aldehyde Dehydrogenase Isozymes[a]

| | Human enzyme | | | | Horse enzyme | |
| | Yoshida[b] | | Greenfield and Pietruszko[c] | | Eckfeldt et al[d] | |
Amino acids	$ALDH_1$	$ALDH_2$	$ALDH_1$	$ALDH_2$	$ALDH_1$	$ALDH_2$
Asp	7.99	8.61	9.71	9.16	8.16	9.19
Thr	5.12	5.57	4.99	5.49	5.40	5.09
Ser	5.22	4.68	5.64	7.75	5.14	4.47
Glu	8.92	9.57	7.61	4.93	9.79	10.06
Pro	4.61	4.91	8.00	7.47	6.15	5.46
Gly	8.75	8.52	9.06	10.00	8.41	8.69
Ala	7.07	8.92	7.75	9.44	7.03	8.94
½Cys	2.0	1.49	—	—	1.76	1.46
Val	6.70	7.92	7.35	10.00	6.65	8.19
Met	1.65	1.69	1.18	1.13	1.88	2.11
Ile	6.32	4.35	5.51	4.37	4.52	3.72
Leu	7.10	6.44	6.43	6.06	7.15	6.33
Tyr	3.06	3.14	2.49	1.97	2.63	2.86
Phe	4.25	4.58	3.94	4.23	4.52	4.22
Lys	6.83	5.56	6.70	6.06	6.65	5.21
His	1.71	1.25	1.58	2.54	1.25	1.24
Arg	3.63	4.14	2.63	2.39	3.14	3.60
Trp	0.78	0.83	—	—	1.13	1.12

[a]Values given are numbers of amino acid residues per 10,000 gram of protein.
[b]Present study.
[c]Calculated from the analytical data by Greenfield and Pietruszko [1977]. Since Cys and Try were not determined in their analysis, the content of a sum of Cys and Try was assumed to be 3.5% (w/w) of the protein for normalization.
[d]Calculated from the analytical data by Eckfeldt et al [1977].

Examination of the immunologically active components of liver extract by two-dimensional starch gel electrophoresis followed by crossed immunoelectrophoresis revealed that an atypical Japanese liver, which had no $ALDH_2$ isozyme, contained (in addition to the active $ALDH_1$ isozyme) an enzymatically inactive, immunologically cross-reactive material (CRM) corresponding to $ALDH_2$ (Fig. 7). $ALDH_1$ and CRM in the crude extract of an atypical Japanese liver were separated from each other by treatment with 5'-AMP-Sepharose 4B, since $ALDH_1$ was absorbed by the affinity column, while CRM had no affinity for the NAD analogue, 5'-AMP.

The existence of CRM corresponding to $ALDH_2$ in an atypical liver leads us to conclude that the absence of $ALDH_2$ isozyme in about 50% of Orientals does not result from a regulatory mutation, a nonsense mutation, or a gene deletion, as previously proposed [Teng, 1981], but must result from a structural mutation in a gene at the $ALDH_2$ locus, resulting in the formation of

Aldehyde Dehydrogenase

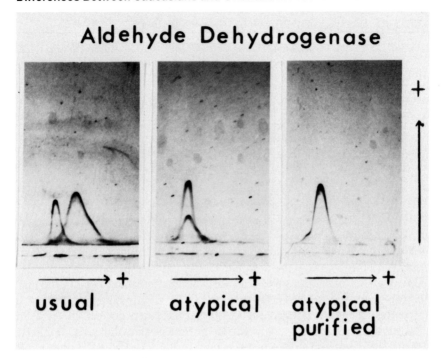

usual   atypical   atypical
purified

Fig. 7. Crossed immunoelectrophoresis of ALDH. First dimension (horizontal): starch gel electrophoresis at pH 7.2; second dimension (vertical): immunoelectrophoresis in agarose gel containing antibody against $ALDH_2$. Left: partially purified enzyme preparation from an usual Caucasian liver. Middle: partially purified enzyme preparation from an atypical Japanese liver. Right: Enzyme preparation from an atypical Japanese liver purified by affinity chromatography with 2'-AMP-Sepharose. Note that an enzymatically inactive but immunologically active component is eliminated by the affinity chromatography (details in Impraim et al [1982]).

enzymatically inactive, abnormal protein. Estimated frequencies of genotypes for the ADH_2 and $ALDH_2$ loci in the Japanese are given in Table III.

IV. ALCOHOL SENSITIVITY AND ENZYME ABNORMALITIES

All investigators agree that a high frequency of acute alcohol intoxication is observed in Orientals, but the figures differ among the investigators. Thus, in Wolff's data about 83% of Oriental individuals showed a flush response [Wolff, 1972, 1973]; about 71% in the study by Ewing et al [1974], and 50%–60% in the studies by Wilson et al [1978], and by Zeiner et al [1979]. These differences could be related to the sampling methods, ie, random population versus adult volunteers with various degrees of predisposition to alcohol, and the test methods for the sensitivity used by these authors.

TABLE III. Genotypes of ADH_2 and $ALDH_2$ in the Japanese[a]

	$ALDH_2^1/ALDH_2^1$	$ALDH_2^1/ALDH_2^2$	$ALDH_2^2/ALDH_2^2$	Σ
ADH_2^1/ADH_2^1	0.015	0.06	0.075	0.15
ADH_2^1/ADH_2^2	0.048	0.192	0.24	0.48
ADH_2^2/ADH_2^2	0.037	0.148	0.185	0.37
Σ	0.10	0.40	0.50	1.00

[a]The frequencies of the atypical ADH_2^2 are based on Stamatoyannopoulos et al [1975]. The frequencies of the atypical $ALDH_2^2$ are based on the observed frequency of absence of $ALDH_2^2$ component (about 50% in Japanese. [Goedde et al, 1979a; Teng, 1981]) and the genetic background of the absence of this component described in the text.

Blood alcohol level and rate of clearance after drinking a moderate amount of alcohol were examined by several investigators. Von Wartburg and Schürch [1968] observed more rapid alcohol elimination in subjects with atypical ADH (ie, 90 mg/kg/h in the normal and 141 mg/kg/h in the atypical), while Edward and Evans [1967] found a faster elimination only in one of the three subjects with atypical ADH; the type of ALDH of their subjects is unknown. In contrast, Fenna et al [1971] reported that the rate of alcohol metabolism, after intravenous injection, was higher in Caucasians than Mongoloids (ie, 145/mg/kg/h and 105 mg/kg/h respectively); the types of ADH and ALDH of these subjects are unknown. Mizoi et al [1979] found no difference in either the maximum blood alcohol level (about 10 mM) or the rate of elimination (about 100 mg/kg/h) between alcohol-flushing and nonflushing Japanese individuals.

The data on acetaldehyde levels after alcohol intake are distributed over a wide range because of difficulties in measuring this very volatile substance and the release of a bound form of acetaldehyde from red blood cells. The values given by Lundquist and Westerfeld [1958], Truitt and Walch [1971], and Stowell et al [1980] (0.1–1.56 g/ml, ie, 2.3–35.9 μM) seem to be more reliable than the higher values (9.3 g/ml in Oriental males and 7.7 g/ml in Caucasian males) reported by Ewing et al [1974]. Mizoi et al [1979] reported that blood acetaldehyde reached an average 0.508 g/ml (ie, 11.5μM) in alcohol-sensitive Japanese and about 0.1 g/ml (ie, 2.3μM) in nonflushing Japanese. According to the recent study by Harada et al [1981], the acetaldehyde level in blood reaches about 2μM in usual individuals, and about 35–40μM in alcohol-sensitive subjects.

As previously suggested, either the atypical ADH_2^2 with high enzyme activity [Stamatoyannopoulos et al, 1975] or the absence of $ALDH_2$ isozyme [Goedde et al, 1979a] could account for an accumulation of acetaldehyde inducing alcohol intoxication. Alternatively, the combination of both ADH and ALDH abnormalities could be involved in the elevation of acetaldehyde level. Based on the available data on ethanol metabolism, one can attempt to evaluate these possibilities. From studies of perfused rat liver, it appears that more than 80% of ethanol administered at a moderate level is oxidized in liver. Most of the acetaldehyde formed is thought to be further oxidized to acetate in liver [Williamson et al, 1969; Eriksson et al, 1975; Braggins et al, 1980]. Multiple metabolic pathways are open to acetaldehyde (ie, ALDH, aldehyde oxidase, xanthine oxidase, and a specific aldolase), but cytosolic $ALDH_1$ and mitochondrial $ALDH_2$ are thought to play a major role in acetaldehyde metabolism in liver. Krebs concluded that in the rat, hepatic ADH activity is sufficiently high to establish near-equilibrium in the reactants of the ADH system and the lactate dehydrogenase system [Krebs, 1966; Williamson et al, 1967]. Thus, the rate of ethanol elimination depends on the concentration of acetaldehyde determined by the ADH step. Krebs' conclusion seems to be an oversimplification, and an apparent near-equilibrium can only be observed in a particular condition [Veech et al, 1972; Braggins et al, 1980]. The study by Braggins et al [1980] suggests that rat liver has comparable capacity for ethanol and acetaldehyde oxidation and that changes in acetaldehyde level could occur by variations of ADH and/or ALDH activities. The situation is basically the same in man. It is known that a partial inhibition of ALDH by calcium carbimide or by disulfiram induces elevation of blood acetaldehyde levels and flushing reaction in man [Stowell et al, 1980]. Conversely, a partial inhibition of ADH by pyrazole decreases acetaldehyde levels and attenuates the symptoms caused by the ALDH inhibitor [Stowell et al, 1980].

As described above, the specific activity (V_{max}) of the pure ADH_2^2 is about 80 times higher than that of the usual ADH_2^1 at physiologic pH, and the ADH activity of crude homogenate of the liver with atypical ADH type is several times higher than that of the usual type liver. But the rate of ethanol oxidation in the atypical liver could not be much higher than that in the usual liver, since a near-equilibrium state is already established in the usual liver, and an additional several-fold increase in potential ADH activity in the atypical liver is not expected to induce substantial shift of the equilibrium state. A decrease in ALDH activity in the atypical liver missing the $ALDH_2$ isozyme could induce elevation of blood acetaldehyde level and flushing, as observed in the subjects administered ALDH inhibitors such as disulfiram and calcium carbimide. These drugs reduce the rate of ethanol elimination in man [Stowell et al, 1980]. By contrast, the rate of ethanol elimination is reported to be identical between alcohol flushing and nonflushing Japanese [Mizoi et al, 1979].

From these findings, a probable genetic cause of alcohol flushing in Orientals is a combination of atypical ADH and atypical ALDH. A higher ADH activity could elevate the acetaldehyde level, which compensates for the decrease in ALDH activity and maintains the rate of ethanol elimination. The degree of acute alcohol intoxication is known to be heterogeneous [Mizoi et al, 1979]. Subjects with atypical ADH type and atypical ALDH type are probably most sensitive, while subjects with usual ADH and atypical ALDH are moderately sensitive. Subjects with atypical ADH and usual ALDH could be only mildly sensitive to alcohol or similar to normal individuals.

A more direct way to elucidate the relationships between the dehydrogenase abnormalities and alcohol sensitivity is obviously the dehydrogenase typing of alcohol-sensitive and alcohol-insensitive individuals. Since it is difficult to obtain biopsy liver samples, Goedde et al [1979b, 1980] tried to distinguish ADH and ALDH types using fibroblast cultures and hair roots and suggested that the atypical ALDH, not atypical ADH, could be related to alcohol flushing. Family pedigree analysis of alcohol sensitivity and unequivocal dehydrogenase typing, possibly using biopsy or autopsy livers, could contribute toward solving the problem. The involvement of other genetic factors besides the abnormalities of ADH and ALDH is not ruled out.

V. SUMMARY AND CONCLUSIONS

Acute alcohol intoxication is far more commonly observed in Orientals than Caucasians. The human liver contains several cytosolic and microsomal ADHs. One of the major cytosolic ADH isozymes controlled by a gene at the ADH_2 locus differs between Caucasians and Orientals. Most Caucasians have the usual enzyme consisting of usual β_1 subunit, while nearly 90% of Orientals have the atypical enzyme consisting of the atypical β_2 subunit. The specific activity of the atypical enzyme is several times higher at pH 10 and nearly 100 times higher at physiologic pH than the usual enzyme. Km values for ethanol, NAD, acetaldehyde, and NADH are several times higher for the atypical enzyme than for the usual enzyme. The usual enzyme is rapidly inactivated by iodoacetate, indicating the existence of an "active-site cysteine" in the molecule. In contrast, the atypical enzyme is resistant to iodoacetate inactivation. Peptide mapping analysis revealed that the active site Cys in the usual β_1 subunit is replaced by His in the atypical β_2 subunit. A remarkable structural homology exists at the active site of horse and human enzymes.

In the usual $\beta_1\beta_1$ enzyme, as in the horse enzyme, the catalytic Zn is expected to link to the sensitive Cys at position 47, His at position 67, and Cys (presumably) at position 174, thus forming the active site. In contrast, the active site of the atypical $\beta_2\beta_2$ enzyme is expected to consist of the catalytic Zn linked to His at position 47, His at position 67, and Cys (presumably) at position 174. The resistance of the atypical $\beta_2\beta_2$ to inactivation by iodoacetate is a direct consequence of the replacement of the sensitive Cys at position 47 by His.

Liver ALDH components also differ between Caucasians and Orientals. Virtually all Caucasians have two major ALDH isozymes, $ALDH_1$ and $ALDH_2$, while approximately 50% of Orientals have only the $ALDH_1$ isozyme (cytosolic) missing $ALDH_2$ isozyme (presumably mitochondrial). $ALDH_1$ consists of four subunits with a molecular weight of 56,500, and $ALDH_2$ consists of four subunits with a molecular weight of 52,600. The two isozymes do not share any common subunit. Examination of liver extracts by two-dimensional crossed immunoelectrophoresis revealed that an atypical Oriental liver with no $ALDH_2$ isozyme contained an enzymatically inactive but immunologically cross-reactive material corresponding to $ALDH_2$, besides the active $ALDH_1$ isozyme. Therefore, the absence of $ALDH_1$ isozyme in atypical Orientals is not due to a regulatory mutation, a gene deletion, or a nonsense mutation, but most probably to a structural mutation in a gene at the *ALDH* locus, resulting in synthesis of enzymatically inactive abnormal protein.

The genetic polymorphism of ADH and of ALDH shows wide differences in frequencies between Orientals and Caucasians. The mechanism of evolutionary divergence of the usual and atypical enzymes would be an interesting subject of study. Despite the rapid development of human chromosome mapping, the gene loci for ADH and ALDH isozymes have not been assigned as yet. The structural study of these loci in Orientals and Caucasians would contribute toward the elucidation of evolutionary processes in these populations.

There is a paradoxical relationship between alcohol sensitivity (ie, acute alcohol intoxication) and alcoholism. Both the Orientals (Japanese, Chinese, Korean) and the American Indians are of Mongoloid origin, and the frequency of alcohol sensitivity is equally high in these populations. The incidence of alcoholism in Orientals is lower than that in Caucasians. In contrast, alcoholism is a serious problem among American Indians and Eskimos. It remains to be studied whether the discrepancy is mainly the result of social and cultural differences or of other hitherto unidentified genetic factor (or factors). Several investigators have suggested that a hepatic ethanol-inducible microsomal ADH and ADH-π play a substantial role in the handling of a high level of alcohol over a long period of time [Orme-Johnson and Zeigler, 1965; Lieber and DeCarli, 1968; Li et al, 1977]. It remains to be determined whether genetic differences of microsomal ADH and ADH-π exist between Orientals and American Indians.

VI. ACKNOWLEDGMENTS

This study was supported by US Public Health Service grants HL-15125 and HL-29515. The author wishes to thank Drs. I.-Y. Huang, C.C. Impraim, and J.F. Lee for their contribution in this study and Mr. G. Wang for technical assistance. The author also thanks Dr. A. Hayashi, Osaka University School of Medicine, for providing autopsy material.

VII. REFERENCES

Berger D, Berger M, von Wartburg JP (1974): Structural studies of human-liver alcohol dehydrogenase isozymes. Eur J Biochem 50:215–225.

Braggins TJ, Crow KE, Bott RD (1980): Acetaldehyde and acetate production during ethanol metabolism in perfused rat liver. Adv Exp Med Biol 132:441–449.

Crow K, Kitson TM, MacGibbon AKH, Bott RD (1974): Intracellular localization and properties of aldehyde dehydrogenase from sheep liver. Biochim Biophys Acta 350:121–128.

Dahl KH, McKinley-McKee JS (1980): Phosphate binding to liver alcohol dehydrogenase studied by the rate of alkylation with affinity labels. Eur J Biochem 103:47–51.

Eckfeldt JH, Yonetani T (1976): Subcellular localization of the F_1 and F_2 isozymes of horse liver aldehyde dehydrogenase. Arch Biochem Biophys 175:717–722.

Eckfeldt JH, Mope L, Takio K, Yonetani T (1976): Horse liver alcohol dehydrogenase: Purification and characterization of two isozymes. J Biol Chem 251:236–240.

Edwards JA, Evans DAP (1967): Ethanol metabolism in subjects possessing typical and atypical liver alcohol dehydrogenase. Clin Pharmacol Ther 8:824–829.

Eklund H, Nordström B, Zeppezauer E, Söderlund G, Ohlsson I, Boiwe T, Söderberg B-O, Tapia O, Bränden C-I (1976): Three-dimensional structure of horse liver alcohol dehydrogenase at 2.4 Å resolution. J Mol Biol 102:27–59.

Eriksson CJP, Marselos M, Koivula T (1975): The role of cytosolic rat liver aldehyde dehydrogenase in the oxidation of acetaldehyde during ethanol metabolism in vivo. Biochem J 152:709–712.

Ewing JA, Rouse BA, Pellizzari ED (1974): Alcohol sensitivity and ethnic background. Am J Psychiatry 131:206–210.

Fenna D, Mix L, Schaefer O, Gilbert JAL (1971): Ethanol metabolism in various racial groups. Can Med Assoc J 105:472–475.

Goedde HW, Harada S, Agarwal DP (1979a): Racial differences in alcohol sensitivity: A new hypothesis. Hum Genet 51:331–334.

Goedde HW, Agarwal DP, Harada S (1979b): Alcohol metabolizing enzymes: Studies of isozymes in human biopsies and cultured fibroblasts. Clin Genet 16:29–33.

Goedde HW, Agarwal DP, Harada S (1980): Genetic studies on alcohol-metabolizing enzymes: Detection of isozymes in human hair roots. Enzyme 25:281–286.

Greenfield NJ, Pietruszko R (1977): Two aldehyde dehydrogenase from human liver: Isolation via affinity chromatography and characterization of isozymes. Biochim Biophys Acta 483:35–45.

Harada S, Agarwal DP, Goedde HW (1981): Acetaldehyde metabolism and polymorphism of aldehyde dehydrogenase in Japanese, abstracted. 6th Int Congr Hum Genet 103.

Impraim CC, Wang G, Yoshida A (1982): Structural mutation in a major human aldehyde dehydrogenase gene results in loss of enzyme activity. Am J Hum Genet 34:837–841.

Jörnvall H (1970): Horse liver alcohol dehydrogenase: The primary structure of the protein chain of the ethanol-active isozyme. Eur J Biochem 16:25–40.

Jörnvall H, Pietruszko R (1972): Structural studies of alcohol dehydrogenase from human liver. Eur J Biochem 25:283–290.

Jörnvall H (1977): The primary structure of yeast alcohol dehydrogenase. Eur J Biochem 72:425–442.

Kitabatake N, Sasaki R, Chiba H (1981): Localization of bovine liver aldehyde dehydrogenase isozymes and their immunological properties. J Biochem 89:1223–1229.

Krebs HA (1966): The role of equilibria in the regulation of metabolism. In Horecker BL,

Stadtman ER (eds): "Current topics in cellular regulation I." New York: Academic Press, pp 45–55.

Li T-K, Bosron WF, Dafeldecker WP, Lange LG, Vallee BL (1977): Isolation of π-alcohol dehydrogenase of human liver: Is it a determinant of alcoholism? Proc Natl Acad Sci USA 74:4378–4381.

Lieber CS, DeCarli LM (1968): Ethanol oxidation by hepatic microsomes: Adaptive increase after ethanol feeding. Science 162:197–198.

Lindros KO, Vihma R, Forsander OA (1972): Utilization and metabolic effect of acetaldehyde and ethanol in the perfused rat liver. Biochem J 126:945–952.

Lundquist F, Westerfeld WW (1958): The kinetics of alcohol elimination in man. Acta Pharmacol Toxicol 14:265–289.

Mizoi Y, Ijiri I, Tasuno Y, Kijima T, Fujiwara S, Adachi J (1979): Relationship between facial flushing and blood acetaldehyde levels after alcohol intake. Pharmacol Biochem Behav 10:303–311.

Orme-Johnson WH, Ziergler DM (1965): Alcohol mixed function oxidase activity of mammalian liver microsomes. Biochem Biophys Res Commun 21:78–82.

Smith M, Hopkinson DA, Harris H (1971): Developmental changes and polymorphism of human liver alcohol dehydrogenase. Ann Hum Genet 34:251–261.

Smith M, Hopkinson DA, Harris H (1972): Alcohol dehydrogenase isozymes in adult human stomach and liver: Evidence for activity of the ADH_3 locus. Ann Hum Genet 35:243–253.

Smith M, Hopkinson DA, Harris H (1973): Studies on the subunit structure and molecular size of the human alcohol dehydrogenase isozymes determined by the different loci, ADH_1, ADH_2, and ADH_3. Ann Hum Genet 36:401–414.

Stamatoyannopoulos G, Chen S-H, Fukui M (1975): Liver alcohol dehydrogenase in Japanese: High population frequency of atypical form and its possible role in alcohol sensitivity. Am J Hum Genet 27:789–796.

Stowell A, Hillbom M, Salaspuro M, Lindros KO (1980): Low acetaldehyde levels in blood, breath, and cerebrospinal fluid of intoxicated humans as assayed by improved methods. Adv Exp Med Biol 132:635–545.

Teng Y-S (1981): Human liver aldehyde dehydrogenase in Chinese and Asiatic Indians: Gene deletion and its possible implication in alcohol metabolism. Biochem Genet 19:107–113.

Truitt EB, Walsh MJ (1971): The role of acetaldehyde in the actions of ethanol. In Kissin B, Begleiter H (ed): "The Biology of Alcoholism, Vol 1: Biochemistry." New York: Plenum Press, pp 161–195.

Veech RL, Guynn R, Veloso D (1972): The time course of the effects of ethanol on the redox and phosphorylation states of rat liver. Biochem J 127:387–397.

von Wartburg JP, Schürch PM (1968): Atypical human liver alcohol dehydrogenase. Ann New York Acad Sci 151:936–946.

Williamson DH, Lund P, Krebs HA (1967): The redox state of free nicotinamide-adenine dinucleotide in the cytoplasm and mitochonria of rat liver. Biochem J 103:514–527.

Williamson JR, Scholz R, Browning ET, Thurman RG, Fukami MH (1969): Metabolic effects of ethanol in perfused rat liver. J Biol Chem 244:5044–5054.

Wilson JR, McClearn GE, Johnson RC (1978): Ethnic variation in the use and effects of alcohol. Drug Alcohol Depend 3:147–151.

Wolff PC (1972): Ethnic differences in alcohol sensitivity. Science 175:449–450.

Wolff PC (1973): Vasomotor sensitivity to alcohol in diverse Mongoloid populations. Am J Hum Genet 25:193–199.

Yoshida A, Impraim CC, Huang I-Y (1981): Enzymatic and structural differences between usual and atypical human liver alcohol dehydrogenases. J Biol Chem 256:12430–12436.

Zeiner AR, Paredes A, Dix Christensen H (1979): The role of acetaldehyde in mediating reactivity to an acute dose of ethanol among different racial groups. Clin Exp Res 3:11–18.

Index

Previous Volumes

Genetic and Structural Dissection of Human Enzymes and Enzyme Defects Using Somatic Cell Hybrids
Thomas B. Shows
Biochemical Genetics Section, Roswell Park Memorial Institute, New York State Department of Health, Buffalo, New York

Mechanisms Involved in the Intracellular Localization of Mouse Glucuronidase
Aldons J. Lusis and Kenneth Paigen
Department of Molecular Biology, Roswell Park Memorial Institute, New York State Department of Health, Buffalo, New York

CONTENTS OF VOLUME 3

Superoxide Dismutases: Occurrence, Structure Function, and Evolution
Joe M. McCord
Department of Biochemistry, University of South Alabama, Mobile, Alabama

Origin and Differentiation of the Soluble α-Glycerolphosphate Dehydrogenase Isozymes in Drosophila Melanogaster
Glenn C. Bewley and Stephen Miller
Department of Genetics, North Carolina State University, Raleigh, North Carolina

Subcellular Localization of Isozymes
Roger S. Holmes and Colin J. Masters
School of Science, Griffith University, Queensland, Australia

Creatine Kinase Isozymes as Diagnostic and Prognostic Indices of Myocardial Infarction
Robert Roberts
Cardiovascular Division, Washington University School of Medicine, St. Louis, Missouri

Isozymic Analyses of Early Mammalian Embryogenesis
R.L. Brinster
Laboratory of Reproductive Physiology, School of Veterinary Medicine, University of Pennsylvania, Philadelphia, Pennsylvania

Molecular Structure, Polypeptide Size, and Genetic Variation of Enzymes
Richard K. Koehn and Walter F. Eanes
Department of Ecology and Evolution, State University of New York, Stony Brook, New York; and the Museum of Comparative Zoology, Harvard University, Cambridge, Massachusetts

CONTENTS OF VOLUME 4

Biochemical and Developmental Genetics of Isozymes in the Mouse, Mus musculus
Michael R. Felder
Department of Biology, University of South Carolina, Columbia, South Carolina

Bioautographic Visualization of Enzymes
Susan L. Naylor
Biochemical Genetics Section, Roswell Park Memorial Institute, New York State Department of Health, Buffalo, New York

Alcohol and Aldehyde Dehydrogenase Isozymes From Mammalian Liver—Their Structural and Functional Differences

Evolutionary Change of Duplicate Genes
Wen-Hsiung Li
Center for Demographic and Population Genetics, University of Texas Health Science Center, Houston

The Genetic Basis of Alkaline Phosphatase Isozyme Expression
T. Stigbrand, J.L. Millán, and W.H. Fishman
Department of Physiological Chemistry, University of Umea, Sweden (T.S., J.L.M.), and La Jolla Cancer Research Foundation, La Jolla, California (J.L.M., W.H.F.)

Isozymes of Phosphofructokinase
Shobhana Vora
Division of Pediatric Hematology, Department of Pediatrics, Columbia University College of Physicians and Surgeons, New York

Glucosephosphate and Triosephosphate Isomerases: Significance of Isozyme Structural Differences in Evolution, Physiology, and Aging
Robert W. Gracy
Department of Biochemistry, North Texas State University/Texas College of Osteopathic Medicine, Denton

Linkage of Mammalian Isozyme Loci: A Comparative Approach
James E. Womack
Department of Veterinary Pathology, Texas A & M University, College Station

Isozymes in Forensic Science
G.F. Sensabaugh
Forensic Science Group, Department of Biomedical and Environmental Health Sciences, School of Public Health, University of California, Berkeley